This edition published by Parragon in 2010

Parragon
Queen Street House
4 Queen Street
Bath BA1 1HE, UK

ISBN: 978-1-4075-3505-0

Created and Produced by David Etherington Design
www.davidetheringtondesign.com

Design: David Etherington, Luke Griffin

Printed in China

365 BRAIN GAMES

GUY CAMPBELL
PAUL MORAN

Bath • New York • Singapore • Hong Kong • Cologne • Delhi
Melbourne • Amsterdam • Johannesburg • Auckland • Shenzhen

INTRODUCTION

We know the importance of keeping our bodies in shape and living a healthy lifestyle, so we walk up stairs to ensure our heart gets a good workout and think nothing of regular ab crunches to keep our stomachs trim. However we often overlook the importance of caring for one of the most important organs in the body—the brain!

365 Brain Games addresses this in a fun and enjoyable way by providing a year-long journey through puzzles that will test and exercise the mind for peak mental fitness. This book will give you a complete cerebral workout as you take on the challenge of a wide range of puzzles including logic tests, number games, picture puzzles, and language riddles.

In addition to these intellectual exercises, many of the daily puzzle entries come with a fascinating fact from the fields of art, history, and science, and an accompanying quote to inform and inspire you. The authors of these words of wisdom are philosophers, scientists, writers, and some of the greatest minds from history, including Albert Einstein, Oscar Wilde, William Shakespeare, and Theodore Roosevelt to name just a few.

So in the pages ahead, tackle the puzzles, study facts, and be inspired by the quotes—and then reap the rewards of an exercised and mentally agile mind.

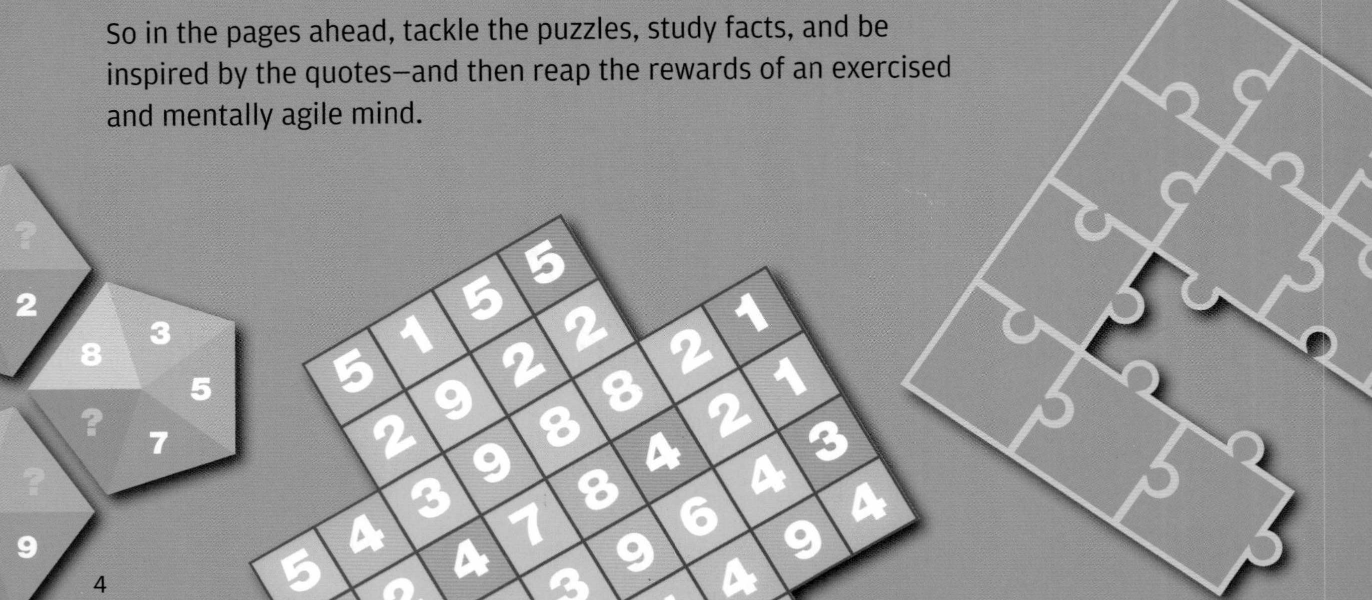

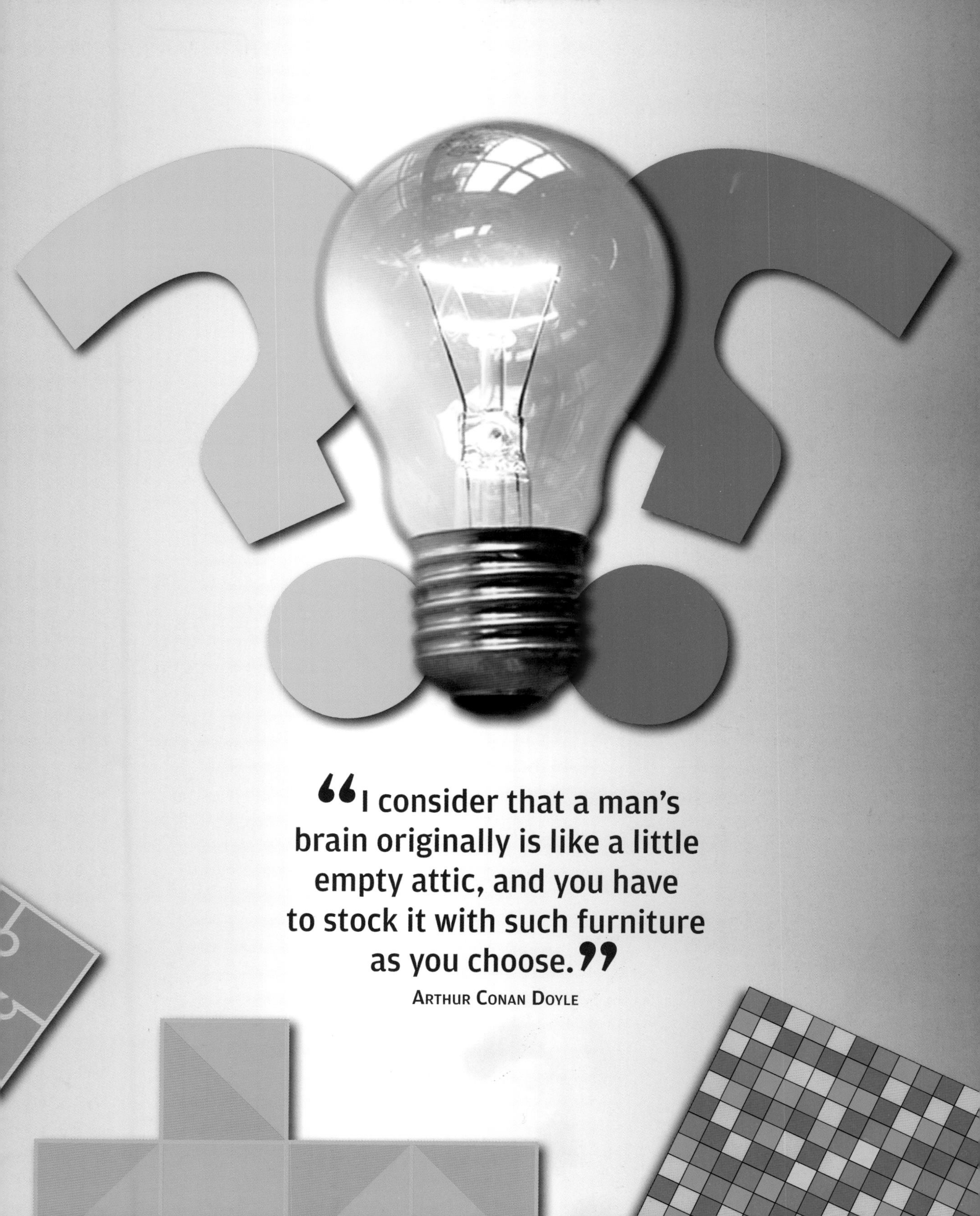
“I consider that a man’s
brain originally is like a little
empty attic, and you have
to stock it with such furniture
as you choose.”
Arthur Conan Doyle

HOW TO USE THIS BOOK

365 Brain Games is uniquely devised to give you the complete mental workout, providing a puzzle a day, as well as fascinating facts and interesting quotes to inform and inspire.

Puzzle number This book contains 365 puzzles and brainteasers, one for every day of the year.

Items you will need
Some puzzles require basic equipment and these are listed here.

 PEN

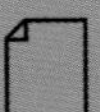 PAPER

 RULER

 COLORED PENS

Difficulty This gauge will inform you of the difficulty of each puzzle. "Easy" puzzles may take only a few minutes to complete while those listed as "Hard" may take more time.

 EASY

 MEDIUM

 HARD

65

DIFFICULTY

Big Pot Bonanza

Mac, Jack and Zac are playing poker. They each won a big pot with their biggest hands of the night, but can you work out their surnames, and then who won how much, with which hand?

- Mac won $250 with his biggest hand, which wasn't four of a kind.
- Brunson had the flush and took more than 100 dollars from Zac with it.
- The $100 dollar pot was won by a full house, but not by Chan or Zac.

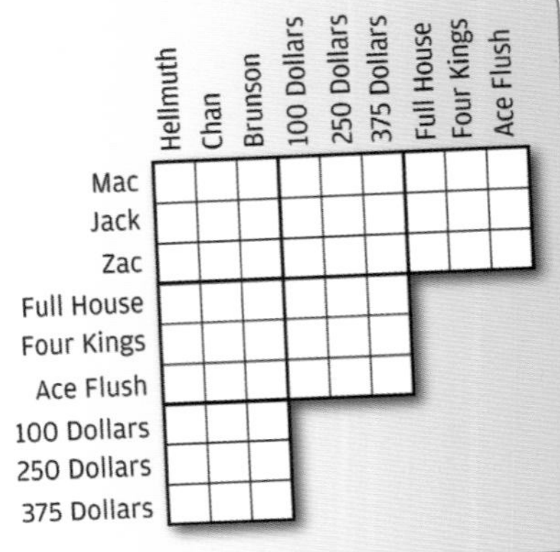

Despite being raised as a Quaker, Richard Nixon was a keen poker player during his two years in the US Navy and even used a portion of his winnings to fund his first foray into professional politics in 1946 when he won a Congressional seat.

66

DIFFICULTY

Robot Research

Which box contains exactly the right bits to build the robot?

"My goal is simple. It is a complete understanding of the universe, why it is as it is and why it exists at all." Stephen Hawking

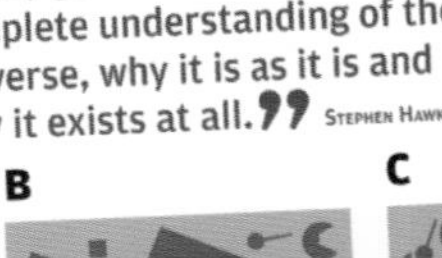

A

B

C

In April 2007, the French TGV train broke its own 1990 world train speed record as it reached 574.8 km/h (357.18 mph) under test conditions.

42

Quotes The words of some of history's greatest minds complement many of the puzzles, offering you encouragement and worldly wisdom.

67

DIFFICULTY

Locate the Letter

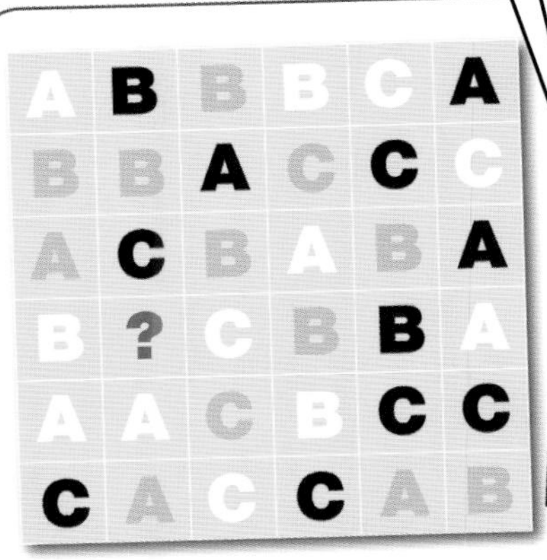

What letter, in what colour, should replace the red question mark so that the grid follows a pattern?

“Every artist should be ahead of his time and behind in his rent.”

KINKY FRIEDMAN

In 1895, Émil... et Levassor... from Paris to Bo... 48 hours and is...

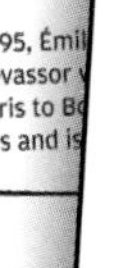

Number Mountain

Replace the question marks with numbers so that each pair of blocks adds up to the block directly above them.

New Zealand's South Island boasts 18 peaks of more than 3,000 metres. The tallest peak is Mount Cook which is 3,754 metres tall.

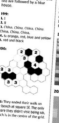

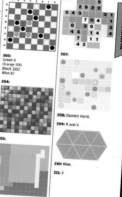

Solutions

Full color solutions and explanations are found at the back of the book, allowing you to work out how the puzzles are solved so next time you will complete them in less time. See pages 202–224.

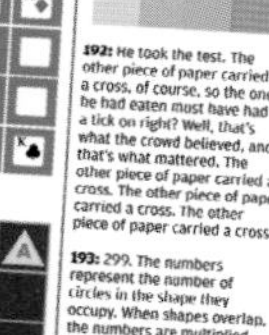

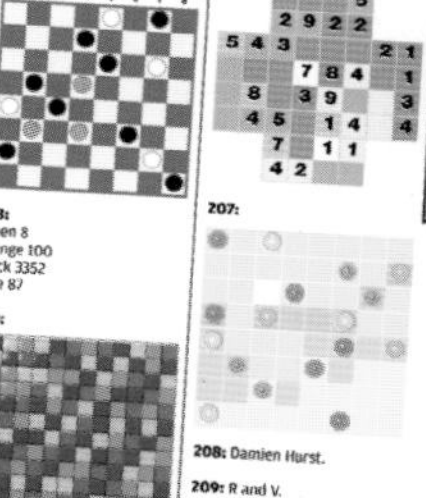

Facts Many of the daily puzzles are accompanied by a fascinating fact or item of trivia to inform and share with friends.

Pirate Hunter

Flintlock Freddy is an inveterate pirate sought throughout the seven seas for 50 counts of villainy. He wears a bandana and an eye patch, but he doesn't have a beard or a hook. Can you clap your eyes on the rogue?

“One secret of success in life is for a man to be ready for his opportunity when it comes.”

Benjamin Disraeli

The Maldives are made up of 1,192 islands. Only 199 are inhabited and out of this figure 87 are exclusive resort islands.

Logical Steps

The balls below have been rearranged. Can you work out the new sequence of the balls from the clues given below?

- Neither the triangle nor the X is next to the square.
- The circle is only next to one other ball, and it isn't the X.
- The star is two balls to the left of the X.

The first (and only) painting van Gogh sold in his lifetime was entitled *Red Vineyard at Arles*. It was exhibited in Brussels in 1890 and sold for 400 francs. It now hangs in the Puskin Museum, Moscow.

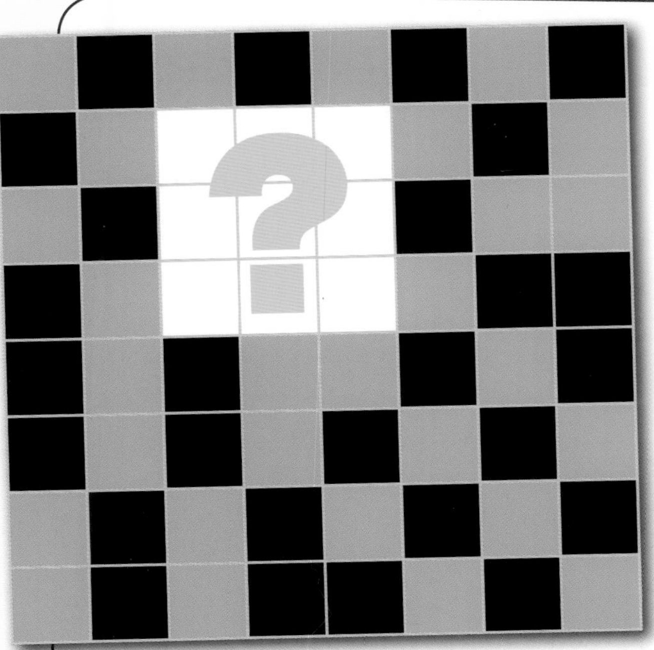

Tricky Tiles

Can you work out which of the squares shown below correctly completes the grid?

“I have often wished I had time to cultivate modesty . . . But I am too busy thinking about myself.”
EDITH SITWELL

The Winter Palace and Hermitage in St. Petersburg, Russia, is the world's largest art gallery. You have to walk 15 miles to see 322 galleries, which hold almost three million pieces of art.

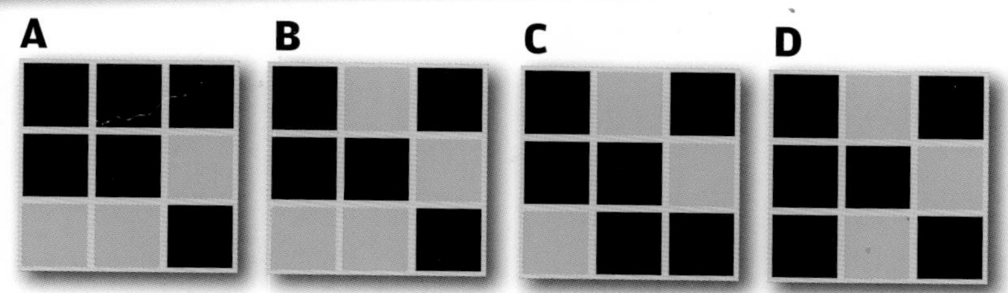

Magic Squares

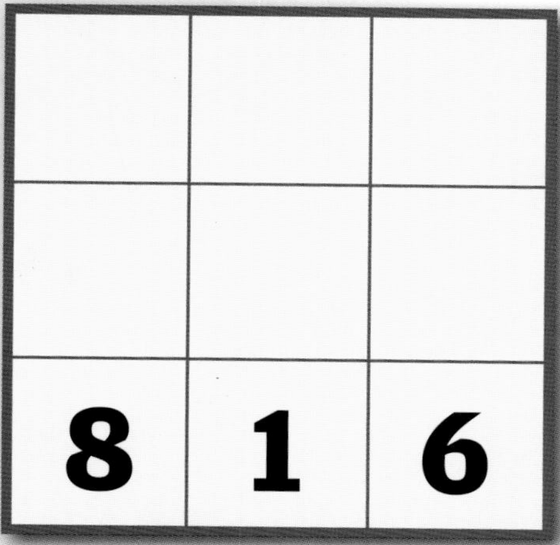

Complete the square using nine consecutive numbers, so that all rows, columns, and large diagonals add up to the same total.

“Magic is believing in yourself; if you can do that, you can make anything happen.” JOHANN WOLFGANG VON GOETHE

With 700 native languages, Papua New Guinea is the world's most linguistically diverse country.

5

DIFFICULTY

Carpet Caper

Charlie is trying to describe on the telephone a rug that he would like to buy. What percentage of this rug is blue, what percentage green, and what cream?

“The toughest thing about success is that you've got to keep on being a success.”

Irving Berlin

6

DIFFICULTY

Crack the Color Code

Can you crack the color code and make your way from one yellow square to the other, moving one square at a time? The blue arrow tells you which way is up.

“To love abundantly is to live abundantly, and to love forever is to live forever.”

Henry Drummond

In ancient Babylon, the bride's father would supply his son-in-law with all the mead (fermented honey beverage) he could drink for a month after the wedding. Because their calendar was lunar, or moon-based, this period of free mead was called the “honey month,” or what we now call the “honeymoon.”

7

DIFFICULTY ★★★

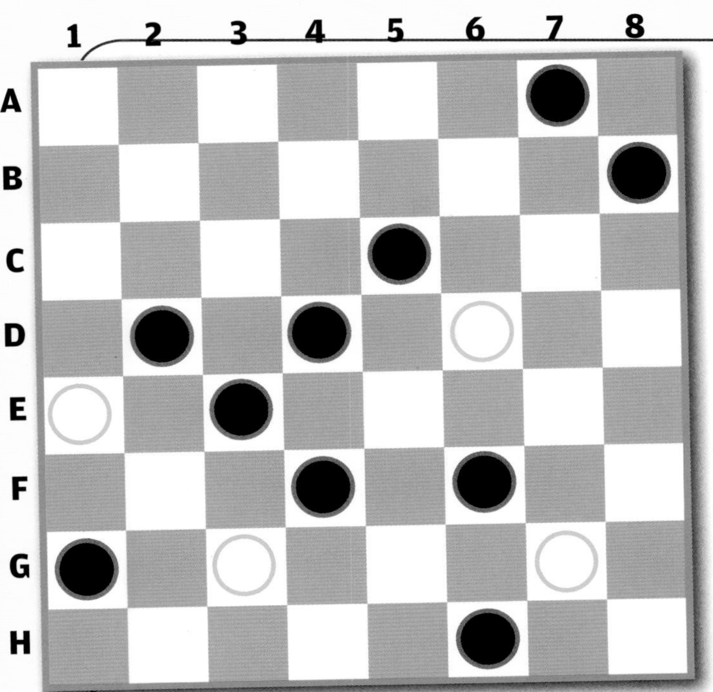

Checkers

Make a move for white so that eight black pieces are left, none of which are in the same column or row.

“Despise the enemy strategically, but take him seriously tactically.”

Mao Tse-tung

From 1788 to 1820, performances of *King Lear* were prohibited on the English stage at the order of reigning monarch, King George III.

8

DIFFICULTY ★☆☆ (1 of 3 stars filled)

Bird’s-eye View

Which of the pictures below represents the correct overhead view of this scene?

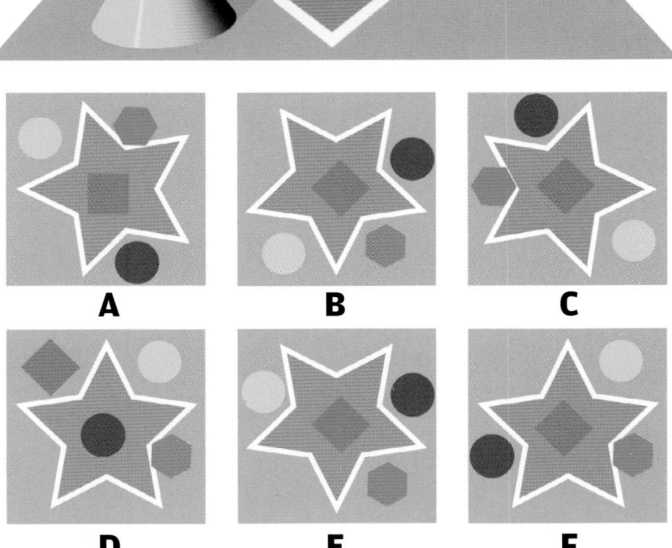

“I seem to have been everywhere in the last 30 years, maybe not in the epicenter but flying around the periphery of extraordinary events and equally extraordinary people.” Rupert Everett

A law was enacted in 1324 that all whales, dolphins, and porpoises found in English waters belonged to the monarchy and were to be known as “Fishes Royal.” The Natural History Museum in London has been responsible for investigating all strandings since 1913.

9

DIFFICULTY

Balancing Act

The arms of these scales are divided into sections—a weight two sections away from the middle will be twice as heavy as a weight one section away. Can you arrange the supplied weights in such a way as to balance the whole scale?

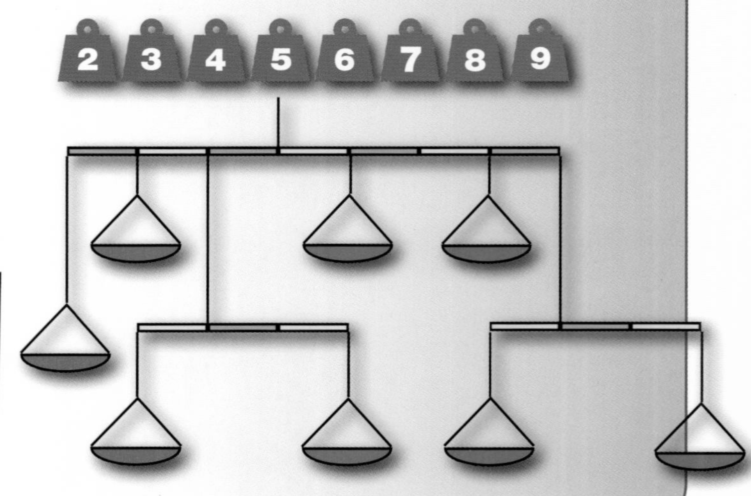

In the 1500s, nautical explorers used the astrolabe, the instrument invented by the Greeks, to calculate latitudes through observation of the height of the sun over the horizon.

10

DIFFICULTY

Complete the Set

Denise has been decorating sets of boxes to give to her friends as presents, but her mischievous son Ben has mixed them up. Can you help her by working out which of the four boxed figures completes the set?

“Everybody knows how to raise children, except the people who have them.”

P. J. O'Rourke

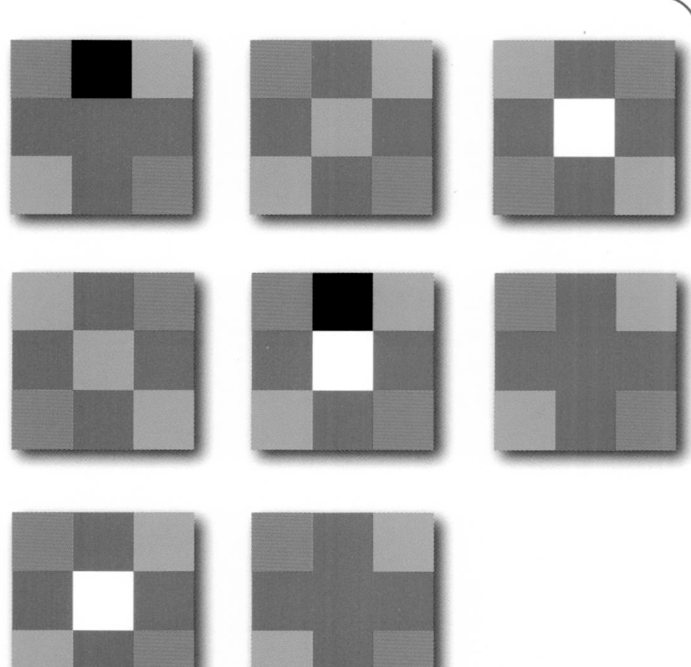

11

DIFFICULTY

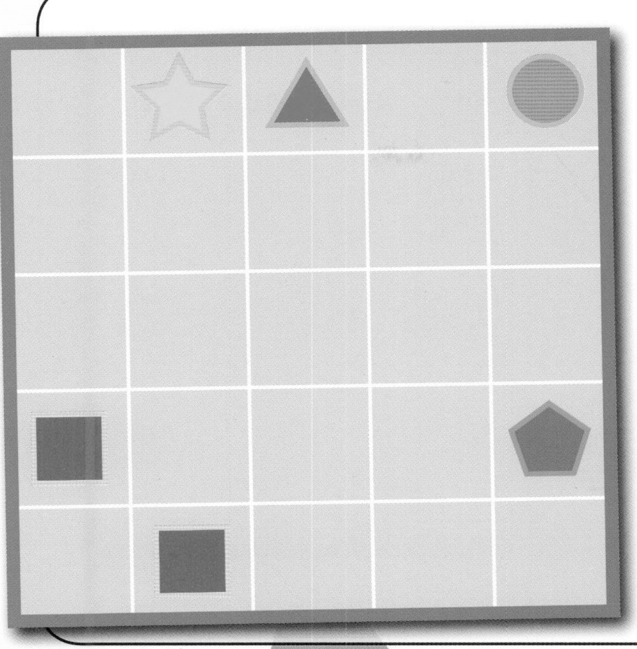

Mind Align

Fill in the empty squares so that each row, column, and long diagonal contains five different symbols.

“If I could read it, I could play it.” Nat King Cole

English physicist and chemist Henry Cavendish not only discovered hydrogen but also determined the mass of the earth.

12

DIFFICULTY

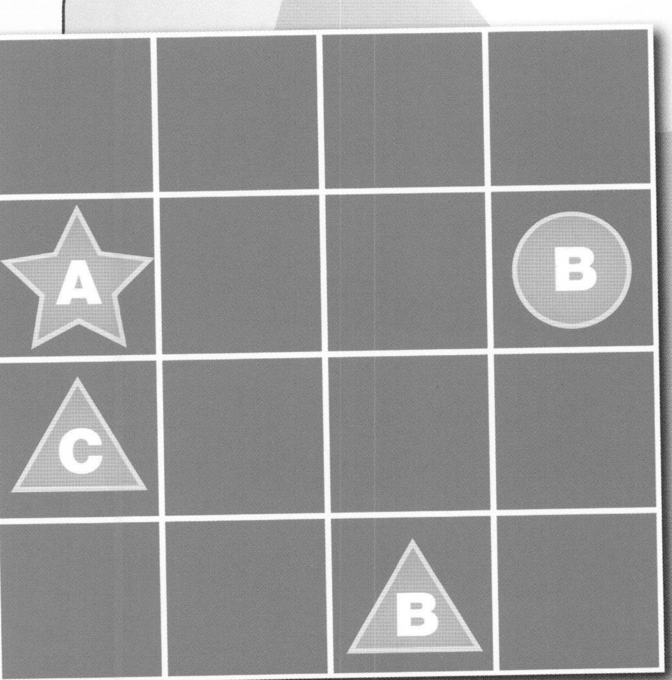

Shape Shuffle

Fill up the shuffle box so that each row, column, and long diagonal contains four different shapes and the letters A, B, C, and D.

“A man may be so much of everything that he is nothing of anything.”

Samuel Johnson

In 1956, the Boston Symphony became the first U.S. orchestra to perform in the Soviet Union. In February 2008, the New York Philharmonic is scheduled to do the same in North Korea.

13

DIFFICULTY

Sudoku Sixpack

Fill up the grid so that every row, column, and long diagonal contains all the numbers 1, 2, 3, 4, 5, and 6.

“What really matters is what you do with what you have.” H. G. Wells

1				2	
	4		3	1	
2		5		3	
4		3			6
	5	2		4	

14

DIFFICULTY

Eight Ball

You're playing stripes in a game of pool, and you've cleaned up all your balls. However, there's a solid ball between the cue and eight balls. Can you see the shot without hitting any other balls?

The first coin-operated billiard table was patented in 1903. A game on the first pay-for-play table cost one penny.

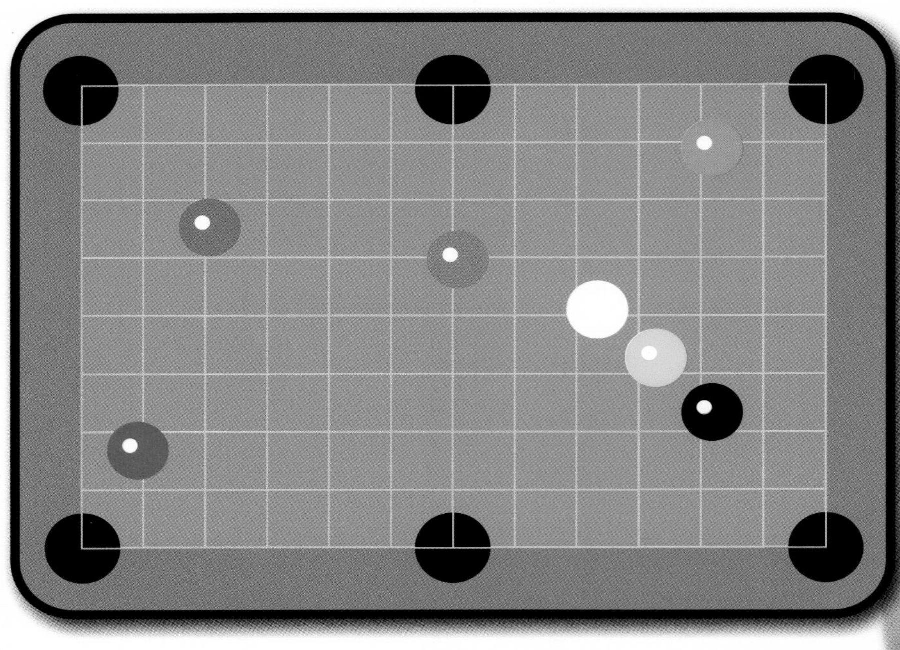

Molecular Mix-Up

Waldo the scientist has got a little confused; which of the molecular shapes is not the same as the others?

> “When a distinguished but elderly scientist states that something is possible, he is almost certainly right. When he states that something is impossible, he is very probably wrong.” ARTHUR C. CLARKE

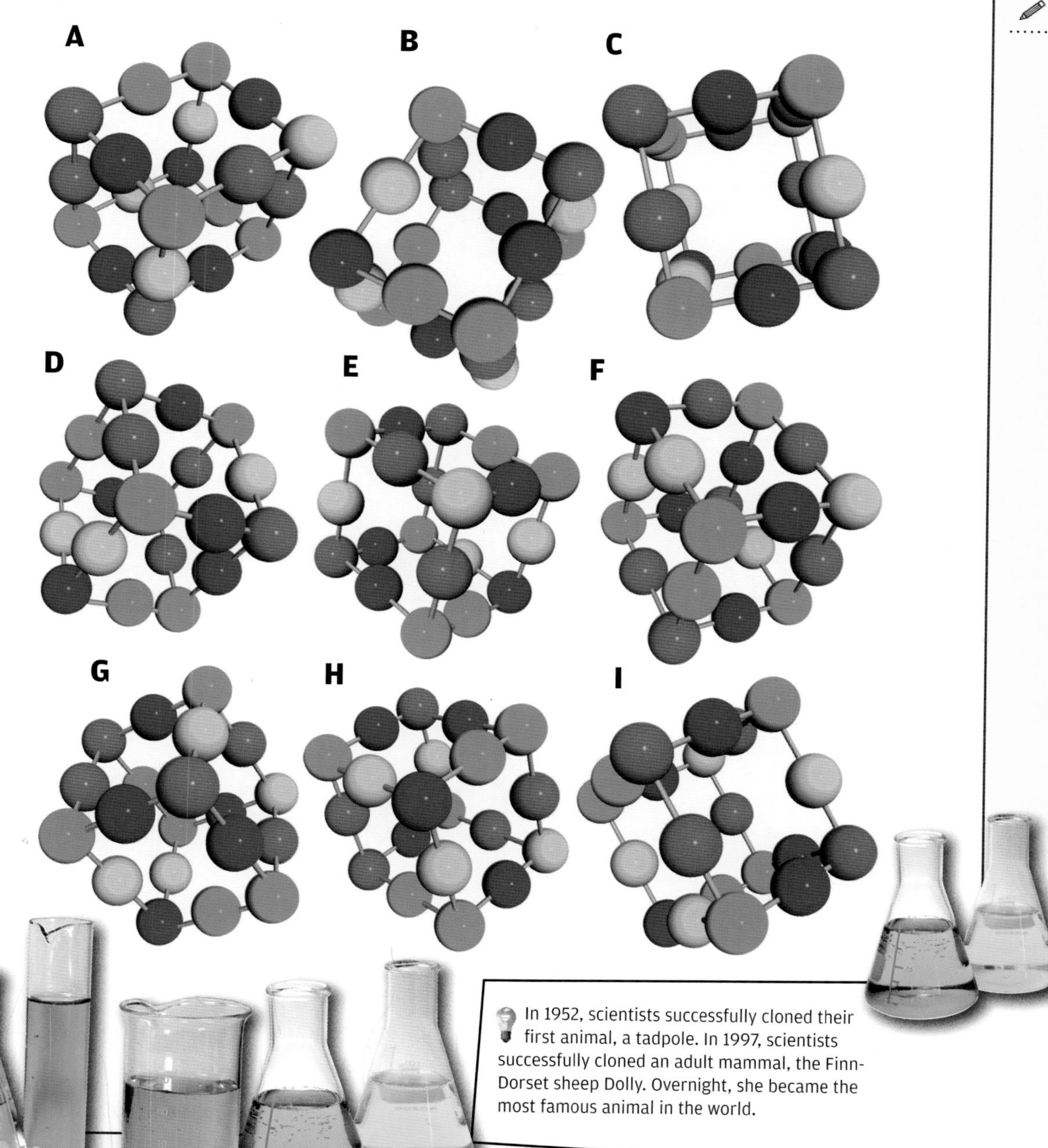

In 1952, scientists successfully cloned their first animal, a tadpole. In 1997, scientists successfully cloned an adult mammal, the Finn-Dorset sheep Dolly. Overnight, she became the most famous animal in the world.

16

DIFFICULTY

Secret Number Sweep

Color in the squares until all the numbers are surrounded by the correct number of shaded squares. When the puzzles is correctly solved the shaded squares will reveal a number!

> **“Everywhere is within walking distance if you have the time.”**
>
> STEVEN WRIGHT

0		3		5		5		4		1	
	3		7		6		7		5		1
2		7		5		4		7		4	
	3		4		1		5		8		3
1		3		2		4		7		4	
	0		0		3		7		7		2
0		0		2		5		7		5	
	3		1		2		5		8		4
3		4		2		1		6		8	
	7		6		4		5		8		4
3		6		7		6		7		4	
1	2		4		5		5	4	4		1

The month of May is named after Maia, the Greek goddess of growth.

17

DIFFICULTY

Loop Link

Connect adjacent dots with either horizontal or vertical lines to create a continuous unbroken loop that never crosses over itself. Some, but not all of the boxes are numbered. The numbers in these boxes tell you how many sides of that box are used by your unbroken line.

> **“Life is just one damned thing after another.”**
>
> ELBERT HUBBARD

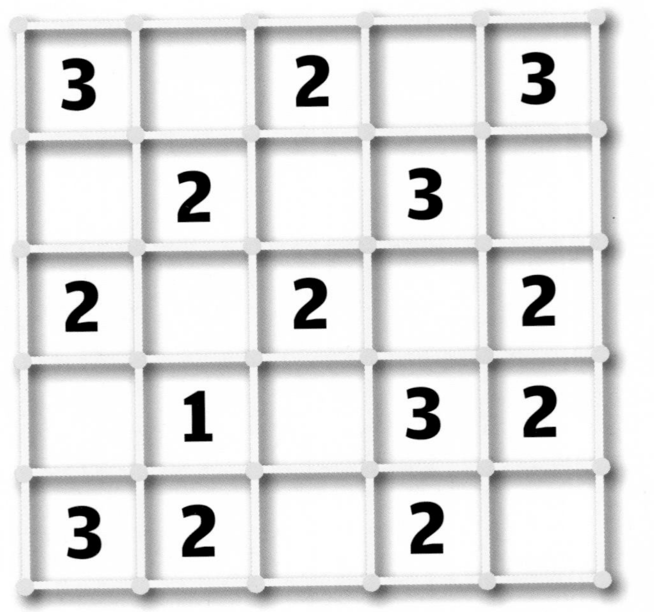

The longest unambiguously documented lifespan is that of Jeanne Calment of France (1875-1997), who was 122 years old. She met Vincent van Gogh at the age of 14.

The top three beef-exporting countries are Brazil, Australia, and Argentina. Brazil is also the world's largest poultry exporter.

Corner Conundrum

18

DIFFICULTY ★★★

Use the numbers in the red corners to make the central number the same way in all three cases. What number should replace the question mark?

On the Radar

19

DIFFICULTY ☆☆★

The numbers in some cells in the grid indicate the exact number of black cells that should border it. Shade these black, until all the numbers are surrounded by the correct number of black cells.

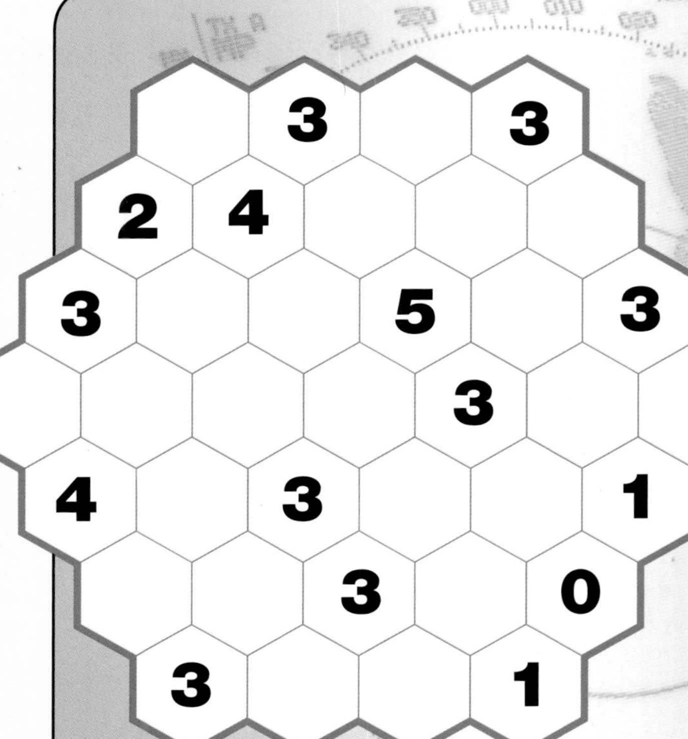

The greatest number of passengers carried by a single commercial airliner is 1,088 by an El Al Boeing 747 during Operation Solomon, which began in May 1991. The purpose of the operation was to evacuate Ethiopian Jews to Israel following the toppling of the Ethiopian government.

> "The knack of flying is learning how to throw yourself at the ground and miss."
>
> Douglas Adams

20

DIFFICULTY

Ride Out!

After the bank robbery, Tex, Six-Gun, and Hoss split up and headed for their hideouts. Can you name each bandit, the horse he rode, and where he escaped to?

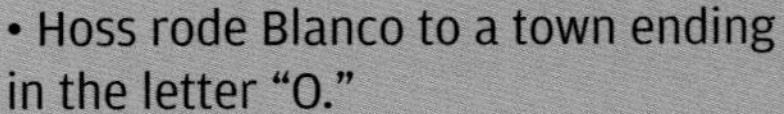

- Hoss rode Blanco to a town ending in the letter "O."
- Six-Gun MacGee didn't ride Sunset, or to Dodge.
- Williams, who wasn't called Tex, didn't ride to Reno.

Rodeos, a popular wild west pastime to test a cowboy's skills, are the only national spectator sport to originate entirely in the United States. A typical rodeo includes a variety of events from calf roping and steer wrestling to saddle bronc and bull riding.

Deluth
Williams
MacGee
Bullet
Sunset
Blanco
Reno
Dodge
Chicago

Tex
Six-Gun
Hoss
Reno
Dodge
Chicago
Bullet
Sunset
Blanco

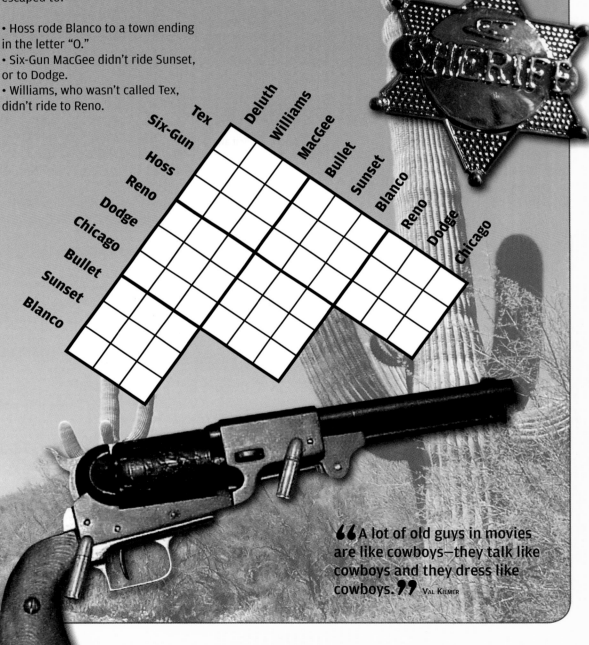

"A lot of old guys in movies are like cowboys—they talk like cowboys and they dress like cowboys." Val Kilmer

21

DIFFICULTY

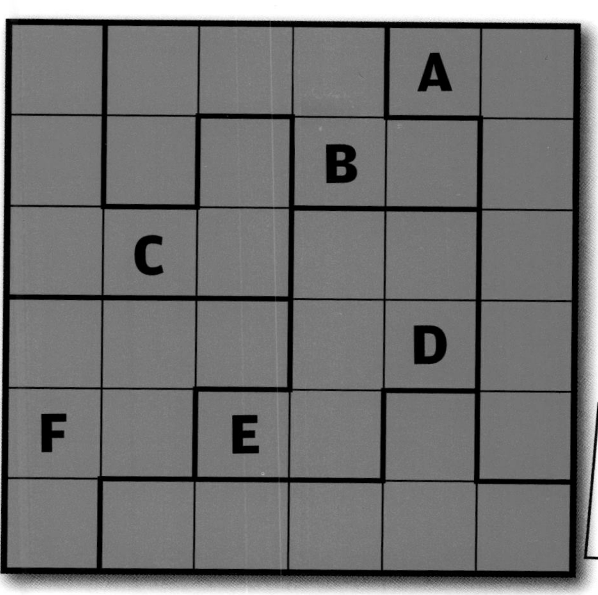

Latin Square

Complete the grid so that every row and column, and every outlined area, contains the letters A, B, C, D, E, and F.

"Abstaining is favorable both to the head and the pocket." W. C. FIELDS

In his will, journalist and newspaper founder Joseph Pulitzer established the Pulitzer Prize to foster excellence in many fields, including journalism. The first awards were given in 1917.

22

DIFFICULTY

Sum People

Each of the different pictures in the box represents a number. The numbers at the end of each row and the bottom of each column are the totals of the numbers in that row or column added together. Can you work out which number each picture represents and so work out what the question mark should be?

In winning the Masters Tournament at Augusta in 1997, Tiger Woods smashed a number of records. He was the youngest player to win the championship. He won by 12 stokes—the greatest margin of victory—and his final four round score of 270, 18 under par, was an Augusta record. He was also the first black player to win a major golf tournament.

23

DIFFICULTY ★

Matching Pair

Only one of the tiles below is unique, the other 14 all have an exact double. Can you find it?

Some of the earliest examples of mosaic patterns on glazed tiles uncovered came from the columns of the temple at Ubaid in Mesopotamia, and are attributed to the second half of the 2nd millennium B.C.

24

DIFFICULTY ★★

More or Less

The arrows indicate whether a number in a box is greater or smaller than an adjacent number. Complete the grid so that all rows and columns contain the numbers 1 to 5.

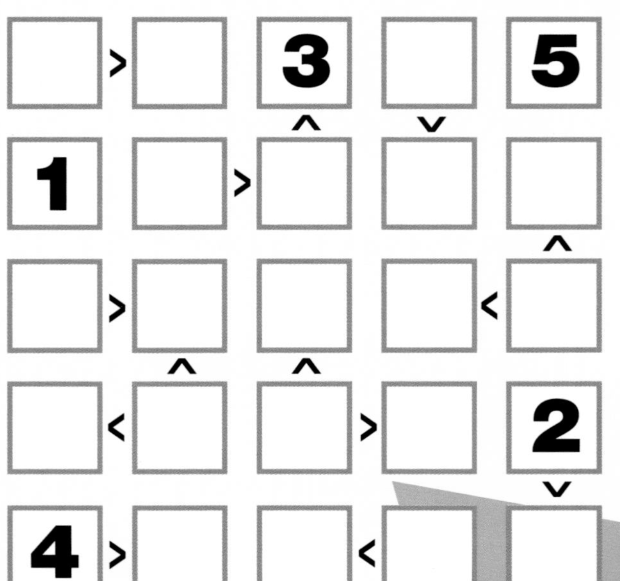

“Even a rich man thinks he has to go down to the office every day. Not because he likes it but because he can't think of anything else to do.”

W. H. AUDEN

The philosopher and writer Jean Paul Sartre declined the Nobel Prize he was awarded in 1964, citing as his reason his consistent refusal to accept any awards.

The annual survey by car-paint manufacturer DuPont found that in 2007, white, by a brief margin, had overtaken silver as the most popular car color.

25 DIFFICULTY

Swatch Switch

There are exactly 24 different ways to arrange four colors next to each other in a line. 23 are shown here, can you work out the order the colors should be in the missing swatch?

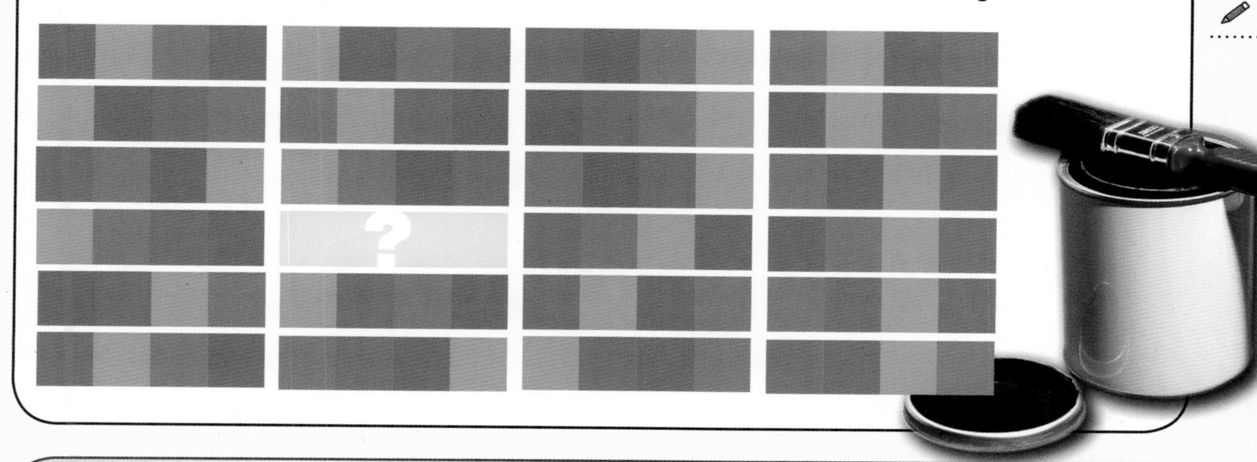

26 DIFFICULTY

Fair's Square

The numbers by each row and column describe black squares and groups of black squares that are adjoining in that row or column. Color in all the black squares and a six number combination will be revealed.

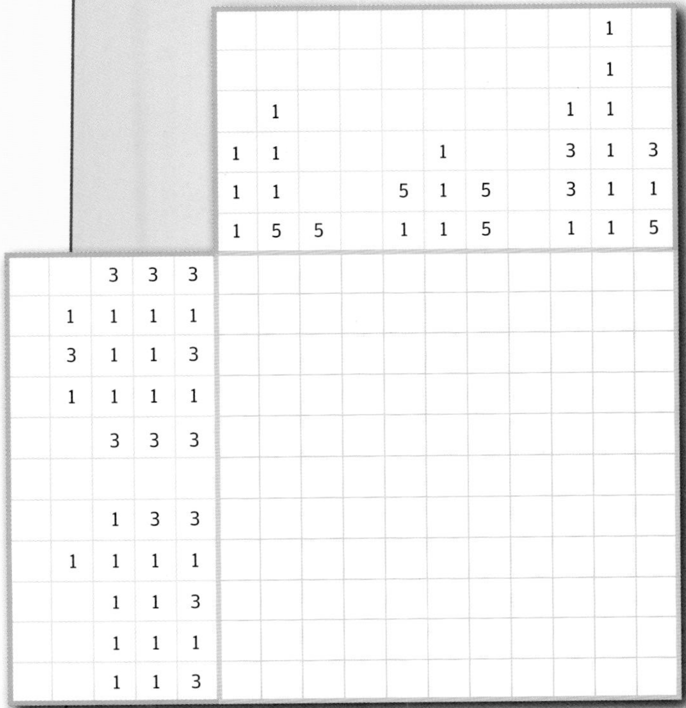

Column clues (top to bottom, columns left to right):

									1	
									1	
	1							1	1	
1	1				1			3	1	3
1	1			5	1	5		3	1	1
1	5	5		1	1	5		1	1	5

Row clues (rows top to bottom):

		3	3	3
	1	1	1	1
	3	1	1	3
	1	1	1	1
		3	3	3
		1	3	3
	1	1	1	1
		1	1	3
		1	1	1
		1	1	3

“Most of the time I don't have much fun. The rest of the time I don't have any fun at all.”

Woody Allen

The world's smallest city block is in Dothan, Alabama, at the intersection of North Appletree, Museum, and Troy Street. The tiny land triangle features a stop sign, a yield sign, a street sign, and a granite marker placed in 1964, stating that it is the world's smallest city block.

27

DIFFICULTY ☆★★

Mine Sweeper

The numbers in some squares in the grid indicate the exact number of black squares that should surround it. Shade these squares until all the numbers are surrounded by the correct number of black squares.

“It’s discouraging to think how many people are shocked by honesty and how few by deceit.” Noel Coward

2			1		2		
		3	3		3	3	
2	3		3		3		2
		4	4	3		2	
3			3		3		1
3				2		2	1
	5		3	2			2
2		2	2		2		

28

DIFFICULTY ☆☆★

Odd Number Out

All these numbers appear twice in the box except one. Can you find it?

“A few honest men are better than numbers.”
Oliver Cromwell

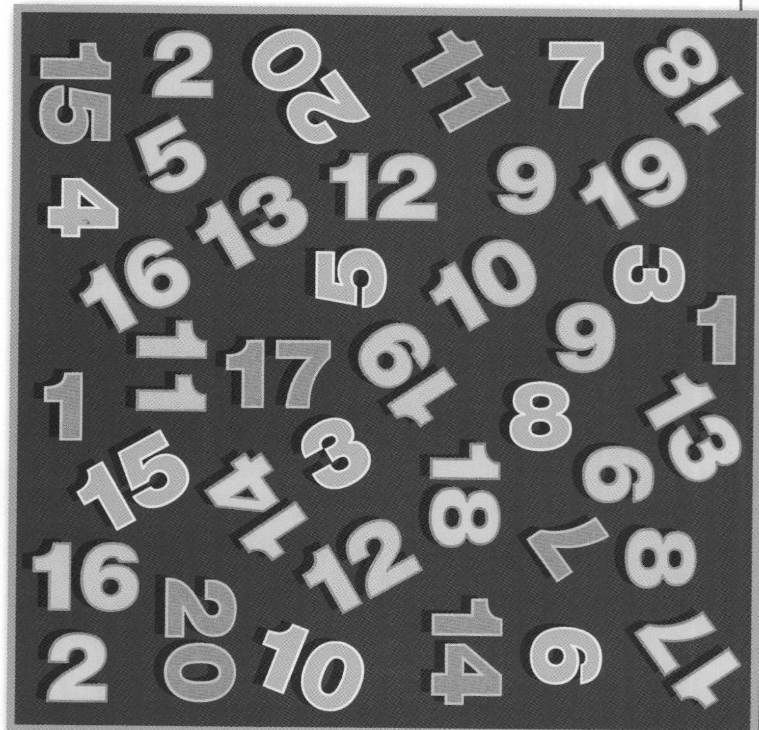

In July 2006, President Lech Kaczynski of Poland swore in his country’s new prime minister—his identical twin brother Jaroslaw.

29

DIFFICULTY ★★★

The South China tiger is believed to be the antecedent of all known species of the big cat.

In the Middle

What numbers should appear in the hubs of these number wheels?

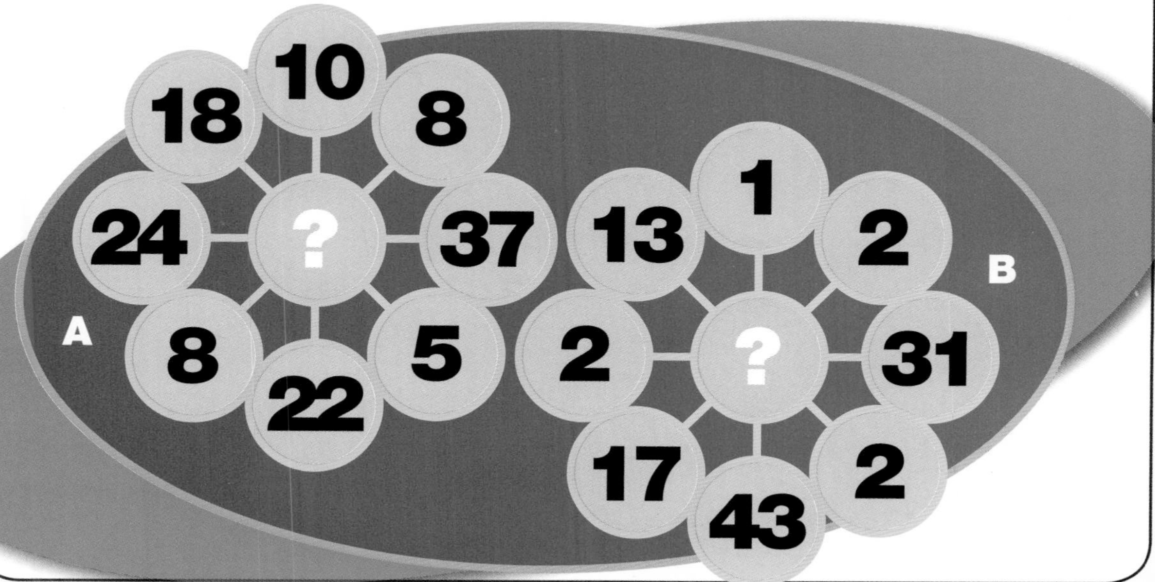

30

DIFFICULTY ★★★

Sudoku

		6		7		5	3	
8			1	3		2		
					2			
9				5			4	
		4			6		8	5
2	8		7	9		6		
	1			6				9
	7					4	2	1
5			4				6	

Complete the grid so that all rows and columns, and each outlined block of nine squares, contain the numbers 1, 2, 3, 4, 5, 6, 7, 8 and 9.

“Have the courage to be ignorant of a great number of things, in order to avoid the calamity of being ignorant of everything.” Sydney Smith

Sudoku is so popular in Japan that sudoku magazines sell over 600,000 copies each month.

31

DIFFICULTY ☆★★

Where's the Pair?

Only two of the shapes below match exactly—can you find them?

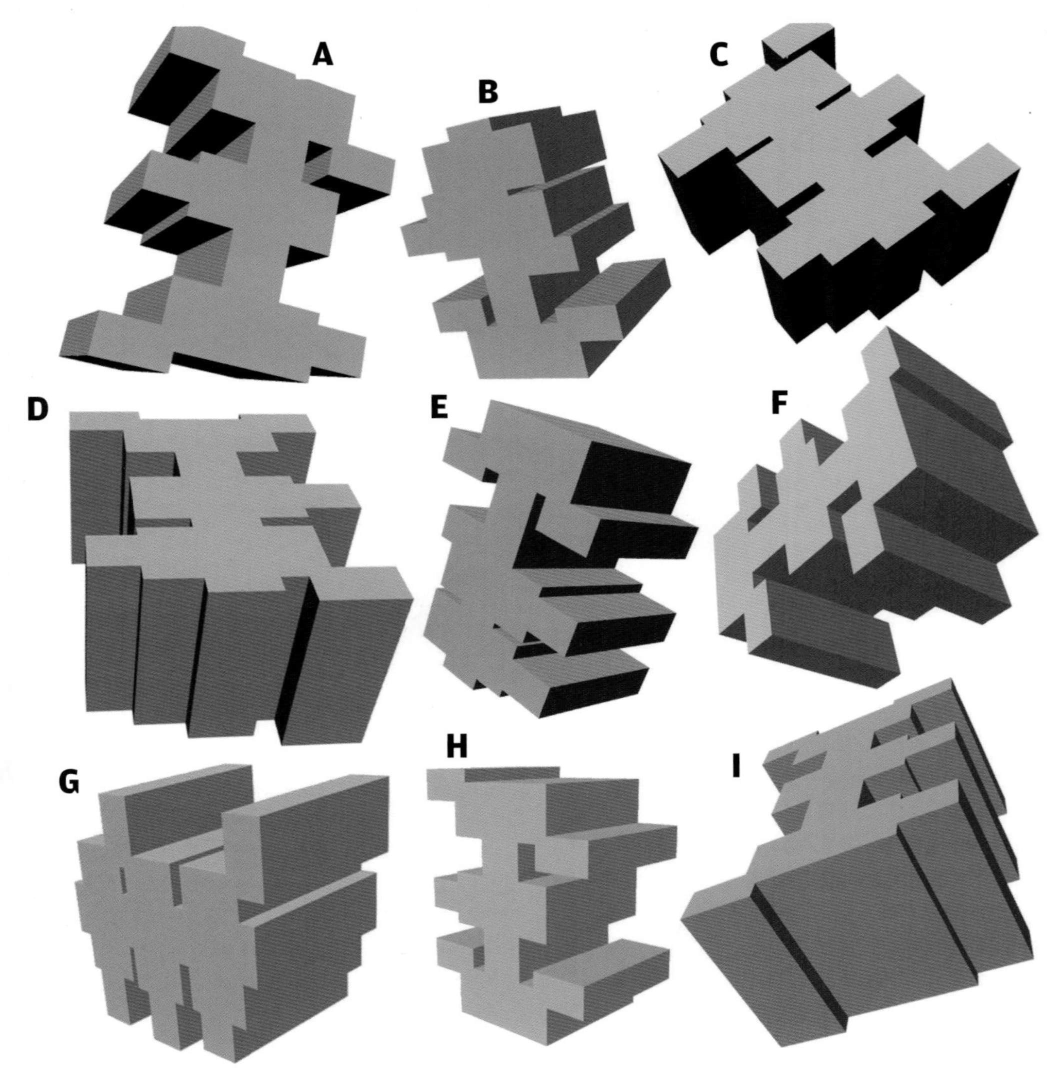

The flower with the world's largest bloom is the *Rafflesia arnoldii*. Found in the rainforests of Indonesia, it can grow to be 3 feet (1 meter) across and weigh up to 15 pounds (7 kilograms). When in bloom it emits a repulsive smell, like rotting meat, which attracts the insects that pollinate the plant.

"I am very interested in the universe—I am specializing in the universe and all that surrounds it." Peter Cook

32

DIFFICULTY

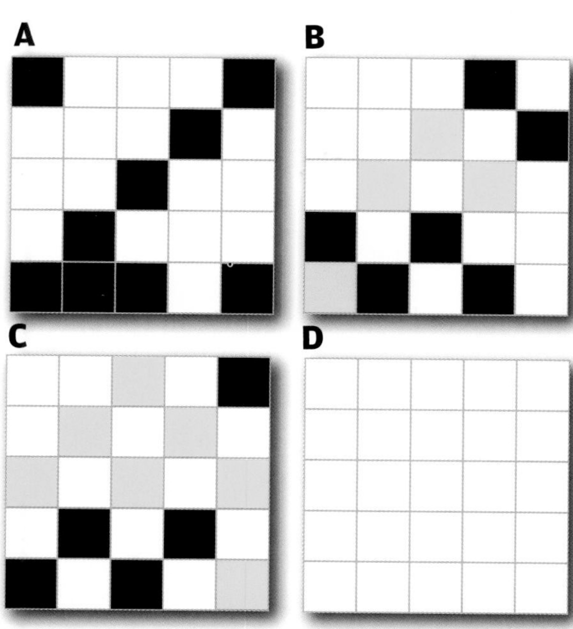

Apply the Rules

The colors of each square in pattern B are directly related to the colors in pattern A. The square colors in pattern C relate to pattern B the same way. Can you apply the same rules and fill in pattern D?

"Boredom is the legitimate kingdom of the philanthropic."

VIRGINIA WOOLF

In its history Brazil has been a colony, an empire, a republic, and has been under military rule. Today, it is a democracy and the fifth largest nation on earth.

33

DIFFICULTY

Make the Cut

Cut two straight lines through this shape to create three shapes that are identical.

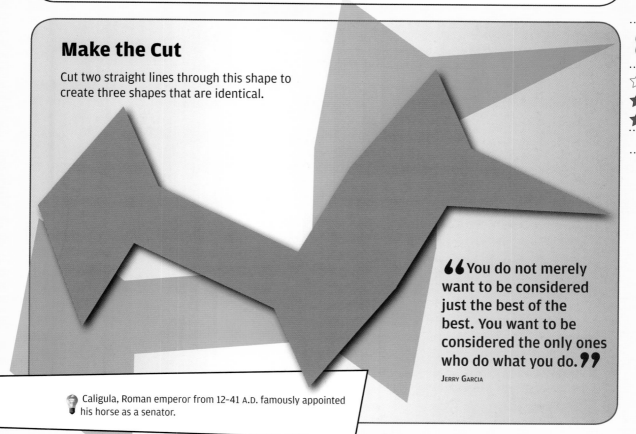

"You do not merely want to be considered just the best of the best. You want to be considered the only ones who do what you do."

JERRY GARCIA

Caligula, Roman emperor from 12-41 A.D. famously appointed his horse as a senator.

34

DIFFICULTY ☆☆★

Next!

In the sequence below, which of the numbered alternatives, A, B, C, or D, should replace the question mark?

In 1912, Alfred Wegener proposed the theory of Continental Drift—the idea that one supercontinent consisting of what we know today as Africa and South America had existed millions of years ago. He called it Pangaea.

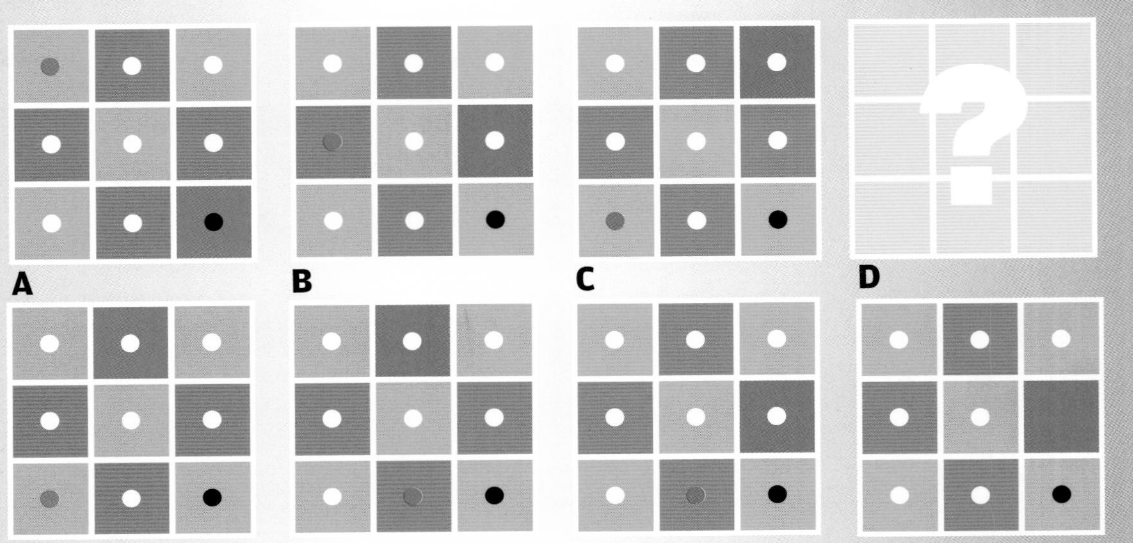

35

DIFFICULTY ★★★

Make it Out

Which of the colored-in sand bucket and shovel images matches the silhouette?

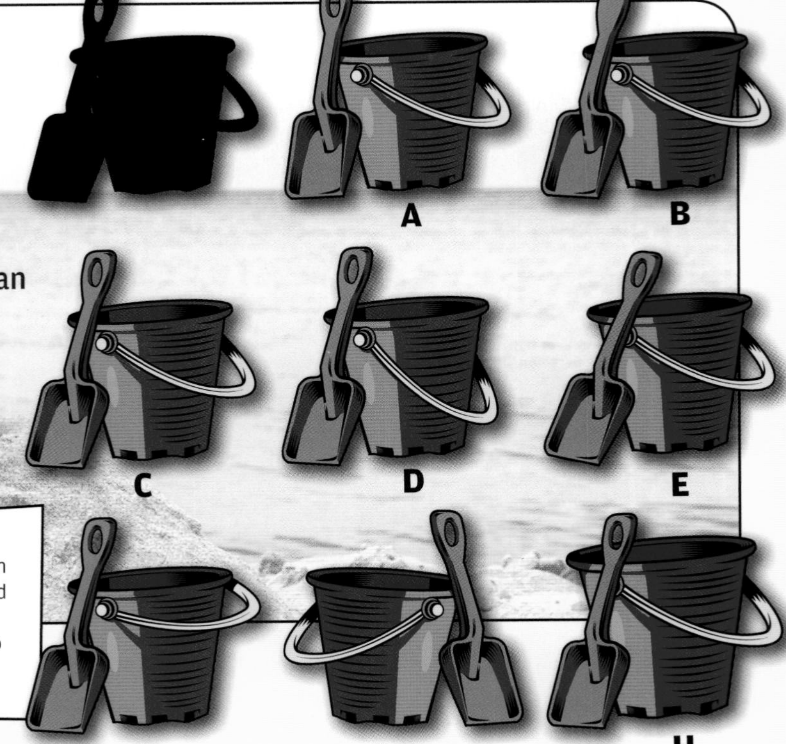

“Every man who possibly can should force himself to a holiday of a full month in a year, whether he feels like taking it or not.” William James

Praia do Cassino, Brazil, is commonly known as the longest beach in the world. Estimated at 158 miles (254 kilometers) long, it stretches from the entrance to the Rio Grande seaport to nearly Chuí, on the border with Uruguay.

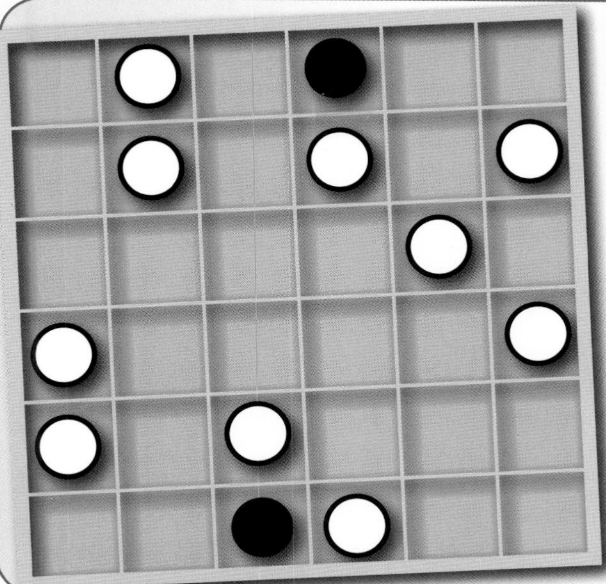

36

DIFFICULTY

Around in Circles

Draw a single continuous line that passes through all the circles. The line must enter and leave each box in the center of one of its four sides.

Black Circle Turn left or right in the box, and the line must pass straight through the next and previous boxes.
White Circle Travel straight through the box, and the line must turn in the next and/or previous box.

“Attitude is a little thing that makes a big difference.”
Winston Churchill

37

DIFFICULTY

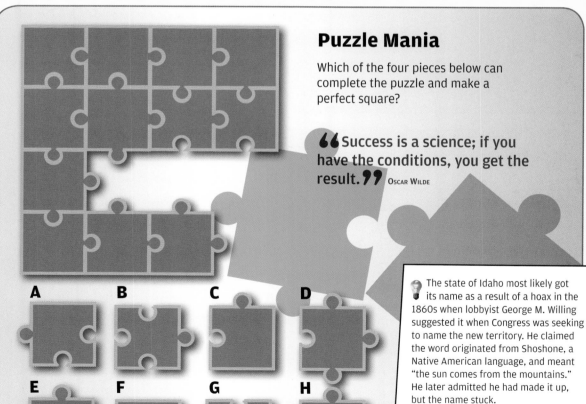

Puzzle Mania

Which of the four pieces below can complete the puzzle and make a perfect square?

“Success is a science; if you have the conditions, you get the result.” Oscar Wilde

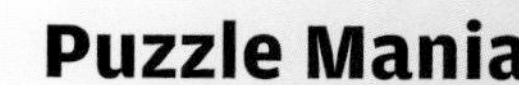

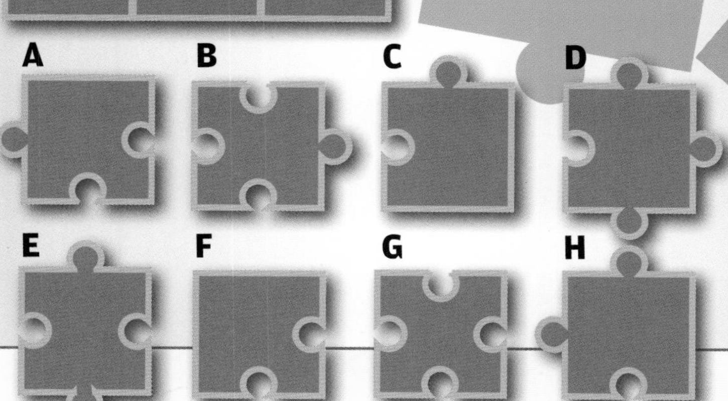

The state of Idaho most likely got its name as a result of a hoax in the 1860s when lobbyist George M. Willing suggested it when Congress was seeking to name the new territory. He claimed the word originated from Shoshone, a Native American language, and meant “the sun comes from the mountains.” He later admitted he had made it up, but the name stuck.

38

DIFFICULTY ☆☆★

Spot the Slate

Two square slates have been broken into four pieces each. Can you reunite them?

The U.S. Bullion Depository at Fort Knox, Kentucky, opened in January 1937. The building cost $560,000 to construct and the materials included 16,000 cubic feet (4,900 cubic meters) of granite, 4,200 cubic yards (3,800 cubic meters) of concrete, 750 tons (680 metric tons) of reinforcing steel, and 670 tons (610 metric tons) of structural steel.

39

DIFFICULTY ☆★★

Invisible Blocks

Assuming all blocks that are not visible from this angle are present, how many blocks have been removed from this 6 x 6 x 6 cube?

"Sometimes paranoia's just having all the facts."

WILLIAM BURROUGHS

In the Middle Ages, fern seeds were thought to be invisible because ferns don't have seeds. They were also said to grant invisibility, as Gadshill from Shakespeare's *Henry IV* claims "We steal as in a castle, cock-sure. We have the recipe of fern-seed, we walk invisible."

40

DIFFICULTY ★☆☆

Can You Cut It?

Cut a straight line through this shape to create two shapes that are identical.

"There can't be any crisis next week. My schedule is already full."

Henry Kissinger

The oldest surviving copy of a news pamphlet was published in Cologne, Germany, in 1470.

41

DIFFICULTY ★★☆

Perfect Pitch

In the field on this map, every tree has one tent found horizontally or vertically adjacent to it. No tent can be in an adjacent square to another tent (even diagonally). The numbers by each row and column tell you how many tents are there. Can you locate all the tents?

		▲		▲			▲	3
▲								0
		▲						2
				▲				1
▲								1
			▲			▲		2
	▲							2
						▲	▲	1
2	1	2	1	2	1	2	1	

"One thing that's certain about the great outdoors: When you come back inside you'll be scratching."

P. J. O'Rourke

▲ TREE

▲ TENT

The world's rarest living creature is the Abingdon Island giant tortoise, which is represented by just one specimen. Because there is no hope of discovering a mate, this particular species is now effectively extinct.

42

DIFFICULTY

Seeing Double

All these shapes appear twice in the box except one. Can you find it?

“Advertising is the rattling of a stick inside a swill bucket.”

George Orwell

Renaissance polymath Leonardo da Vinci is believed to have invented scissors.

43

DIFFICULTY

Lucky Number

What's the missing number?

Gambling was legalized in Las Vegas, Nevada, in 1931. The first people to be issued a gambling license were Mayme V. Stocker and J. H. Morgan, on 20 March 1931. Their three-month license cost $1,410.

15

12

16

?

44

DIFFICULTY

Fit Together

Which of the two honeycomb shapes below can be paired up to create the top shape?

A

B

C

> “If God had wanted us to bend over, he would have put diamonds on the floor.” JOAN RIVERS

D

E

F

During World War II, Academy Award statues were made of plaster instead of the usual gold to mark the war effort.

45

DIFFICULTY

Going in Circles

Use the corner circles to make the central number the same way in all three cases. What number should replace the question mark?

The rock group Pink Floyd took their name from two blues musicians—Pink Anderson and Floyd Council.

46

DIFFICULTY

Boxed Up

The value of each shape is the number of sides each shape has, multiplied by the number within it. So a square containing the number 4 has a value of 16. Find a block of four squares (two squares wide by two squares high) with a total value of exactly 100.

"A lot of fellows nowadays have a B.A., M.D., or a PhD. Unfortunately they don't have a J.O.B." Fats Domino

Sir Hans Sloane was a British physicist and collector of curiosities in the eighteenth century. Upon his death in 1753 he bequeathed his collection to the nation and formed the basis of the British Museum, which opened six years later.

47

DIFFICULTY

What's Coming Next?

The sequence below follows a logical pattern. Can you work out the color and shape of the next in line?

Sir Hans Sloane was responsible for the invention of milk chocolate. While traveling in Jamaica he found the local drink of cocoa and water much more palatable if mixed with milk.

"Success is having to worry about every damn thing in the world, except money." Johnny Cash

All at Sea

The numbers on the side and bottom of the grid indicate occupied squares or groups of consecutive occupied squares in each row or column. Can you finish the grid so that it contains four cruisers, three launches, and two buoys, and the numbers tally?

"As a general rule, nobody has money who ought to have it."
BENJAMIN DISRAELI

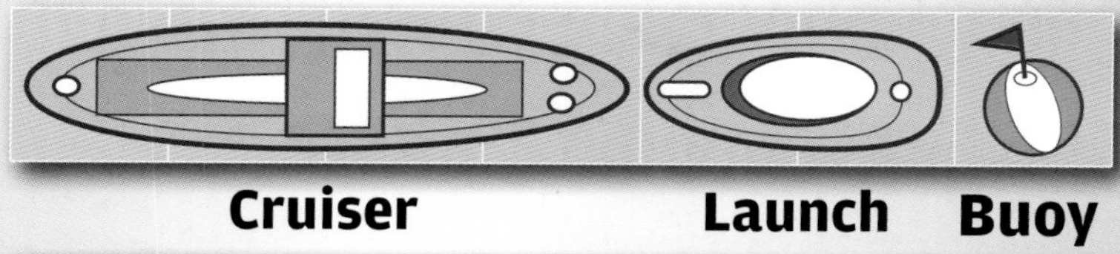

Cruiser Launch Buoy

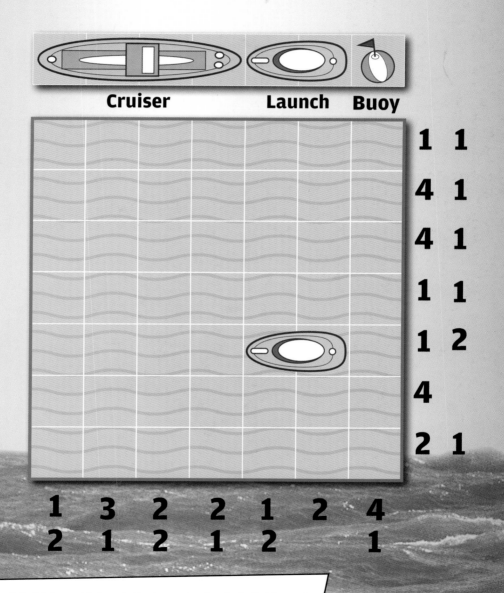

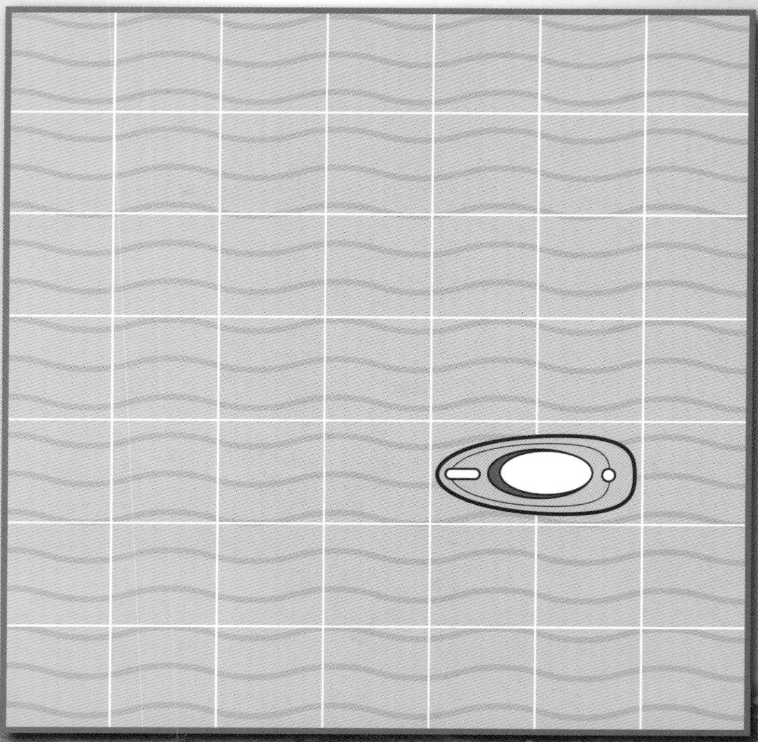

							Row clues
							1 1
							4 1
							4 1
							1 1
				Launch	Launch		1 2
							4
							2 1
1 2	3 1	2 2	2 1	1 2	2	4 1	

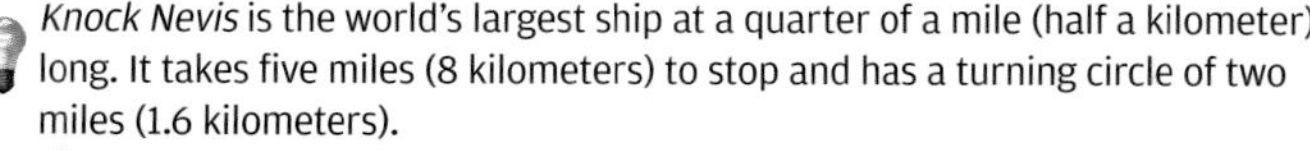

Knock Nevis is the world's largest ship at a quarter of a mile (half a kilometer) long. It takes five miles (8 kilometers) to stop and has a turning circle of two miles (1.6 kilometers).

49

DIFFICULTY

Taking Shape

What shape, in what color, should replace the question mark so that the grid follows a pattern?

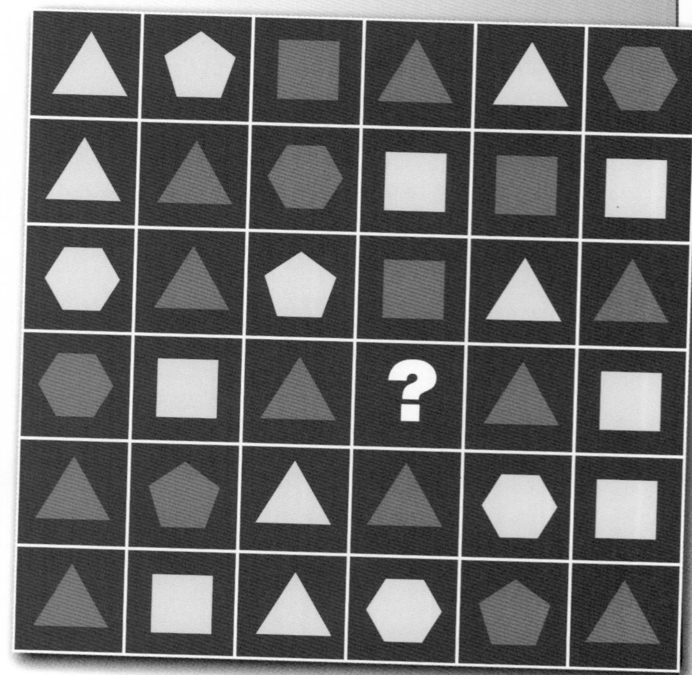

“A man’s worth is no greater than his ambitions.”

Marcus Aurelius

French writer Voltaire is the man responsible for the theory that a falling apple provided the impetus for Newton’s theory of gravity. Voltaire claimed to have been told the story by Newton’s niece.

50

DIFFICULTY

Pentagon Puzzler

The numbers on these pentagons follow a pattern. Your task is to uncover the secret to the pattern and fill in the blanks to complete the puzzle.

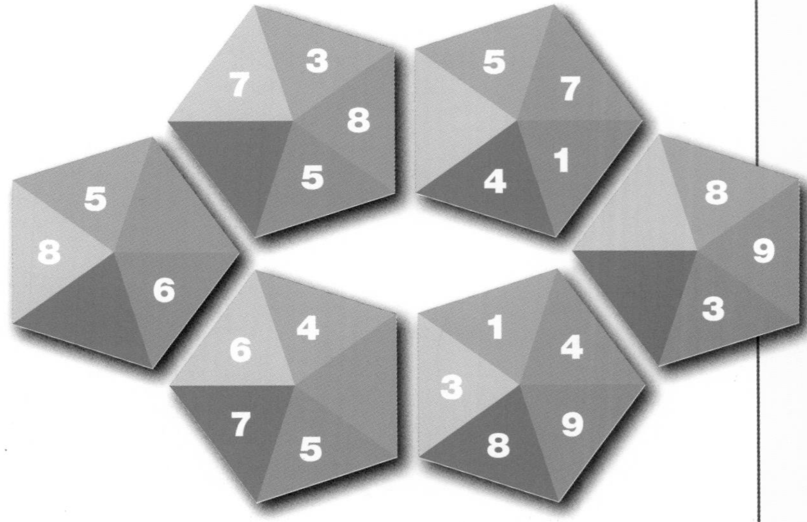

“Dreams are renewable. No matter what our age or condition, there are still untapped possibilities within us and new beauty waiting to be born.”

Dale E. Turner

Despite being over 60 years old and the world’s fourth largest building (in terms of floor space), the Pentagon is still thought to be one of the most efficient office buildings in the world. Although the giant Department of Defense HQ at Arlington, Virginia, contains 17 ½ miles (12 kilometers) of corridors it takes only seven minutes to walk between any two points in the building.

51

DIFFICULTY

In the Hole

Which of the squares below correctly completes the grid?

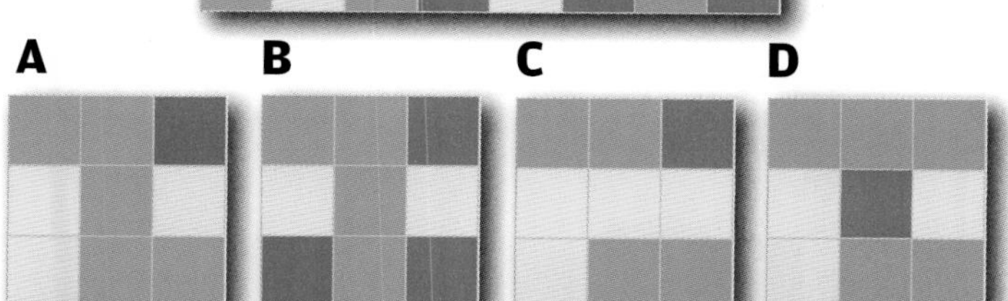

“Maybe, just once, someone will call me ‘sir’ without adding, ‘you’re making a scene.’”

HOMER SIMPSON

The Gulf Stream originates in the western Caribbean Sea and flows through the Gulf of Mexico and the Straits of Florida. It moves north driven by prevailing trail winds along the east coast of the United States to Cape Hatteras in North Carolina, where it turns northeast toward Europe.

52

DIFFICULTY

Jumbled Puzzle

Which of the four pieces below can complete the jigsaw and make a perfect square?

“Blessed is he who expects nothing for he shall never be disappointed.”

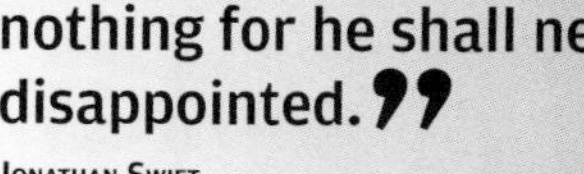

JONATHAN SWIFT

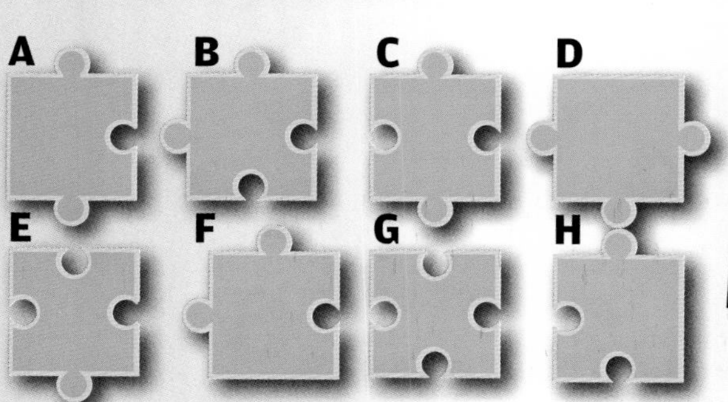

In 1954, Ann Hodge from Alabama was struck by a nearly 9-pound (4-kilogram) meteorite, which crashed through her ceiling and struck her after bouncing off her radio, leaving her badly bruised. It was the first recorded incidence of a human being struck by a meteorite.

53

DIFFICULTY

Knight's Move

Find an empty square in the grid that is one chess knight's move away from a blue, red, and yellow circle. A knight's move is an "L" shape—two squares sideways, up or down in any direction, followed by one square to the left or right.

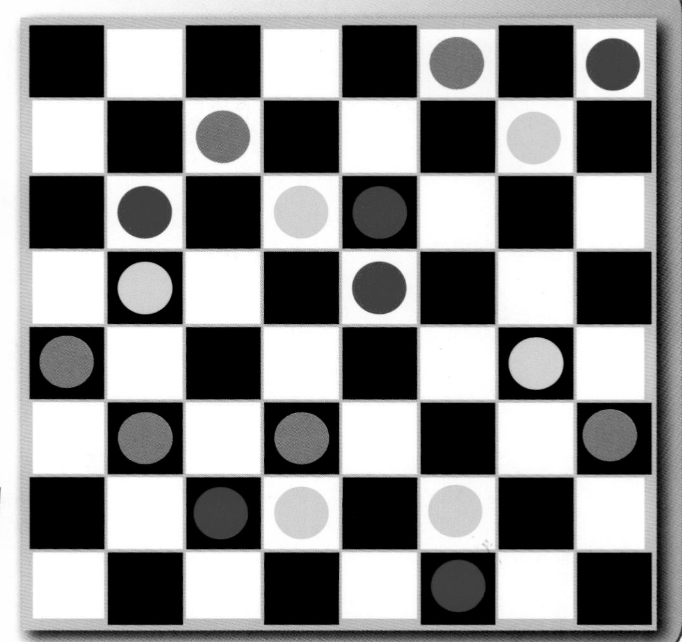

"My loathings are simple: stupidity, oppression, crime, cruelty, and soft music."

VLADIMIR NABOKOV

The word "checkmate" comes from the Persian phrase "Shah Mat," which means "the King is dead."

54

DIFFICULTY

Center of Attention

What numbers should appear in the hubs of these number wheels?

There are three sovereign countries that are completely surrounded by other countries: Lesotho (South Africa), San Marino, and the Vatican City (the last two in Italy).

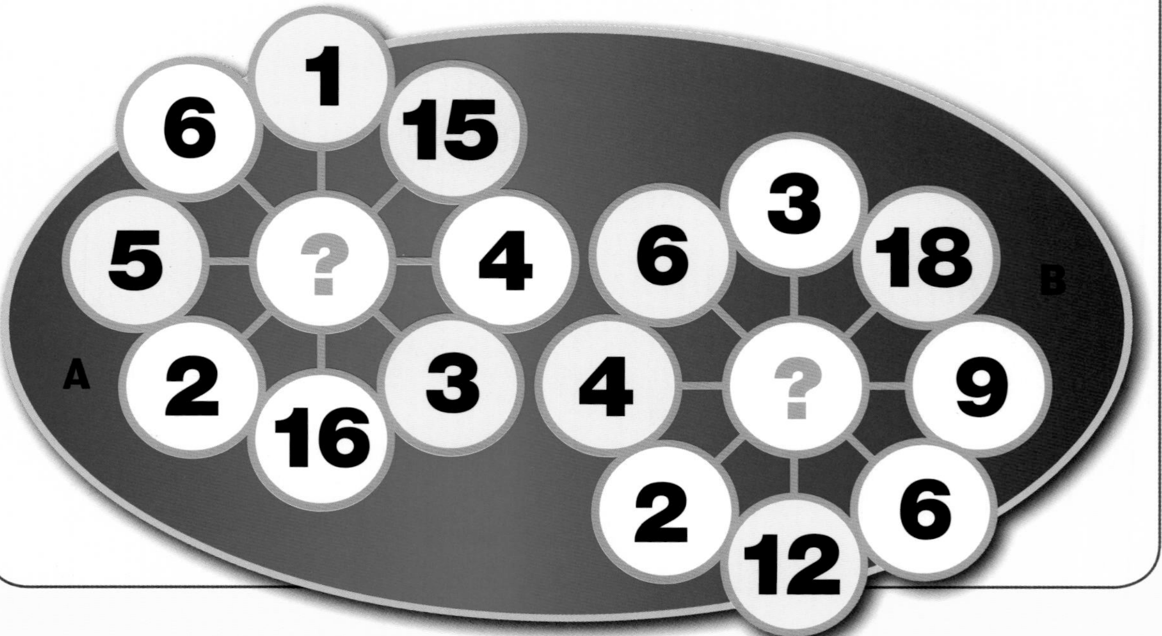

55

DIFFICULTY

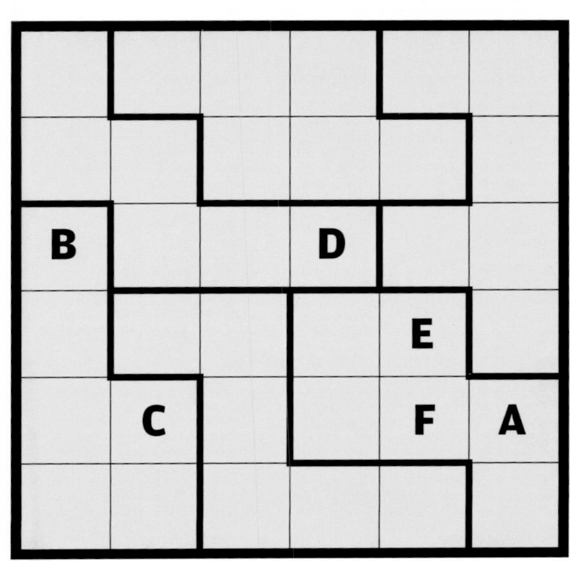

Squared Off

Complete the grid so that every row and column, and every outlined area, contains the letters A, B, C, D, E, and F.

“Occasionally he stumbled over the truth, but hastily picked himself up and carried on as if nothing had happened.” Stanley Baldwin

A Motorola telecommunications engineer was the first person to make a call using a cellular phone. On a Manhattan street on April 3, 1973, he called a friend who worked for a rival company to let him know they'd made the breakthrough.

56

DIFFICULTY

2		3		2			1
			2		2	3	
	4	1		1			3
			1			5	
4		4			3		
		6			3		3
				5			
1	3		4			2	0

Black Out

The numbers in some of the squares in the grid indicate the exact number of black squares that should surround it. Shade these squares until all the numbers are surrounded by the correct number of black squares.

“Have a nice day, dear. Don't drive over any mines or anything.” Basil Fawlty

The longest acceptance speech in Academy Award history was delivered by Greer Garson in 1943 upon winning Best Actress for *Mrs. Miniver*. It lasted five minutes and 30 seconds.

57

DIFFICULTY

Loopy Numbers

Connect adjacent dots with either horizontal or vertical lines to create a continuous unbroken loop that never crosses over itself. Some but not all of the boxes are numbered. The numbers in these boxes tell you how many sides of that box are used by your unbroken line.

"I have but one lamp by which my feet are guided, and that is the lamp of experience. I know no way of judging of the future but by the past." EDWARD GIBBON

2	2		2	3
	3	1	2	
2				2
3	2		3	
3	1	2		2

58

DIFFICULTY

Mechanical Matrix

Engine mechanic Jack Willis has discovered that he has been delivered too many parts. He knows eight of the parts that he definitely needs but can you assist him in working out which of the four boxed figures completes the set?

"The government solution to a problem is usually as bad as the problem." MILTON FRIEDMAN

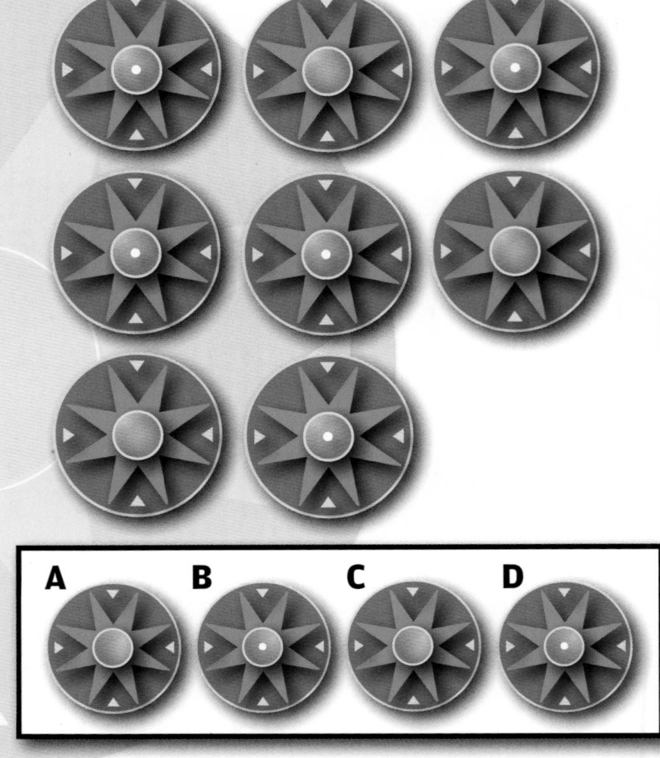

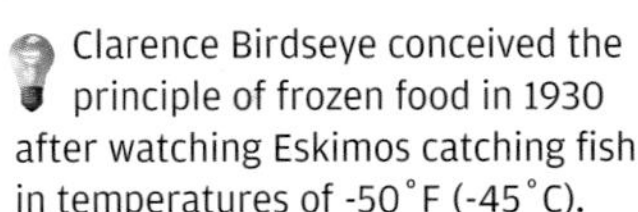

Clarence Birdseye conceived the principle of frozen food in 1930 after watching Eskimos catching fish in temperatures of -50°F (-45°C).

The Finns are the world's greatest coffee drinkers, consuming on average 25 pounds (11 kilograms) every year per person.

Magic Squares

59

DIFFICULTY

Complete the square using nine consecutive numbers, so that all rows, columns, and diagonals add up to the same total.

"I believe in equality for everyone—except reporters and photographers." MOHANDAS GHANDI

Find the Way

60

DIFFICULTY

The arrows indicate whether a number in a box is greater or smaller than an adjacent number. Complete the grid so that all rows and columns contain the numbers 1 to 5.

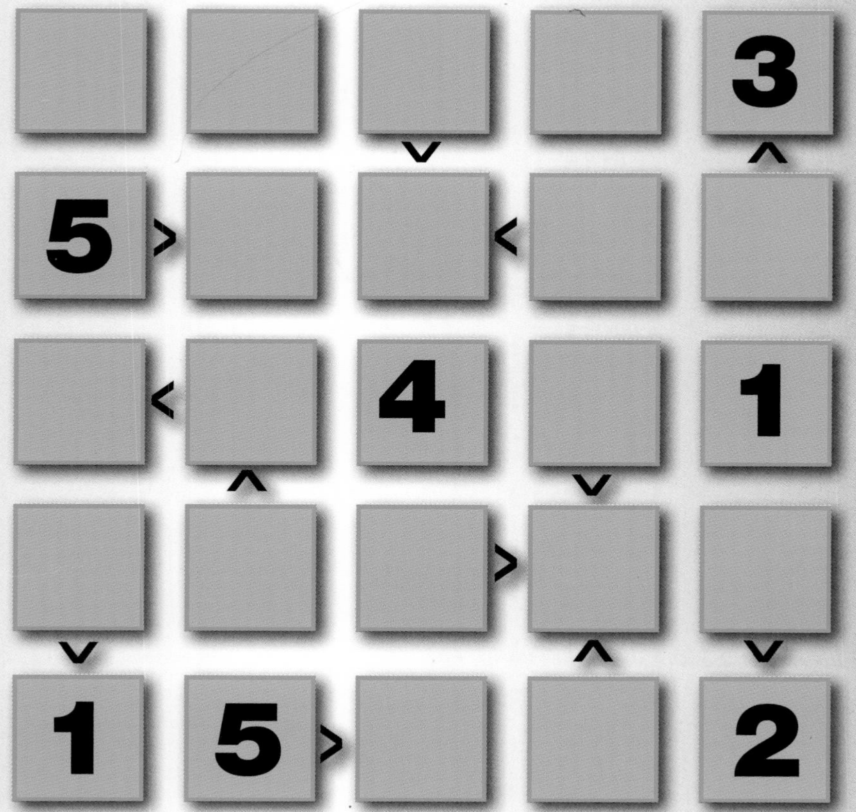

 The UN Declaration of Human Rights is 1,772 words long.

61

DIFFICULTY ★★★

Sudoku

Complete the grid so that all rows and columns, and each outlined block of nine squares, contain the numbers 1, 2, 3, 4, 5, 6, 7, 8, and 9 only once.

“Acting is merely the art of keeping a large group of people from coughing.”
RALPH RICHARDSON

						5	4	3
2		6		3			7	
7				6	9		1	
9				2		3		
	4		5		8			2
6		7	8			1		
					3			4
8			6	1				9

62

DIFFICULTY ☆★★

Picture Logic

The numbers by each row and column describe black squares and groups of black squares that are adjoining. Color in all the black squares and a six-number combination will be revealed.

“Manners are especially the need of the plain. The pretty can get away with anything.”
EVELYN WAUGH

Column clues (left to right, top to bottom):

Col 1	Col 2	Col 3	Col 4	Col 5	Col 6	Col 7	Col 8	Col 9	Col 10	Col 11
1 1 1 1	1 1 1 1	5 5		3 1 5	1 1 1 1 1 1	1 3 1 3		5 1	1 1 1 1	5 5

Row clues (top to bottom):

Row	Clue
1	3 3 3
2	1 1 1 1
3	3 3 3
4	1 1 1 1
5	3 3 3
6	
7	3 3 3
8	1 1 1
9	1 3 1
10	1 1 1 1
11	1 3 1

The most expensive bottle of wine ever sold was a bottle of 1787 Château Lafite from the cellar of Thomas Jefferson, which sold at Christie’s auction house, London, for $160,000 in December 1985.

63

DIFFICULTY

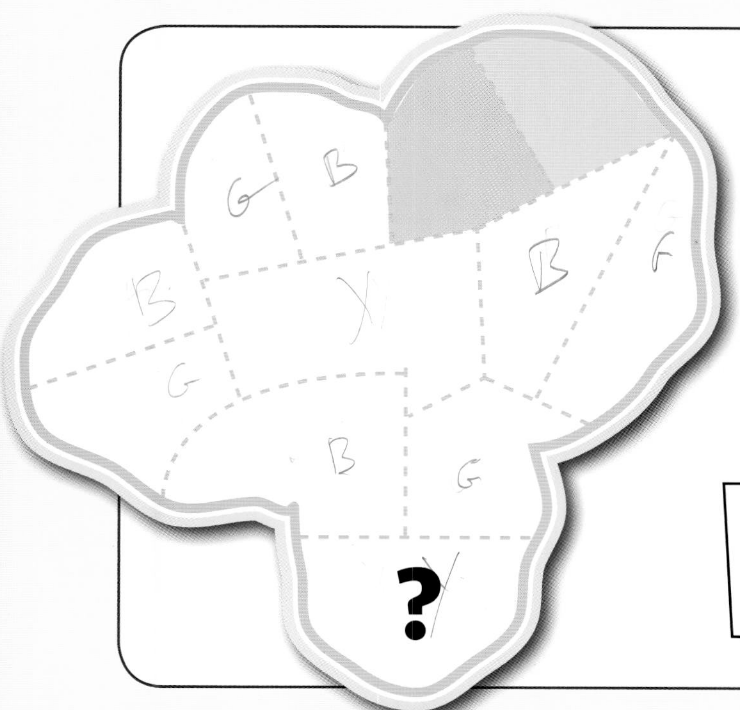

Map Attack

This map can only be colored in with three colors—blue, yellow, and green. Assuming no two adjacent areas can be colored the same, what color will the area containing the question mark be?

“Speak softly and carry a big stick.” THEODORE ROOSEVELT

Regarded as the world's longest motorable road, the Pan-American Highway runs for 15,000 miles from Fairbanks, Alaska, to Brasilia, Brazil.

64

DIFFICULTY

3R	3D	2D	1L
2D	OPEN	1L	3L
1R	2D	1R	1U
1U	2R	2U	1D
4U	4U	1U	1L

Safecracker

To open the safe, all the buttons must be pressed in the correct order before the “open” button is pressed. What is the first button you must press in your sequence?

“No people is wholly civilized where a distinction is drawn between stealing an office and stealing a purse.”
THEODORE ROOSEVELT

The Ivy League is made up of the northeastern universities of Brown, Columbia, Cornell, Dartmouth, Harvard, Princeton, Pennsylvania, and Yale.

Big Pot Bonanza

Mac, Jack, and Zac are playing poker. They each won a big pot with their biggest hands of the night, but can you work out their last names, and then who won how much, with which hand?

- Mac won $250 with his biggest hand, which wasn't four of a kind.
- Brunson had the flush and took more than $100 from Zac with it.
- The $100 pot was won by a full house, but not by Chan or Zac.

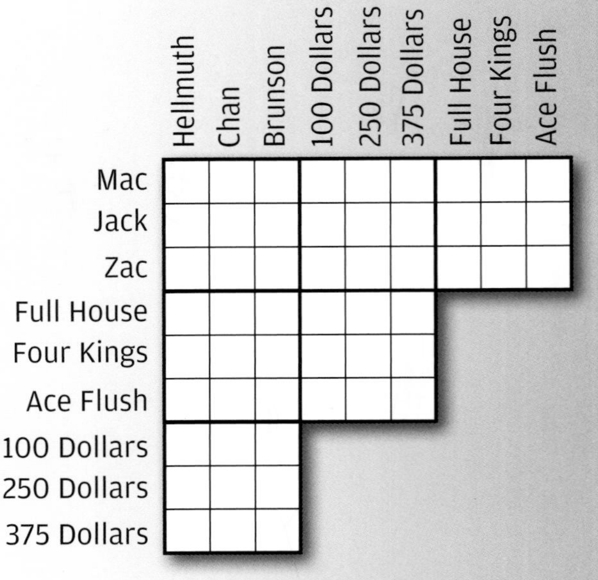

	Hellmuth	Chan	Brunson	100 Dollars	250 Dollars	375 Dollars	Full House	Four Kings	Ace Flush
Mac									
Jack									
Zac									
Full House									
Four Kings									
Ace Flush									
100 Dollars									
250 Dollars									
375 Dollars									

Despite being raised as a Quaker, Richard Nixon was a keen poker player during his two years in the U.S. Navy, and he even used a portion of his winnings to fund his first foray into professional politics in 1946, when he won a Congressional seat.

Robot Research

Which box contains exactly the right parts to build the robot?

"My goal is simple. It is a complete understanding of the universe, why it is as it is, and why it exists at all." STEPHEN HAWKING

A

B

C

In April 2007, the French TGV train broke its own 1990 world train-speed record as it reached 357.18 mph (576 kph) under test conditions.

67

DIFFICULTY ★★★

Locate the Letter

A	B	B	B	C	A
B	B	A	C	C	C
A	C	B	A	B	A
B	?	C	B	B	A
A	A	C	B	C	C
C	A	C	C	A	B

What letter, in what color, should replace the red question mark so that the grid follows a pattern?

> "Every artist should be ahead of his time and behind in his rent."
>
> KINKY FRIEDMAN

In 1895, Émile Levassor driving a Panhard et Levassor won a 745-mile (1,200 kilometer) road race from Paris to Bordeaux and back. The journey took 48 hours and is regarded as the first proper motor race.

68

DIFFICULTY ★★★

Number Mountain

Replace the question marks with numbers so that each pair of blocks adds up to the block directly above them.

> "There are many paths to the top of the mountain, but the view is always the same."
>
> CHINESE PROVERB

178

? ?

? ? ?

27 ? ? 16

11 ? 10 ? 7

? ? ? ? ? 1

New Zealand's South Island boasts 18 peaks of more than 9,800 feet (3,000 meters). The tallest peak is Mount Cook, which is 12,300 feet tall (3,754 meters).

69

DIFFICULTY

Same Difference

By examining the relationships of the following shapes, can you identify the next shape?

The first countries to broadcast television were: Germany, the Great Britain and the United States (1936); France and Poland (1937); the Soviet Union (1938); and Japan and Italy (1939).

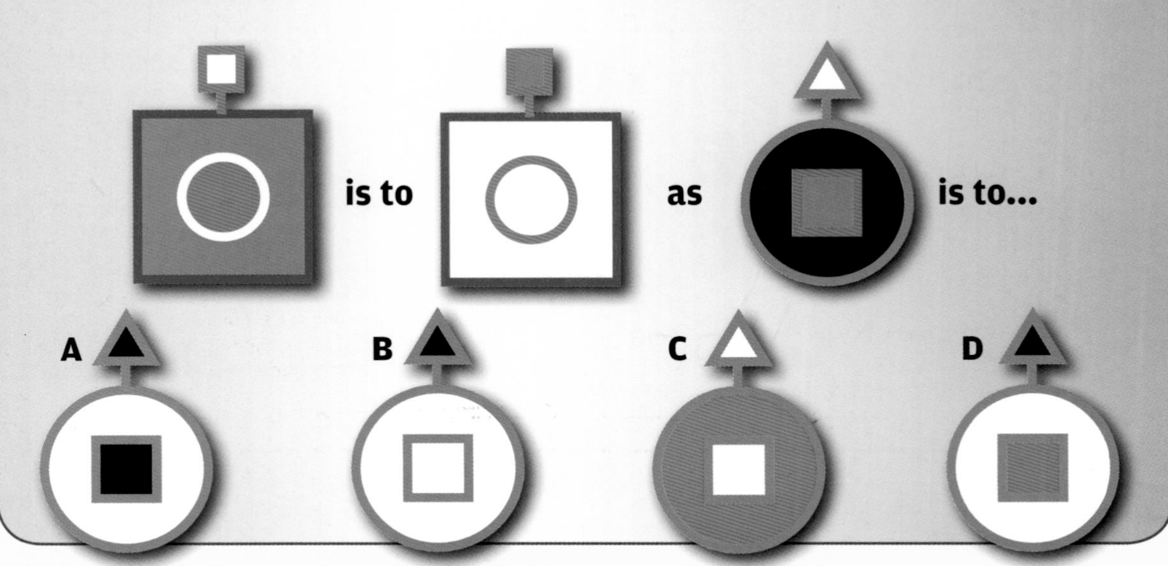

70

DIFFICULTY

Weigh to Go

The colored balls represent the numbers 1, 2, 3, 4, and 5. Can you work out which is which, and then how many red balls are needed to balance the final scale?

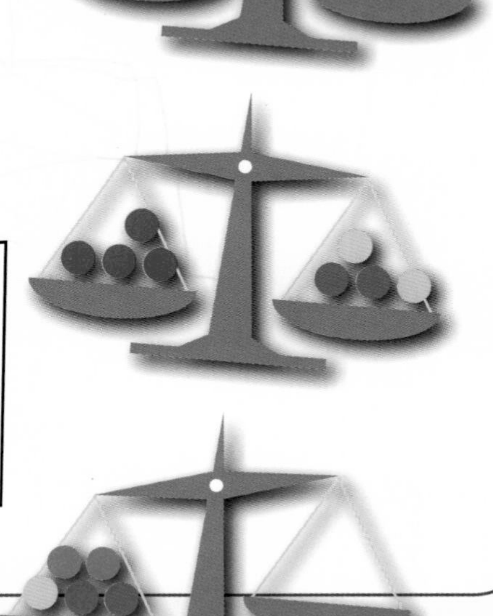

"Read not to contradict and confute, nor to believe and take for granted . . . but to weigh and consider." Francis Bacon

The first abacus was almost certainly based on a flat stone covered with sand or dust. Words and letters were drawn in the sand; eventually numbers were added and pebbles used to aid calculations. The Babylonians used this dust abacus as early as 2,400 B.C.

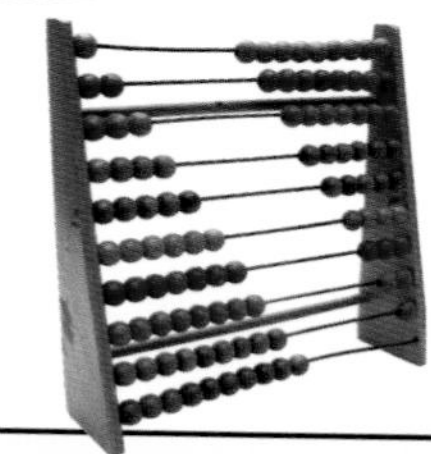

71

DIFFICULTY

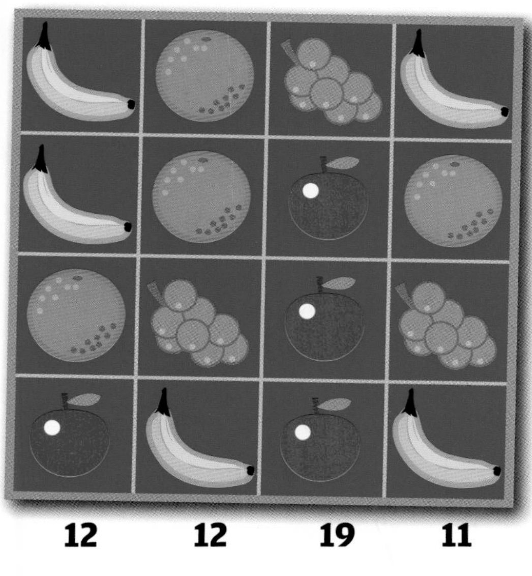

Fruitful Task

Each of the different pictures in the box represents a number. The numbers at the end of each row and the bottom of each column are the totals of the numbers in that row or column added together. Work out which number each picture represents and then work out what the question mark should be?

“Anybody can make history. Only a great man can write it.”

OSCAR WILDE

The first known published crossword puzzle was created by a journalist named Arthur Wynne from Liverpool, England. It first appeared in the Sunday newspaper, the *New York World,* on December 21, 1913.

72

DIFFICULTY

Grand Prix Puzzle

This racing car is made up of building bricks that are all the same size. Can you work out what percentage is gray, blue, black, and red?

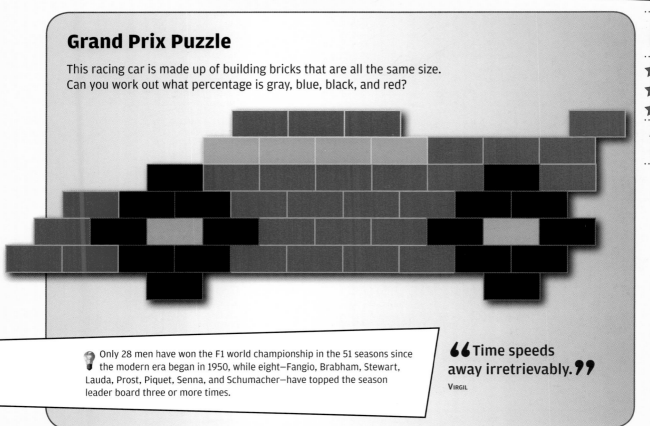

Only 28 men have won the F1 world championship in the 51 seasons since the modern era began in 1950, while eight–Fangio, Brabham, Stewart, Lauda, Prost, Piquet, Senna, and Schumacher–have topped the season leader board three or more times.

“Time speeds away irretrievably.”

VIRGIL

73

DIFFICULTY ★★☆

View to a Clue

The four squares at the bottom can all be found in the picture grid. Can you track them down? Beware: They may not be the right way up.

> “Everything in nature is lyrical in its ideal essence, tragic in its fate, and comic in its existence.” GEORGE SANTAYANA

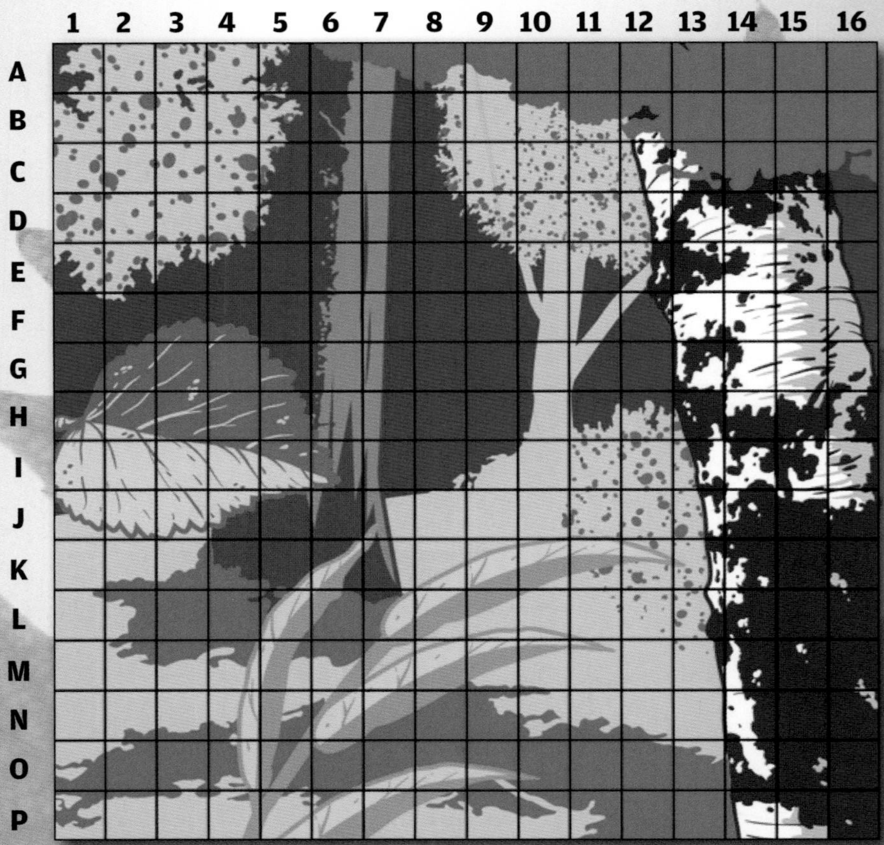

	1	2	3	4	5	6	7	8	9	10	11	12	13	14	15	16
A																
B																
C																
D																
E																
F																
G																
H																
I																
J																
K																
L																
M																
N																
O																
P																

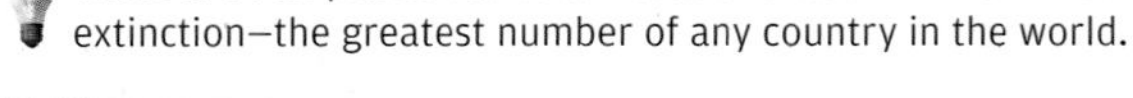

There are 952 plants native to Ecuador that are under threat of extinction—the greatest number of any country in the world.

74

DIFFICULTY

Cubism

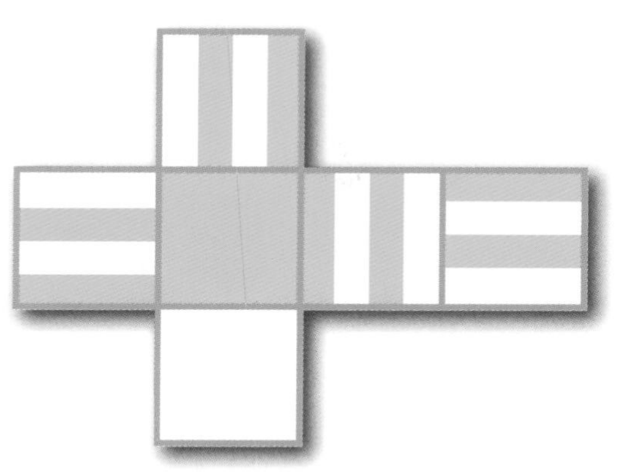

The shape left can be folded to make a cube. Which of the four cubes pictured below could it make?

“What people call fate is mostly their own stupidity.”

Arthur Schopenhauer

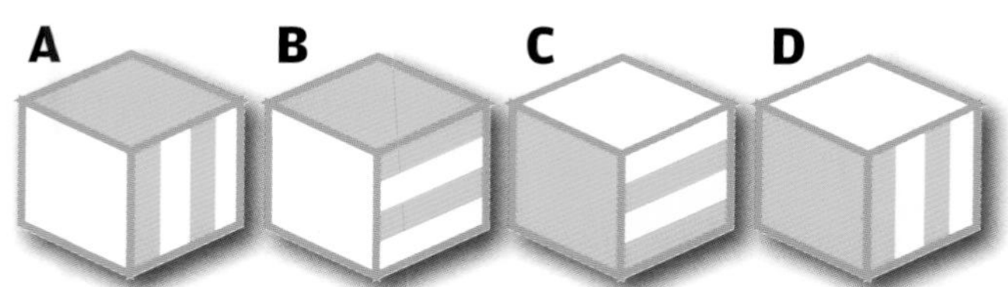

The British Secret Service Bureau was set up in 1909 in response to the threat posed to the Great Britain’s naval ports by spies from Germany. It was renamed MI5 (Military Intelligence, Section 5) in 1916 and again as the Security Service in 1931, although MI5 is still popularly used today.

75

DIFFICULTY

Do you Remember Me?

Study these images for a minute, cover them up with a sheet of paper, and then answer the five questions shown below.

On February 28, 1953, Frances Crick walked into The Eagle pub in Cambridge, England, and announced that he and James Watson “had found the secret of life”—the two Cambridge academics had discovered DNA.

Questions:

1. How many of the men have handkerchiefs that match their ties?
2. How many of the blond men have yellow ties?
3. How many men with red ties have white handkerchiefs?
4. What color is the background on the man with the green suit?
5. What color tie has the blond man on the blue background?

76

DIFFICULTY

To Follow

In the sequence below, which of the numbered alternatives, A, B, C, or D, should replace the question mark?

American Olympic athlete Ray Ewry is the holder of the most athletics gold medals. They were won in the standing jump and triple jump events of the 1900, 1904, 1906, and 1908 Games.

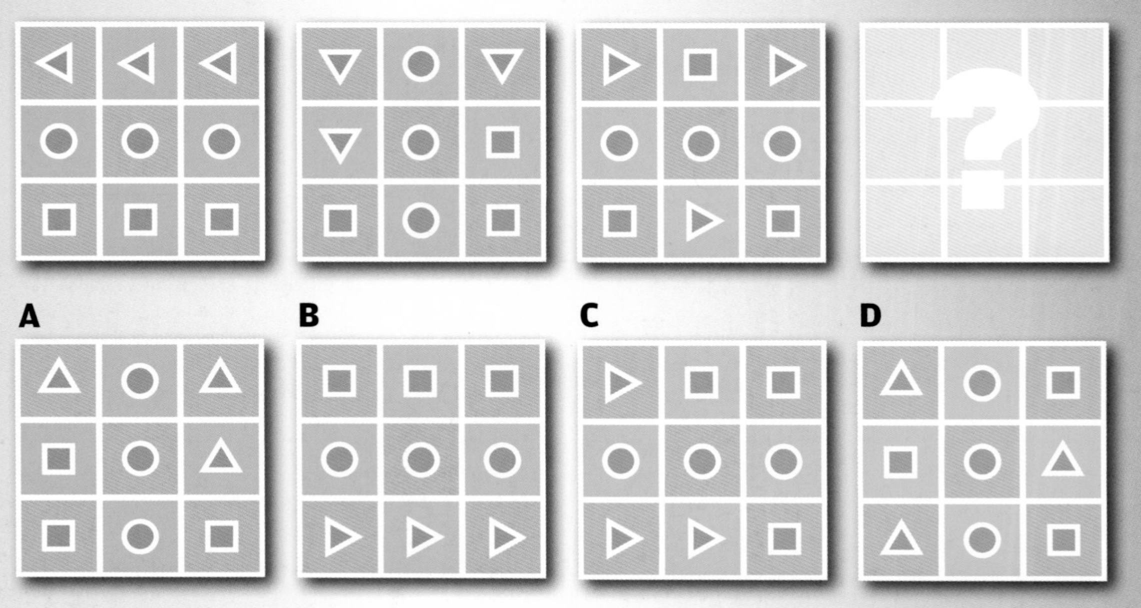

77

DIFFICULTY

Dinosaur Dilemma

Can you work out the approximate area that the dinosaur part of this image takes up?

“If size did matter, the dinosaurs would still be alive.” Wendelin Wiedeking

The smallest known dinosaur is the Compsognathus, which was the size of a chicken. The largest was the Sauroposeidon, which means “earthquake god lizard.” It weighed 60 tons (61,000 kilograms) and stood 60 feet (18 meters) tall.

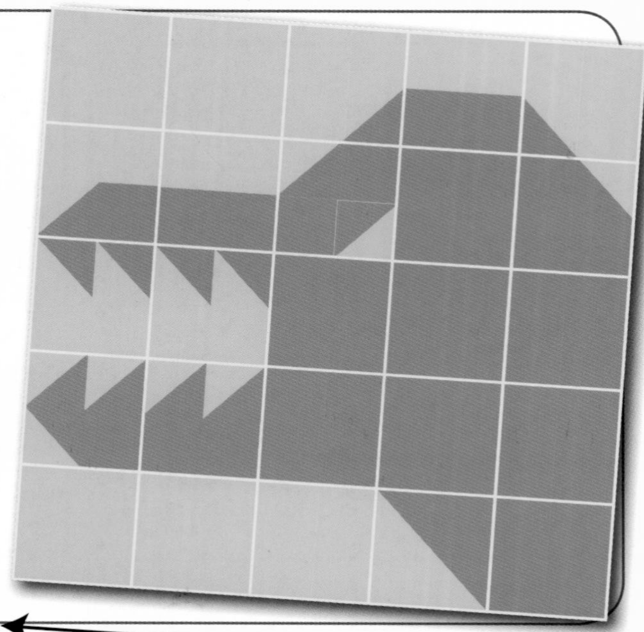

100 inches/254 centimeters

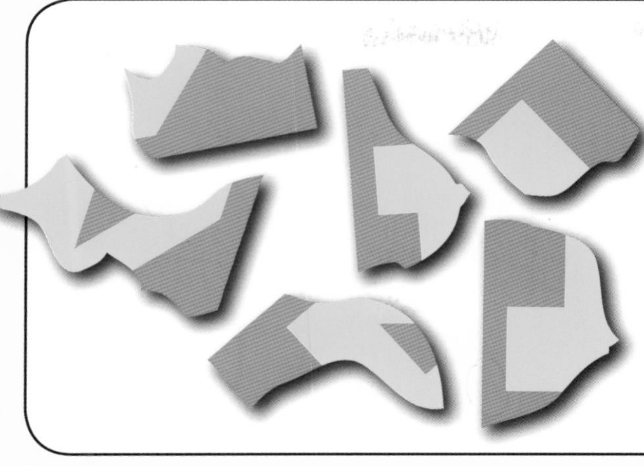

78

DIFFICULTY

All Sewn Up

Reassemble these torn pieces and you will reveal what?

“The most happy marriage I can picture or imagine to myself would be the union of a deaf man to a blind woman.” S. T. Coleridge

79

DIFFICULTY

The Chinese consider it bad luck to turn a fish over at the table. The superstition is originally attributed to South China's fishing families, who believed bad luck would ensue and a fishing boat would capsize if the fish were up-ended.

Cats and Cogs

Turn the handle in the indicated direction . . . Does the cat in the basket go up or down?

“A cat is more intelligent than people believe, and can be taught any crime.” Mark Twain

80

DIFFICULTY

Fruit Formula

The islands of Zanga, Binoo, and Biro Biro export fruit around the world. Can you work out in which sea or ocean the islands are, and which island produces which fruit for which country?

- Zanga is not in the Pacific Ocean, and its mangoes are not exported to the USA.
- Australia imports the coconuts, which are not from Binoo.
- Biro Biro is in the Caribbean.

The tiny Andean country of Ecuador is the world's biggest exporter of bananas. The fruit is second only to oil in terms of economic importance for the country.

81

DIFFICULTY

Follow That

The sequence below follows a logical pattern. Work out what design should come next?

"The chief distinction of a diplomat is that he can say no in such a way that it sounds like yes." LESTER BOWLES PEARSON

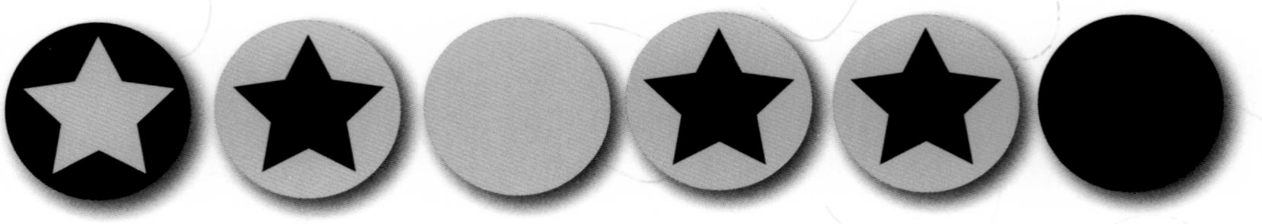

On October 16, 1923, brothers Walt and Roy Disney founded the Walt Disney Company; it was originally known as the Disney Brothers Cartoon Studio.

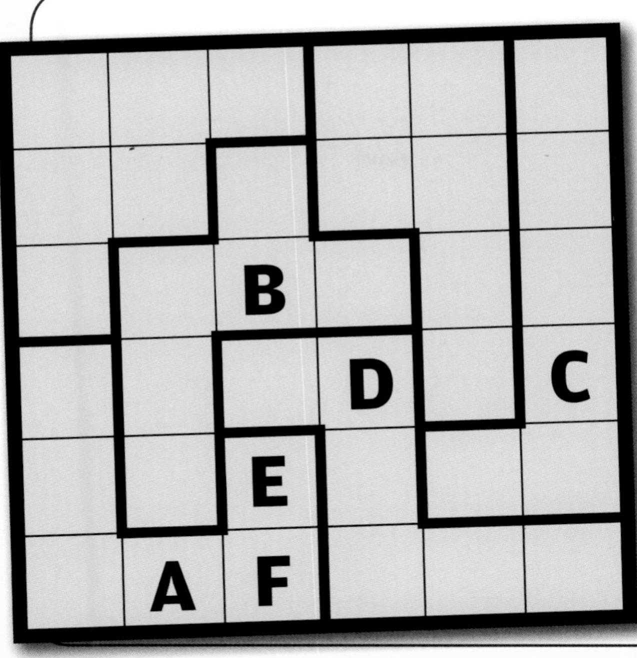

Squared Off

82

DIFFICULTY ★★★

Complete the grid so that every row and column, and every outlined area, contains the letters A, B, C, D, E, and F.

"In a time of universal deceit, telling the truth becomes a revolutionary act." George Orwell

Mining in the Witwatersrand Basin region of South Africa has unearthed one-third of all the gold ever mined on the planet.

Block Party

83

DIFFICULTY ☆★★

Assuming all blocks that are not visible from this angle are present, how many blocks have been removed from this 6 x 6 x 6 cube?

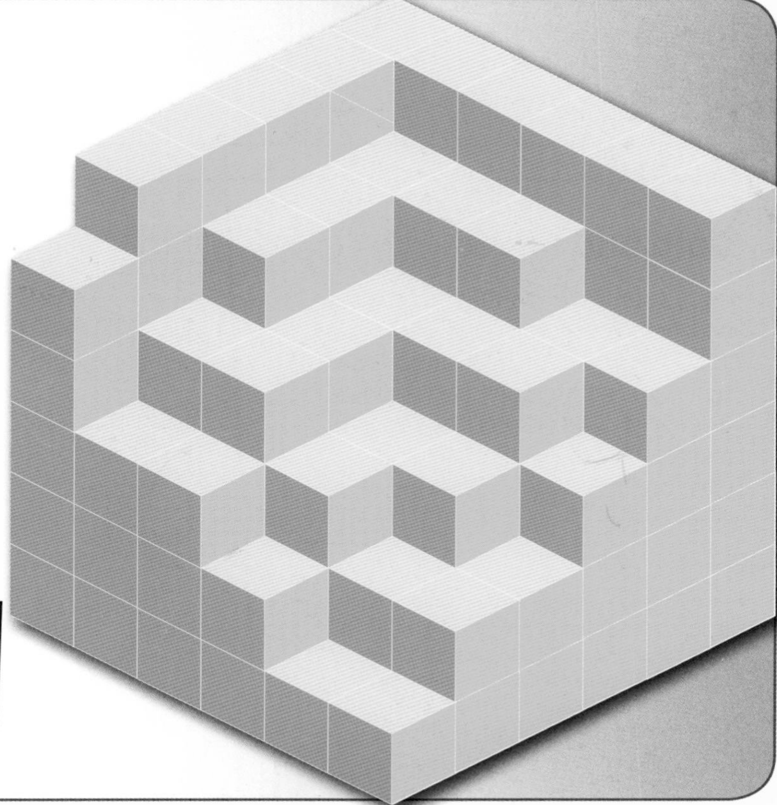

"Maybe the most that you can expect from a relationship that goes bad is to come out of it with a few good songs." Marianne Faithfull

The 2006 U.S. census put the population at 299,398,484. It had risen by 6.4% since 2000.

84

DIFFICULTY ★★★

Box Values

The value of each shape is the number of sides each shape has, multiplied by the number within it. So a square containing the number 4 has a value of 16. Find a block of four squares (two squares wide by two squares high) with a total value of exactly 60.

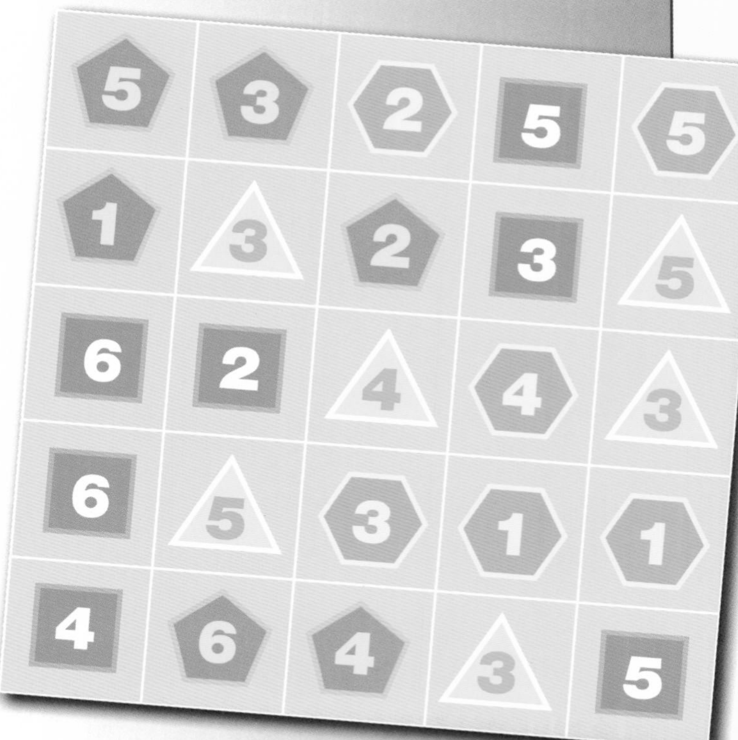

"I read the newspapers avidly. It is my one form of continuous fiction." ANEURIN BEVAN

The world's deepest bar can be found four miles (six kilometers) south of Johannesburg city center in what used to be a donkey stable for a thriving gold-mining reef in the 1920s. Known as Shaft 14, it is 741 feet (226 meters) underground.

85

DIFFICULTY ☆★★

Gold and Silver

Every gold coin has a silver coin found horizontally or vertically adjacent to it. No silver coin can be in an adjacent square to another silver coin (even diagonally). The numbers by each row and column tell you how many silver coins are there. Can you find all the silver coins?

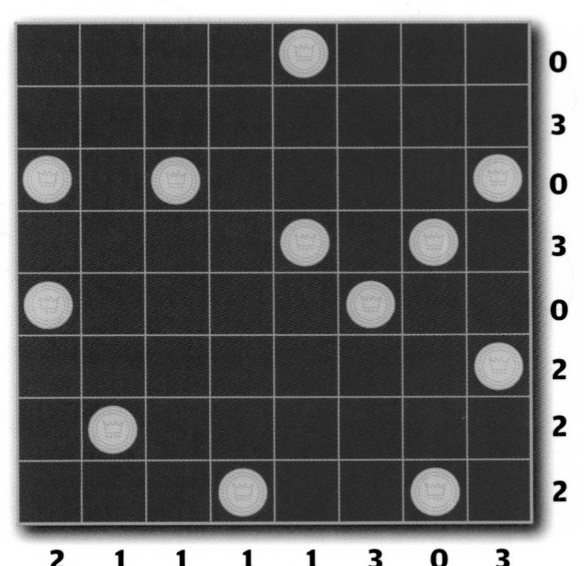

Gold is so malleable that an ounce of gold can be stretched to a length of over 50 miles (85 kilometers) or beaten into a sheet to cover 100 square feet (30.5 square meters).

Piecing It Together

Which four of the pieces below can complete the puzzle and make a perfect square?

“Sex appeal is 50 percent what you’ve got and 50 percent what people think you’ve got.” SOPHIA LOREN

86

DIFFICULTY

King Henry III became ruler of England in 1216, when he was just nine years old, and ruled until his death in 1272. During his reign a polar bear was kept at the Tower of London. It was a gift from King Haakon IV of Norway.

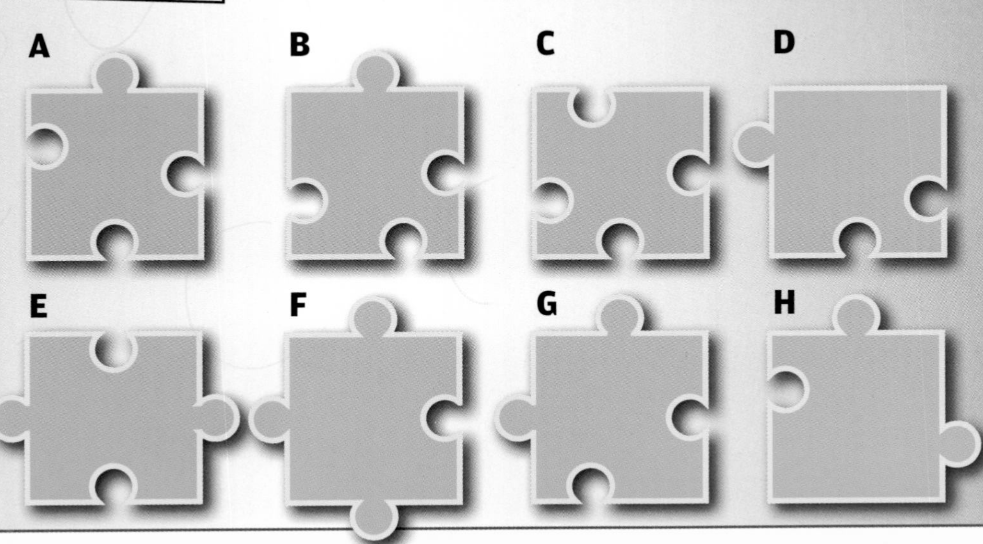

87

DIFFICULTY

Seeing Double

All these icons appear twice in the box except one. Can you find it?

“If I have seen farther than others, it is because I was standing on the shoulders of giants.” Sir Isaac Newton

President Theodore Roosevelt was not only the first serving president to ride in an automobile, but also the first serving president to travel outside the country when he visited Panama in November 1906.

88

DIFFICULTY

Make the Cut

Cut two straight lines through this shape to create three shapes that are identical.

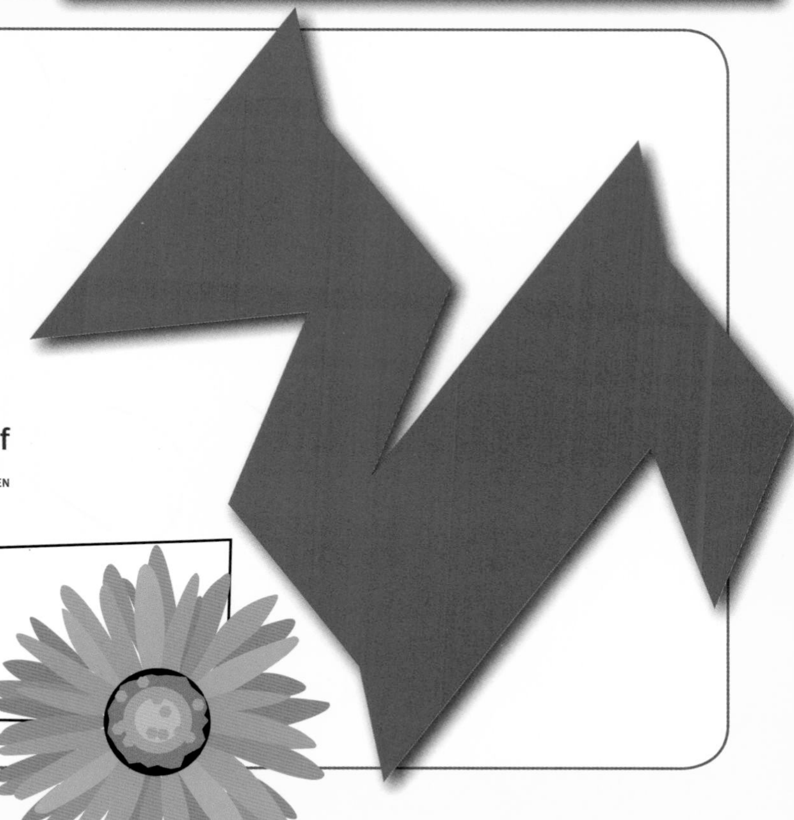

“A national political campaign is better than the best circus ever heard of, with a mass baptism and a couple of hangings thrown in.” H. L. Mencken

The word “April” is derived from the Latin *aperie*, which translates as “to open” and was used to describe the first flowering of spring.

The Next Step

Which of the four boxed figures completes the sequence?

"Standing in the middle of the road is very dangerous; you get knocked down by the traffic from both sides." MARGARET THATCHER

?

The world's first traffic light was installed outside the Houses of Parliament in London, England, in 1868. At this point the only traffic was pedestrian or horse-drawn buggies. It was a revolving gas lantern with red and green signals. Unfortunately, the light exploded in 1869, injuring a policeman.

90

DIFFICULTY

Super Sudoku

Complete the grid so that all rows and columns, and each outlined block of nine squares, contain the numbers 1, 2, 3, 4, 5, 6, 7, 8, and 9.

“I believe that every human has a finite number of heartbeats. I don’t intend to waste any of mine running around doing exercises.”

Neil Armstrong

	7				5		4	
			1		6			
2			3			1		8
		5				3		
			4	1				
3		9			7			6
7			8		4		3	
		2		9		5		
	5		6				8	1

As a boy, cult film director David Lynch attained the rank of Eagle Scout– the highest in the Boy Scout movement. On his 15th birthday Lynch, as an Eagle Scout, served as an usher at the inauguration of President John F. Kennedy.

91

DIFFICULTY

Knitty Gritty

Old Mother Jones loves to knit when she’s worried. This month her daughter is learning to drive and she has produced 238 scarves, 71 pom-pom hats, and 41 beanie hats. As a percentage of total production, how much of her output were hats?

“In every conceivable manner, the family is link to our past, bridge to our future.” Alex Haley

One of the earliest known examples of knitting was finely decorated cotton socks found in Egypt at the end of the first millennium A.D. The first knitting trade guild was started in Paris in 1527.

Complete the Masterpiece

The painting *Four Suns Over Tokyo* is in three colors only: purple, yellow, and green. No two areas of the same color border each other. What color is the top right-hand corner?

“Art is born of the observation and investigation of nature.” Cicero

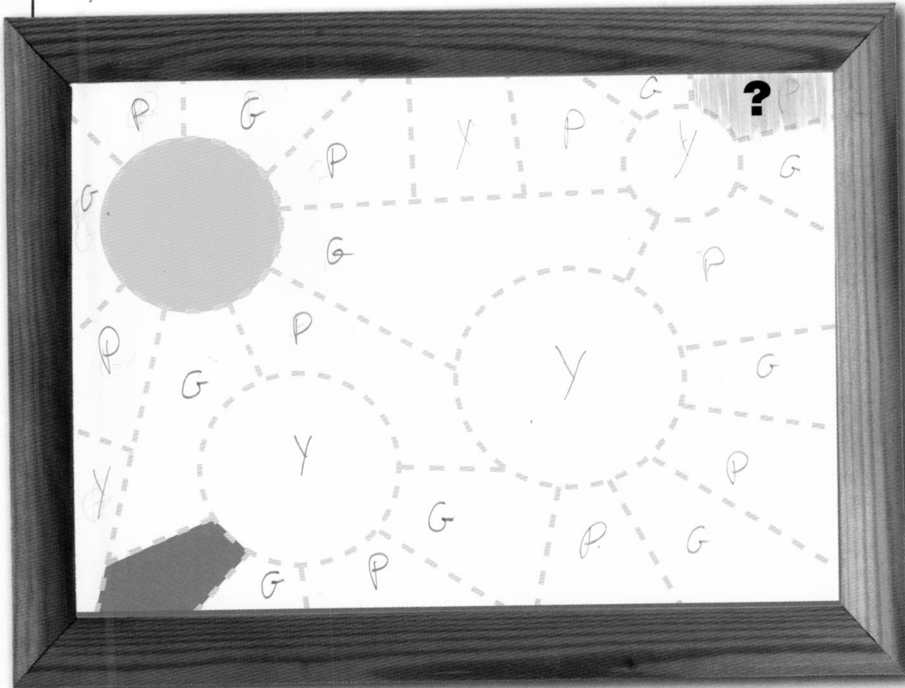

The amount of energy poured onto the earth from the sun every 15 minutes is roughly equivalent to the earth's electricity needs for a year.

93 DIFFICULTY

3			3		3		1
		4		3			2
	4		2		3	4	
	3	2			2		3
4		3	1	3		4	
				2		4	
	4		2		3		2
1		1			2	2	

Black Out

The numbers in some squares in the grid indicate the exact number of black squares that should surround it. Shade these squares until all the numbers are surrounded by the correct number of black squares.

“Darkness is only driven out with light, not more darkness.” Martin Luther King Jr.

94

DIFFICULTY ★

Cowboy Lineup

Hoss McGrew is wanted in six counties for rustling chickens. He always wears a hat with no band on it, a vest and a neckerchief. Can you pick him out of the lineup?

“Love is the ultimate outlaw. It just won’t adhere to any rules. The most any of us can do is sign on as its accomplice.” Tom Watson

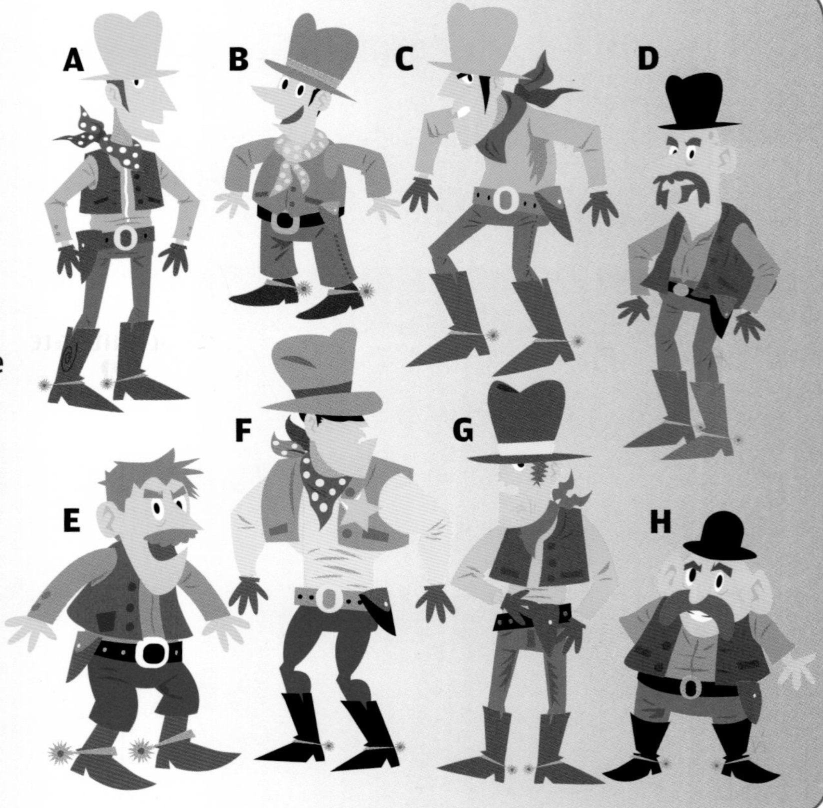

There were 17,576 possible rotor settings on the original Enigma code machine used in World War II to break secret codes.

95

DIFFICULTY ★★

Coming Together

These seven pieces can be assembled into a green square. What is on it?

“No matter how old a mother is, she watches her middle-aged children for signs of improvement.” Florida Scott-Maxwell

96

DIFFICULTY

Level Loads

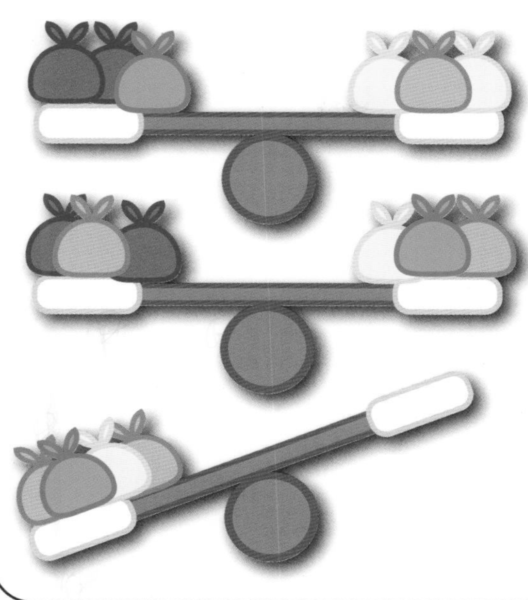

The colored sacks—green, blue, brown, yellow, and black—represent the numbers 1, 2, 3, 4, and 5. Which one is which, and how many black sacks are needed to balance the bottom seesaw?

“There is always a heavy demand for fresh mediocrity. In every generation the least cultivated taste has the largest appetite.” Paul Gauguin

The Russian KGB was created in 1954. At its peak, it was the world's largest secret-police and espionage organization. After playing a part in a failed coup attempt to overthrow Mikhail Gorbachev, it lost influence and was finally dissolved when the Soviet Union collapsed.

97

DIFFICULTY

Car Countdown

Each of the different pictures in the box represents a number. The numbers at the end of each row and the bottom of each column are the totals of the numbers in that row or column added together. Can you work out which number each picture represents and so work out what the question mark should be?

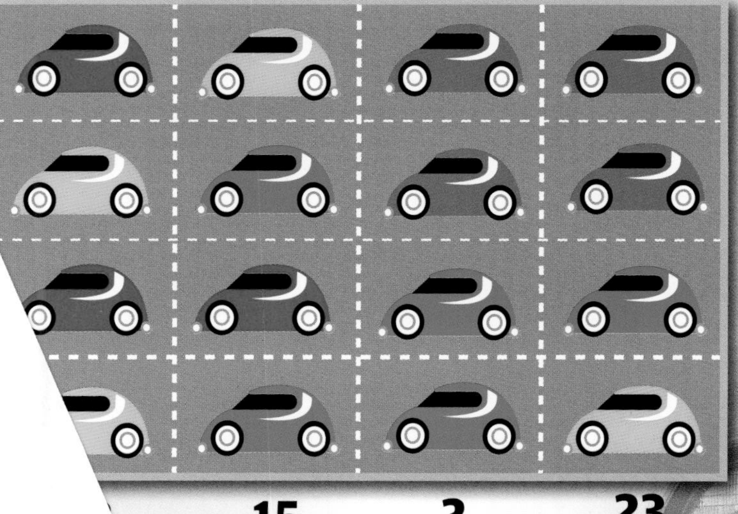

“The best car safety device is a rearview mirror with a cop in it.” Dudley Moore

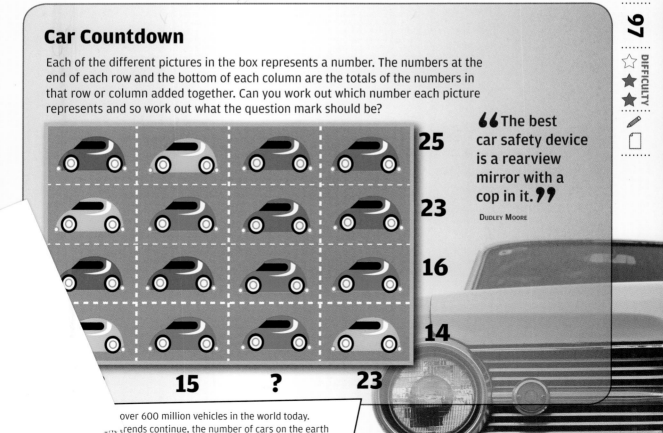

over 600 million vehicles in the world today. ... trends continue, the number of cars on the earth ...uble in the next 30 years.

Loopy Numbers

Connect adjacent dots with either horizontal or vertical lines to create a continuous unbroken loop that never crosses over itself. Some but not all of the boxes are numbered. The numbers in these boxes tell you how many sides of that box are used by your unbroken line.

3	3	2	2	2
		1		
2	3		2	3
	2	1		2
3		2		3

Until July 9, 2007, the Argentine capital Buenos Aires had not seen snow for 89 years.

Make the Cut

Can you fold a straight line through this shape to create two shapes that are identical?

“It took man thousands of years to put words down on paper, and his lawyers still wish he wouldn’t.” Mignon McLaughlin

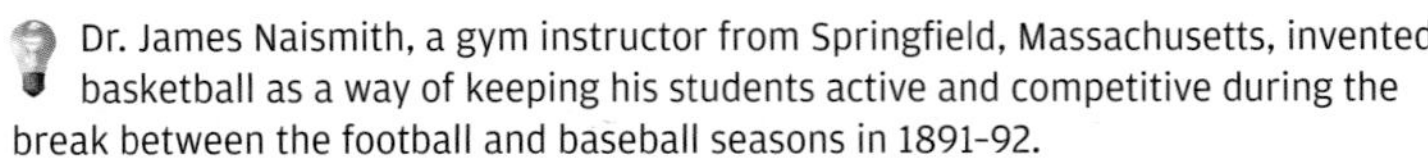
Dr. James Naismith, a gym instructor from Springfield, Massachusetts, invented basketball as a way of keeping his students active and competitive during the break between the football and baseball seasons in 1891–92.

100

DIFFICULTY ☆☆★

What's the Difference?

Can you spot ten differences between these two pictures of a bird relaxing on a Sunday morning?

Ernest Hemingway was a civilian in Cuba during World War II, but he added surveillance capabilities to his own private boat so he could guard the waters against German submarines.

101

DIFFICULTY ★★★

Star Corner

Use the corner stars to make the central number the same way in all three cases. What number should replace the question mark?

“We make war that we may live in peace.” ARISTOTLE

Scientists have developed a currency durable enough to be used in space in anticipation of future space tourism. It is called the Quasi Universal Intergalactic Denomination, or Quid.

102

DIFFICULTY ☆★★

Reach for the Stars

Can you find three perfect five-pointed stars in this colorful collection?

“A man gazing on the stars is proverbially at the mercy of the puddles in the road.”

ALEXANDER SMITH

The amount of power transmitted by the Galileo spacecraft's radio is about the same amount used by a refrigerator lightbulb—about 20 watts.

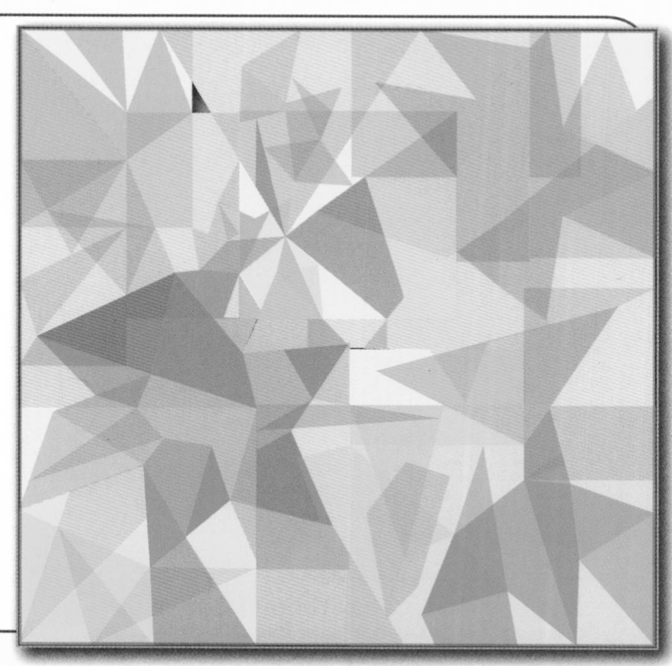

103 DIFFICULTY

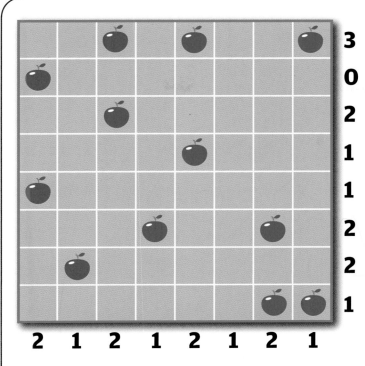

Apples and Pears

		🍎		🍎			🍎	3
🍎								0
		🍎						2
				🍎				1
🍎								1
			🍎			🍎		2
	🍎							2
						🍎	🍎	1
2	1	2	1	2	1	2	1	

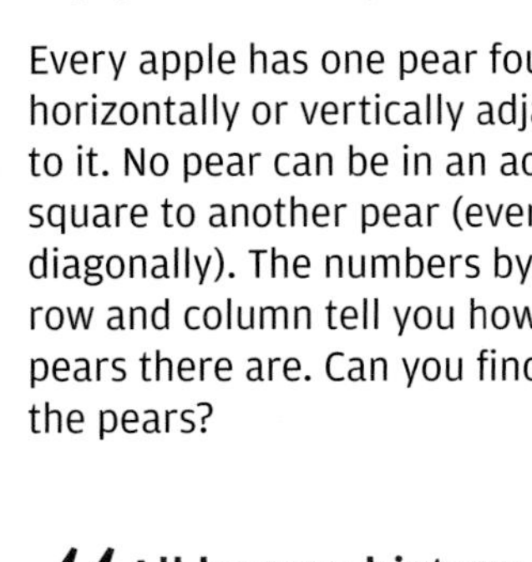

Every apple has one pear found horizontally or vertically adjacent to it. No pear can be in an adjacent square to another pear (even diagonally). The numbers by each row and column tell you how many pears there are. Can you find all the pears?

“All human history attests that happiness for man—the hungry sinner!—since Eve ate apples, much depends on dinner.”

Lord Byron

Over 7,500 varieties of apples are grown throughout the world. In 2006-7 the People’s Republic of China led the world in commercial apple production, with almost 27 million tons (24 million metric tons), followed by the United States, with almost five million tons. In 2006-7, commercial world production of apples was over 48 million tons (43 million metric tons).

104 DIFFICULTY

What’s Coming Next?

The sequence below follows a logical pattern. What is the color and shape next in line?

?

President Ronald Reagan was such a huge baseball fan that he worked as a radio announcer for the Chicago Cubs—a job that provided him with a springboard into acting.

105

Kitchen Capers

One of these pictures of Pierre the chef is an exact mirror image of the first one. Can you find it?

“Great eaters and great sleepers are incapable of anything else that is great.” Henry IV of France

The world’s most expensive sandwich, created by London chef Scott McDonald, costs $170. Its ingredients are Wagyu beef, fresh lobe foie gras, black truffle mayonnaise, brie de meaux, arugula, red pepper and mustard confit, and plum tomatoes.

106

Knight’s Move

Find an empty square in the grid that is one chess knight’s move away from a blue, red, and yellow circle. A knight’s move is an “L” shape—two squares sideways, up or down in any direction, followed by one square to the left or right.

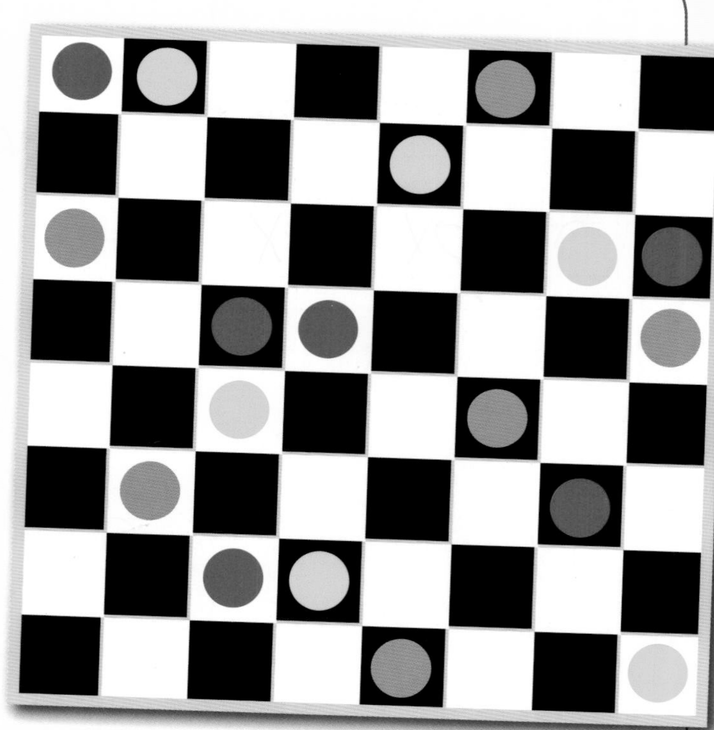

“I failed to make the chess team because of my height.”
Woody Allen

In 1980, after 24 hours and 30 minutes, consisting of 193 moves, Yedael Stepak beat Yaakov Mashian in the world’s longest decided chess game.

Haunted

107

DIFFICULTY

Honeycomb Halves

Tyler is a keen beekeeper and he is collecting his prized honeycomb to sell at the county fair. He is trying to make sure that each jar is exactly the same. Which two honeycomb shapes shown below will pair up to create the top shape?

"The men of experiment are like the ant; they only collect and use. But the bee . . . gathers its materials from the flowers of the garden and of the field, but transforms and digests it by a power of its own."

LEONARDO DA VINCI

A

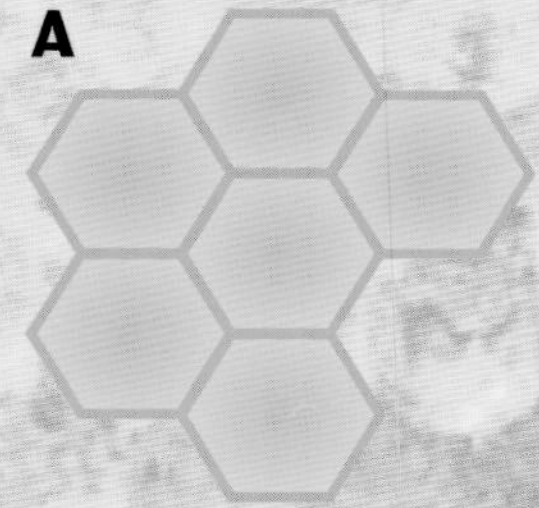

B

C

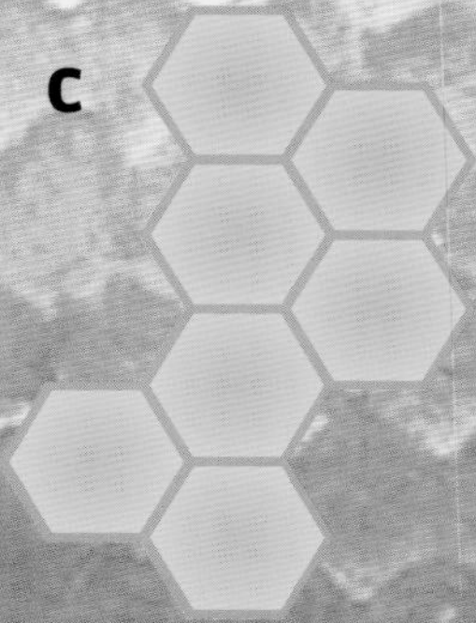

D

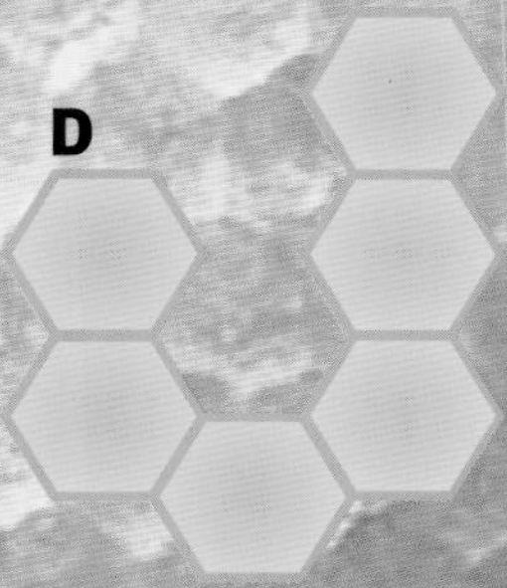

E

F

Honeybees can direct other bees to food by dancing. The movements tell them the location and direction of the food.

108 DIFFICULTY

Ticket to Ride

These ten pieces of a train ticket can be assembled to spell the name of a world city. Which one?

According to the chronicler Raphael Holinshed, there were an estimated 72,000 executions carried out in England during the reign of Henry VIII, including two of his wives.

109 DIFFICULTY

Star Spotter

Three stars can be seen in different directions in the night sky. Can you find out what star type they all are, where they can be found, and where we should be looking?

- Ipson 7 is not in the constellation of Orion, nor is it a white dwarf star. It can be seen in the west.
- The neutron star can be seen in the east. It is not Jalafrey 2.
- Zan 10 can be found in the constellation of Capricorn.

	Taurus	Orion	Capricorn	Red Dwarf	White Dwarf	Neutron	East	West	North
Ipson 7									
Jalafrey 2									
Zan 10									
East						
West						
North						
Red Dwarf			
White Dwarf			
Neutron			

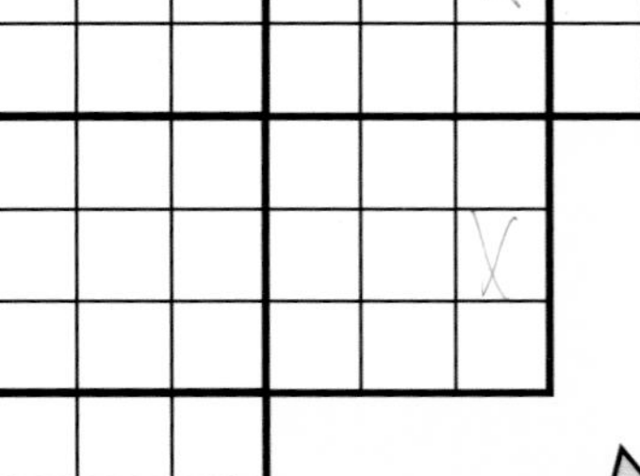

In 1963, Russian Valentina Vladimirovna Tereshkova became the first woman to enter space as a crew member of *Vostok 6*.

110

DIFFICULTY ★★★

Will It Fit?

Black Beard the pirate has a big wooden box measuring 4 yards (4 meters) wide, 3 yards (3 meters) deep and 3 yards (3 meters) high. His 4-inch (10 centimeter) wide mast has broken into two pieces, one 5 yards (5 meters) long and one 5 yards and 20 inches (5.5 meters) long. Can he get either, neither or both of the pieces into the box?

"A stone thrown at the right time is better than gold given at the wrong time." PERSIAN PROVERB

The world's largest coral reef ecosystem, the Great Barrier Reef, is home to approximately 1,500 species of fish, 400 species of corals, 4,000 species of mollusks, 500 species of seaweed, 215 species of birds, 16 species of sea snake, and 6 species of sea turtle.

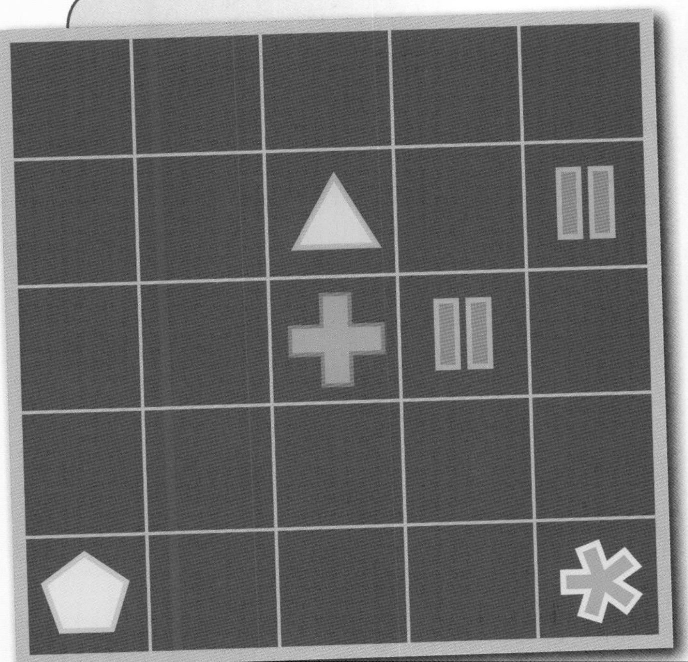

111

DIFFICULTY ☆☆★

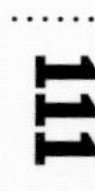

Shape Shifting

Fill in the empty squares so that each row, column, and long diagonal contains five different symbols.

"Man must shape his tools lest they shape him." ARTHUR MILLER

The Nintendo Game Boy is the world's most popular video-game system. Between 1989 and 2000, more than 100 million units were sold.

112

DIFFICULTY ★★★

Odd One Out!

Which of the shapes below is not the same as the other ones?

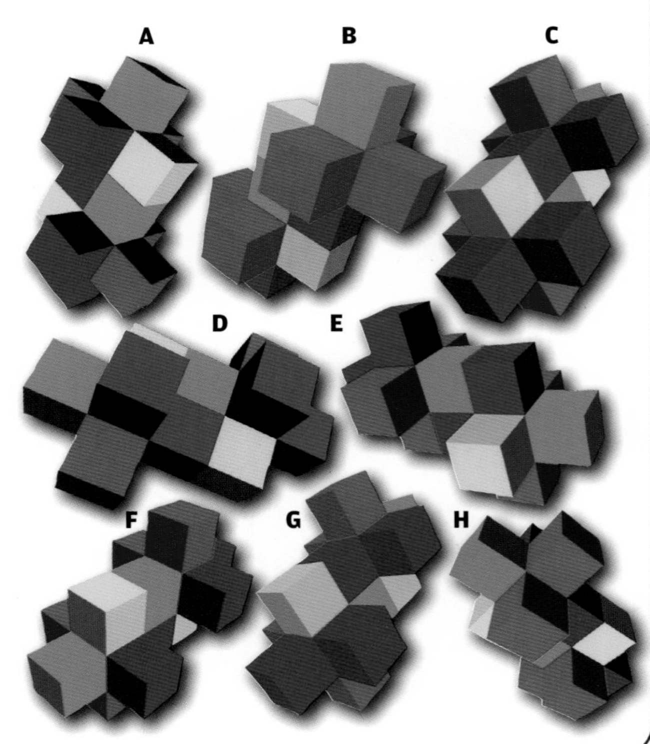

“All that we are is the result of what we have thought. If a man speaks or acts with an evil thought, pain follows him. If a man speaks or acts with a pure thought, happiness follows him, like a shadow that never leaves him.” Buddha

The quiz show *Deal or No Deal,* in which contestants try to win money randomly concealed within identical sealed boxes, was created by Dutch producers Endemol and has been syndicated in over 40 countries all over the world.

113

DIFFICULTY ☆★★

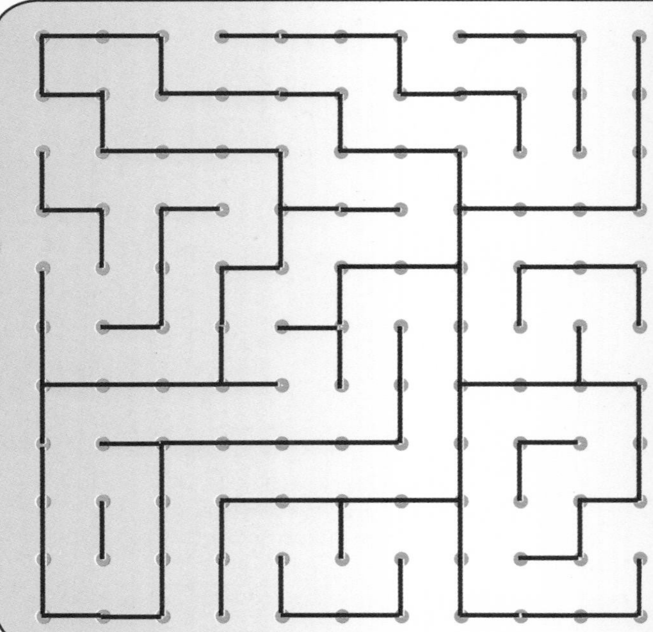

It's Your Turn

Playing the game of boxes, each player takes it in turns to join two adjacent dots with a line. If a player's line completes a box, the player wins the box and has another chance. It's your turn in the game, left. To avoid giving your opponent a lot of boxes, what's your best move?

“Man should forget his anger before he lies down to sleep.” Mohandas Gandhi

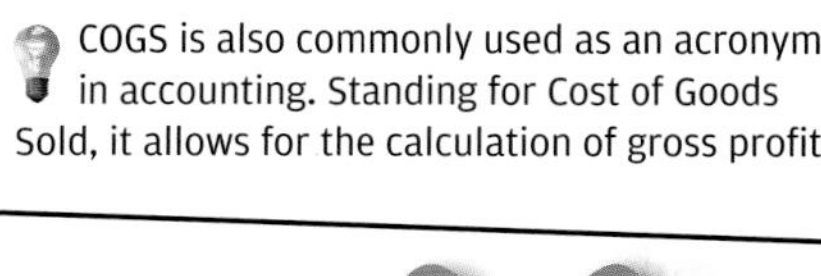

COGS is also commonly used as an acronym in accounting. Standing for Cost of Goods Sold, it allows for the calculation of gross profit.

114

DIFFICULTY

Revolutions

Cog A has 16 teeth, cog B has 10, and cog C has 8. How many revolutions must cog A turn completely to make the letters the right way up on all three cogs?

> **“Talent wins games, but teamwork and intelligence wins championships.”**
>
> Michael Jordan

115

DIFFICULTY

Radio Signals

In the sequence below, which of the numbered alternatives, A, B, C, or D, should replace the question mark?

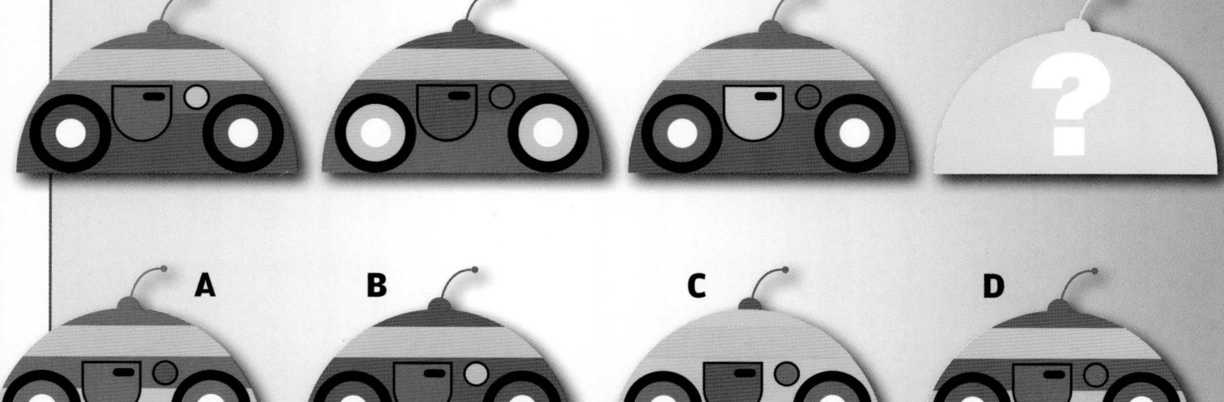

The following are the most played songs on radio: “Stand By Me” by Ben E. King, “Dock Of The Bay” by Otis Redding, “Never My Love” by The Association, and “Yesterday” by The Beatles. However the most played is “You’ve Lost That Lovin’ Feelin” by The Righteous Brothers, with over eight million plays.

116

DIFFICULTY ★★★

Nice Moves!

To complete Mario's world renowned dance move, all the steps below must be taken in the correct order. What is the first step in the dance sequence?

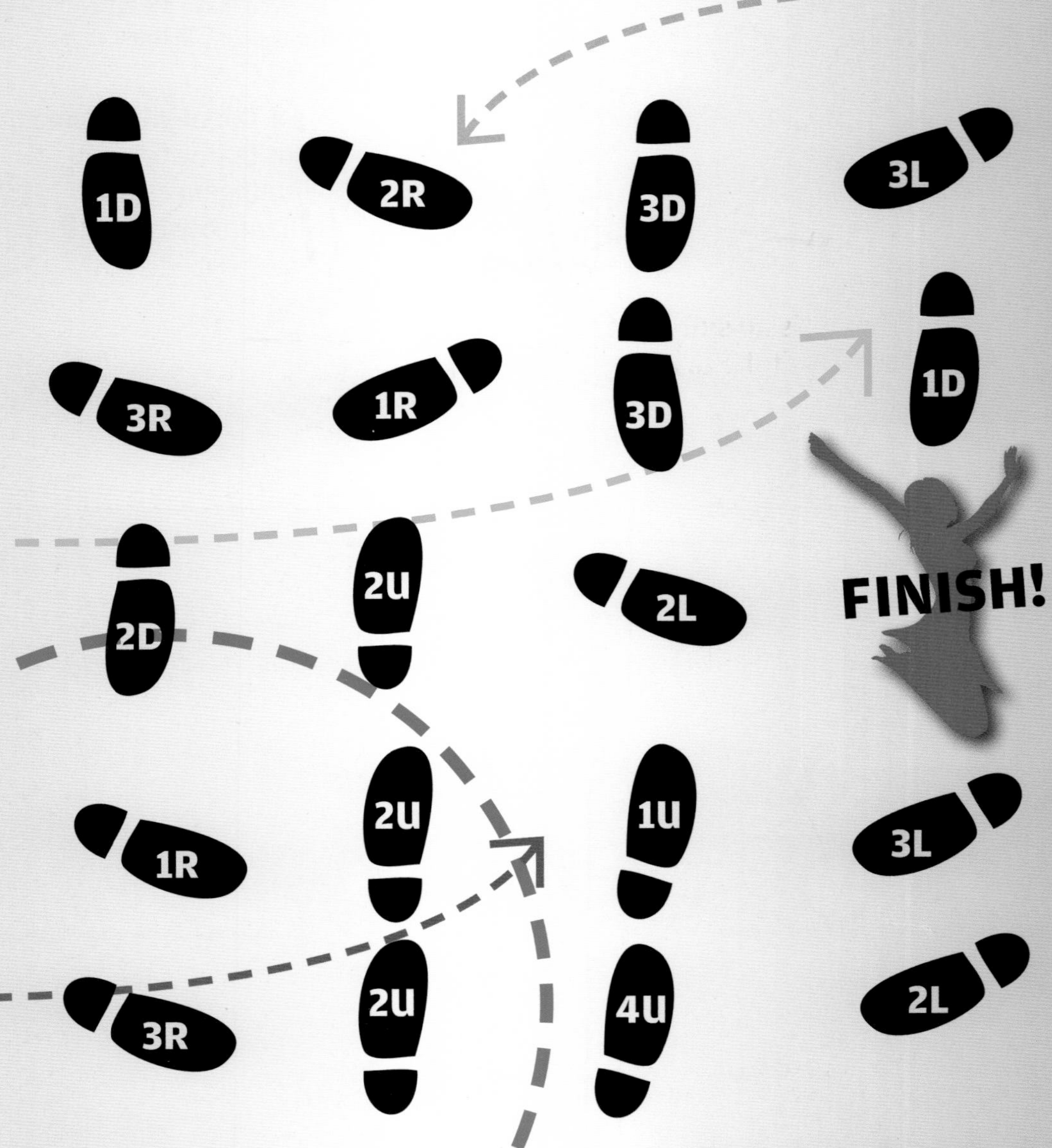

The original name of belly dance is *Raqs Sharqi*, which means 'Dance of the Orient'. In France, it got dubbed *danse du ventre*, which literally means "belly dance" due to the flutter of the dancer's stomach. It is believed that belly dancing was created to help prepare women for birth.

"To be fond of dancing was a certain step towards falling in love." JANE AUSTEN

117

DIFFICULTY ★

Weigh To Go

The colored balls represent the numbers 1, 2, 3, 4, and 5. Which one is which, and how many blue balls are needed to balance the final scale?

“Charity is no substitute for justice withheld.”

SAINT AUGUSTINE

Every cubic foot of water weighs about 64 pounds (29 Kilograms). Only 2.5 percent of the water on the earth is not salty. Of this, only about 0.3 percent is available for drinking. The rest is trapped in ice and groundwater.

118

DIFFICULTY ★

Back Together

Roger is trying to fix two broken roof tiles that have fallen from his farmhouse roof. Can you reunite them?

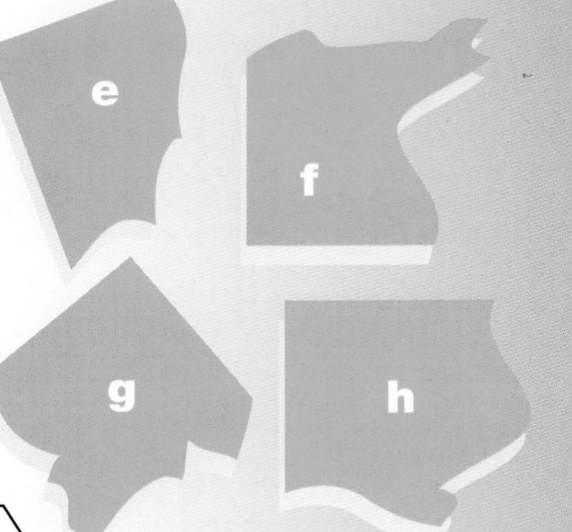

“There are no extra pieces in the universe. Everyone is here because he or she has a place to fill, and every piece must fit itself into the big jigsaw puzzle.” DEEPAK CHOPRA

The oldest known house in the world is a remarkable dwelling found at Mezhirich, Ukraine. It is made of mammoth bones and was built about 15,000 years ago.

119

DIFFICULTY

Equal Shapes

Cut a straight line through this shape to create two shapes that are identical.

“A man’s true character comes out when he’s drunk.”

CHARLIE CHAPLIN

Charlie Chaplin once won third prize in a Charlie Chaplin look-alike contest.

120

DIFFICULTY

Going in Circles

Draw a single continuous line around the grid that passes through all the circles. The line must enter and leave each box in the center of one of its four sides.

Black Circle: Turn left or right in the box, and the line must pass straight through the next and previous boxes.
White Circle: Travel straight through the box, and the line must turn in the next and/or previous box.

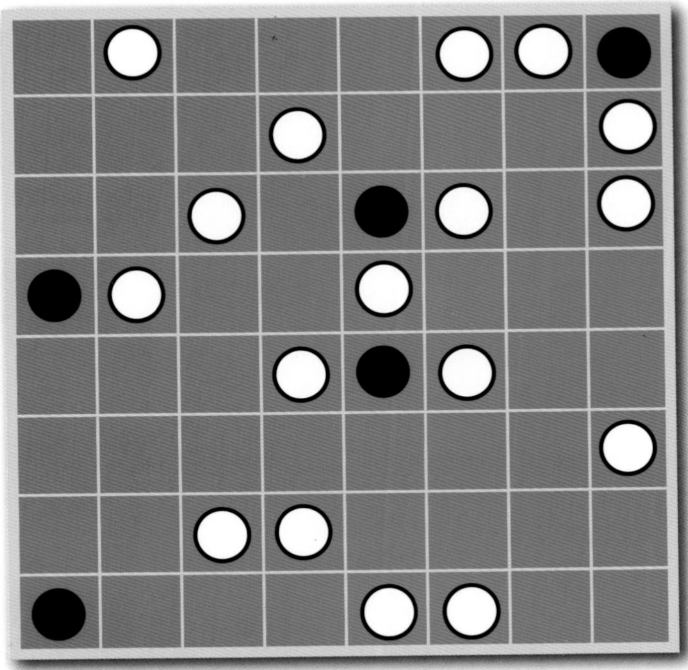

Inventor Sir Charles Fothergill Wheatstone coined the term “microphone” in 1827. A musical man, he also invented the accordian two years later.

121

DIFFICULTY

Sudoku

8		9	6	1	4			3
	2				9	6	7	
5		3	7				4	
		6	9		7	4	8	5
4	3							
7			8		6	3		
9		1	2			8		6
6		7			3		2	
	5		4		8	7		1

Complete the grid so that all rows and columns, and each outlined block of nine squares, contain the numbers 1, 2, 3, 4, 5, 6, 7, 8, and 9.

Every four days the world's population increases by one million people.

“Three grand essentials to happiness in this life are something to do, something to love, and something to hope for.”

JOSEPH ADDISON

122

DIFFICULTY

Find the Letter

What letter, in what color, should replace the red question mark so the grid follows a pattern?

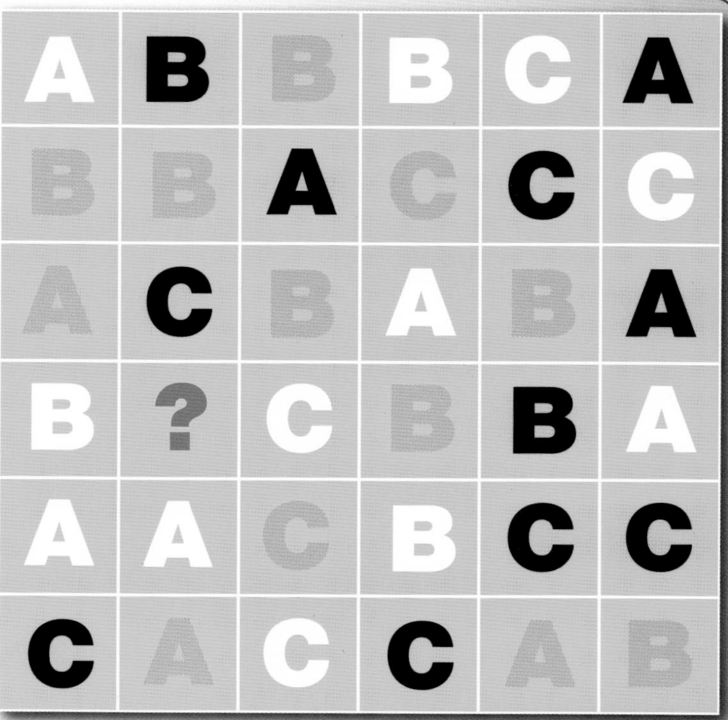

“Honesty is the first chapter in the book of wisdom.”

THOMAS JEFFERSON

Between 1848 and 1852, at the height of the brief Gold Rush period, the population of California swelled from 14,000 to 223,000. In 1850, California officially became a state.

123

DIFFICULTY ★★★

Sum Total

Replace the question marks with mathematical symbols (+, -, x, or ÷) to make the equation.

In 1642, at only 19 years old, the French mathematician Blaise Pascal invented the world's first calculator, a mechanical device operated through the use of a stylus. It was only capable of addition and subtraction, and Pascal himself was the only person who knew how to repair it.

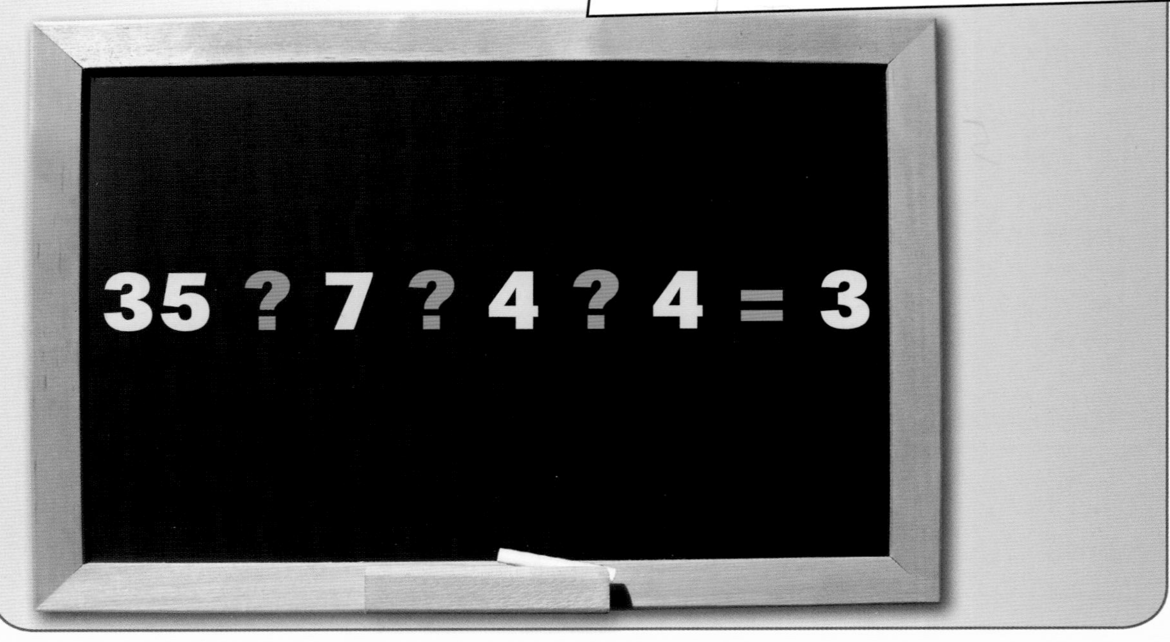

124

DIFFICULTY ☆★★

Salt and Pepper

Every saltshaker has a pepper mill found horizontally or vertically adjacent to it. No pepper mill can be in an adjacent square to another one (even diagonally). The numbers by each row and column tell you how many pepper mills are there. Can you locate all of them?

SALT

PEPPER

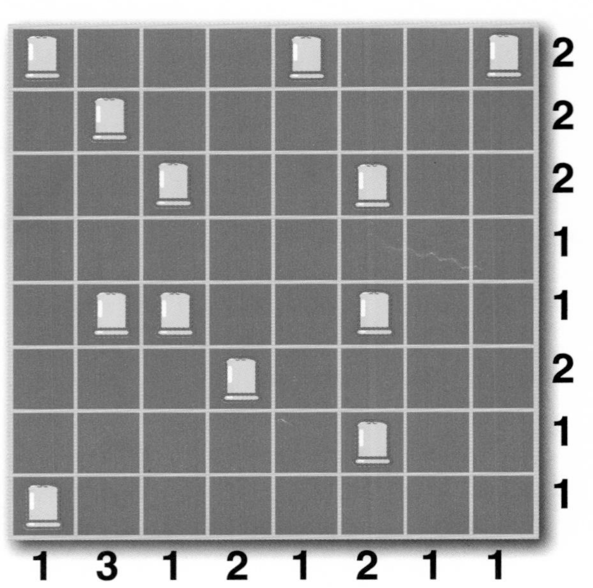

It is believed that Roman soldiers were at certain times paid with salt, and this is still evident in the English language. The word "salary" derives from the Latin word *salarium,* that means payment in salt.

125

DIFFICULTY ★★☆

Come Together

Michael just has to fill the shape on the left to complete the tiling of his bathroom. Which two shapes below will pair up to finish the job?

A B C D E F

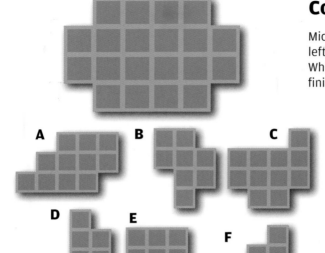

“The harder I work, the luckier I get.” Samuel Goldwyn

The world's largest restroom is in Chongqing, China, and can support as many as 1,000 people using it at the same time. Additionally, it offers radio and television to entertain users of this mammoth restroom.

126

DIFFICULTY ★☆☆

Where Next?

			>					
^		^				v		
		5	>			2	>	
v								^
			<			3	<	
		^						
					>			4
v								
1			<				>	

The arrows indicate whether a number in a box is greater or smaller than an adjacent number. Complete the grid so that all rows and columns contain the numbers 1 to 5.

“God loved the birds and invented trees. Man loved the birds and invented cages.” Jacques Deval

In one year, an acre of trees can absorb as much carbon as is produced by a car driven up to 8,700 miles (14,000 kilometers).

127

DIFFICULTY

Puzzle Pieces

Jessie is struggling to finish the jigsaw puzzle; which of the four pieces shown below complete the puzzle and make a perfect square?

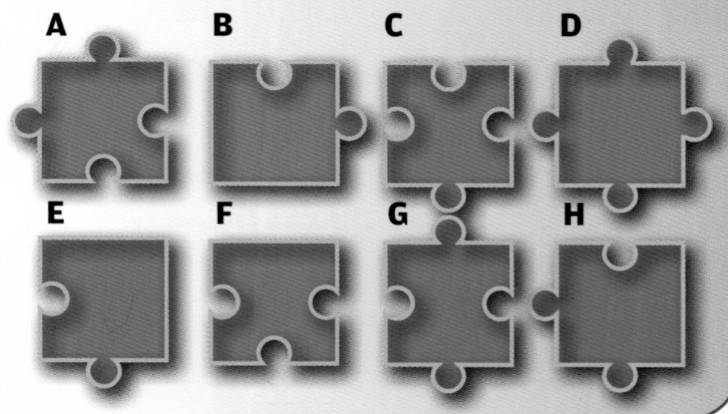

“A man who won’t die for something is not fit to live.”
MARTIN LUTHER KING JR.

John Spilsbury, a London engraver and mapmaker, produced the first jigsaw puzzle in around 1760. Spilsbury mounted one of his maps on a sheet of hardwood and cut around the borders of the countries using a fine-bladed saw. The end product was an educational pastime, designed as an aid in teaching children their geography. The idea caught on and, until about 1820, jigsaw puzzles remained primarily educational tools.

128

DIFFICULTY

Squared Off!

Complete the grid so that every row and column, and every outlined area, contains the letters A, B, C, D, E, and F.

		E		B	
	A				C
			F		B
D					
		C			A

“When science finally locates the center of the universe, some people will be surprised to learn they’re not it.” BERNARD BAILEY

The German philosopher Friedrich Nietzsche was also Professor of Classics at the University of Basel in Switzerland.

129

DIFFICULTY

Pulley Puzzler

Turn the handle in the indicated direction. Does the weight go up or down?

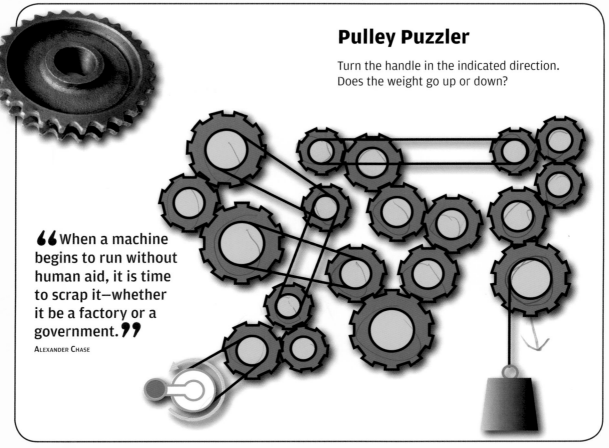

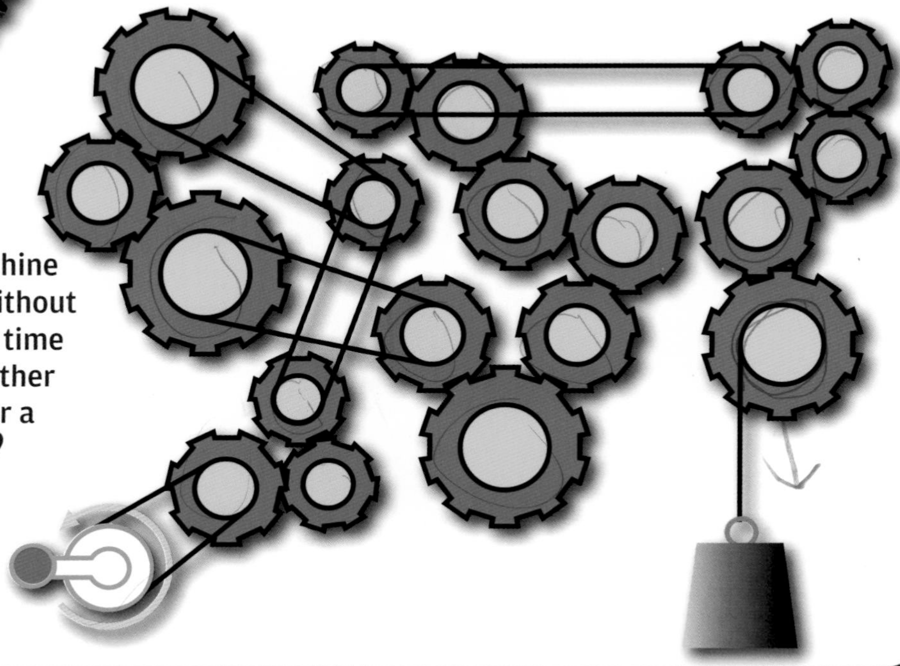

“When a machine begins to run without human aid, it is time to scrap it—whether it be a factory or a government.”

ALEXANDER CHASE

130

Hidden Answer

The value of each shape is the number of sides each shape has, multiplied by the number within it. So a square containing the number 4 has a value of 16. Find a block of four squares (two squares wide by two squares high) with a total value of exactly 70.

“Hope never abandons you; you abandon it.”

GEORGE WEINBERG

131

DIFFICULTY

Loopy Numbers

Connect adjacent dots with either horizontal or vertical lines to create a continuous unbroken loop that never crosses over itself. Some but not all of the boxes are numbered. The numbers in these boxes tell you how many sides of that box are used by your unbroken line.

"Friendship with oneself is all important because without it one cannot be friends with anybody else in the world."
Eleanor Roosevelt

132

DIFFICULTY

Hue Goes There?

Three of the sections below can be found in our main grid, one cannot. Can you spot the section that doesn't belong?

"The artist must create a spark before he can make a fire and before art is born, the artist must be ready to be consumed by the fire of his own creation." Auguste Rodin

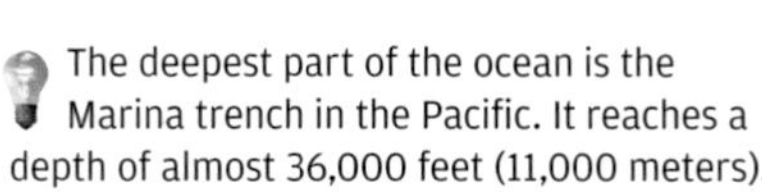

The deepest part of the ocean is the Marina trench in the Pacific. It reaches a depth of almost 36,000 feet (11,000 meters).

133

DIFFICULTY

Next in Sequence

The sequence below follows a logical pattern. Can you work out the color and shape next in line?

German composer Johannes Brahms was in his early forties before he composed his first symphony.

134

DIFFICULTY

Tic-Tac-Toe

3	4	3	4	5	4	4
5			O	X		6
4				O		3
2		O				6
5	O				X	3
3			O	X		4
4	5	3	4	4	5	3

The numbers around the edge of the grid describe the number of X's in the vertical, horizontal, and diagonal lines connecting with that square. Complete the grid so that there is an X or O in every square.

"He who postpones the hour of living is like the rustic who waits for the river to run out before he crosses." Horace

Formerly the residence of the Dali Lama, the Potala Palace in Tibet contains over 1,000 rooms and 10,000 individual shrines. It is 13 stories high and 1,180 feet (360 meters) wide. It is now a museum by decree of the Chinese government.

135

DIFFICULTY

The Great Divide

Divide the grid into four equally sized, equally shaped parts, each containing one each of the five colored stars.

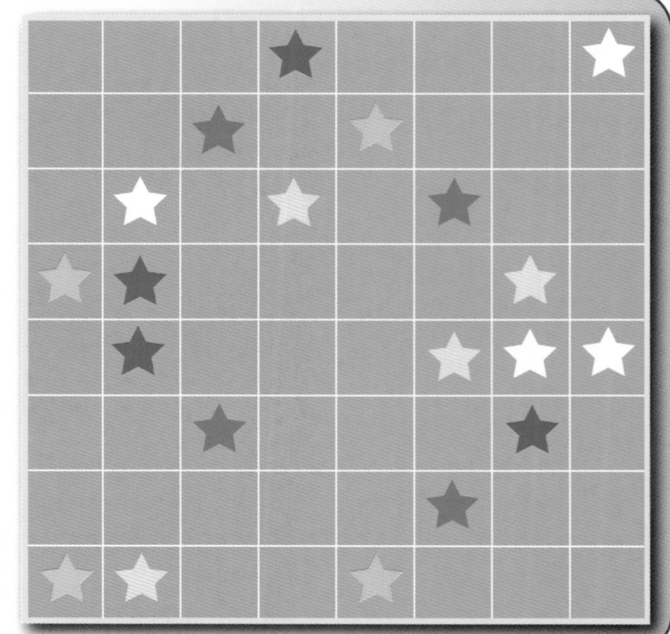

“Failures are divided into two classes—those who thought and never did, and those who did and never thought.”

JOHN CHARLES SALAK

136

DIFFICULTY

Chocolate Chunks

This chocolate bar contains dark, white, and milk chocolate segments. The manufacturers produce the bar to a strict patented pattern. Which of the square chunks shown below correctly completes the bar?

“There is nothing better than a friend, unless it is a friend with chocolate.”

CHARLES DICKENS

Chocolate was introduced into the United States in 1765. When cocoa beans were brought from the West Indies to Dorchester, Massachusetts.

Shaping Relations

137

DIFFICULTY ☆★★

By examining the relationships of the following designs, can you identify the next one?

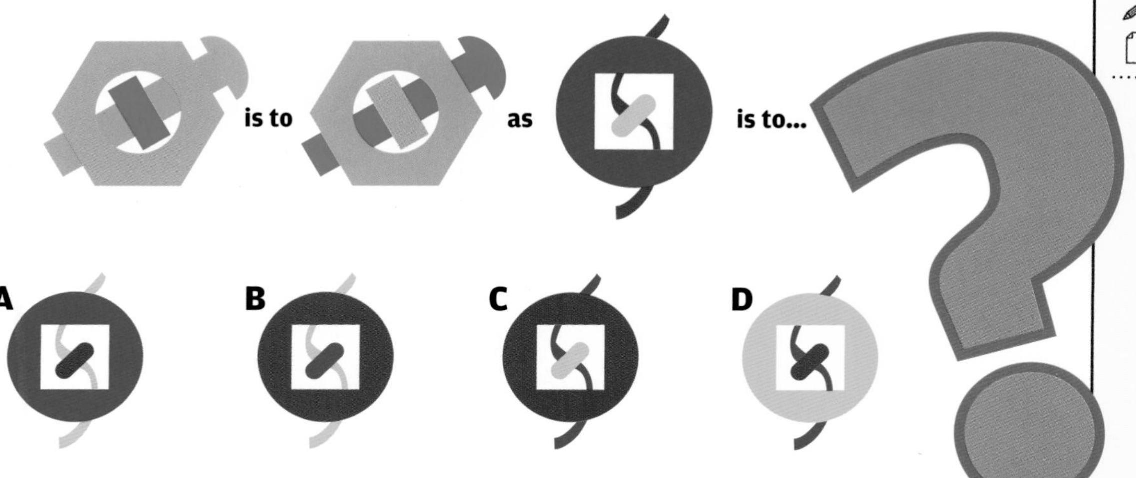

How Many Bricks?

138

DIFFICULTY ☆★★

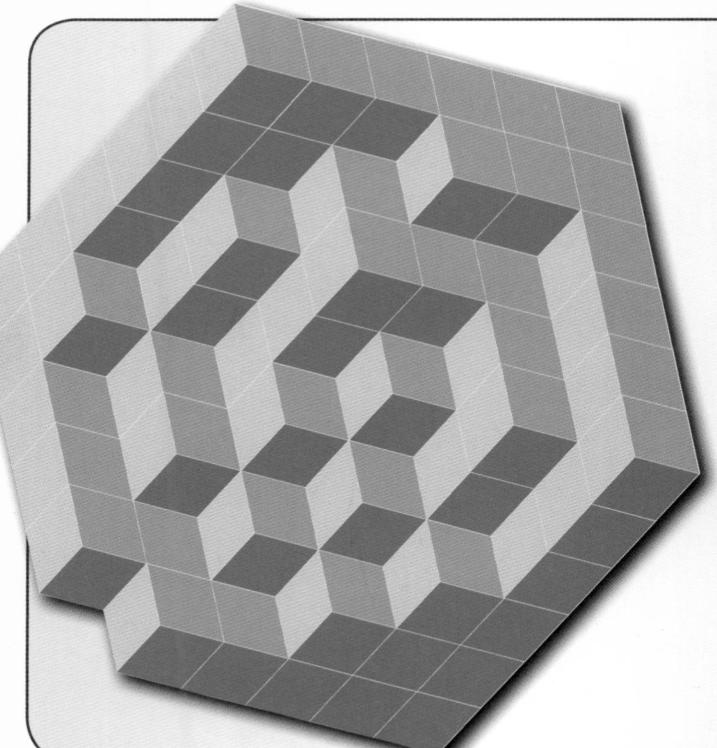

Assuming all blocks that are not visible from this angle are present, how many blocks have been removed from the cube?

“Better to be a strong man with a weak point, than to be a weak man without a strong point. A diamond with a flaw is more valuable than a brick without a flaw.”

William J. H. Boetcker

139

DIFFICULTY ★★★

Spin of the Wheel

The roulette ball is dropped into the wheel at the 0 section. When the ball falls into a number, 15 seconds later, it has traveled at an average speed of 13 feet (4 meters) per second clockwise, while the wheel has traveled at an average 6½ feet (2 meters) per second in the other direction. The ball starts rolling 20 inches (50 centimeters) away from the wheel's centre. Where does it land? Take pi as having a value of exactly 3.2.

"Every man is rich or poor according to the proportion between his desires and his enjoyments." SAMUEL JOHNSON

The odds of winning roulette are slightly better if playing in Europe rather than North America. The U.S. version has two zero spots versus Europe's one, cutting your chances of the jackpot from 1 in 37 to 1 in 38.

140

DIFFICULTY ★

Solitary Letter

All these letters appear twice in the box except one. Can you find it?

"Time is my greatest enemy." EVITA PERON

The Rosetta Stone, the key to deciphering Egyptian hieroglyphs, was made out of granite.

Stars, Suns & Moons

Work out which number is represented by which symbol, and fill in the question mark.

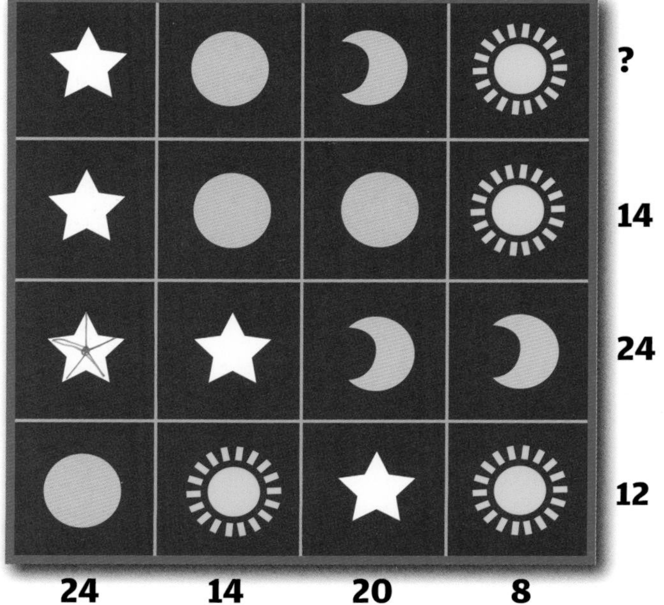

"The sun and the moon and the stars would have disappeared long ago . . . had they happened to be within the reach of predatory human hands." HENRY ELLIS

141

DIFFICULTY

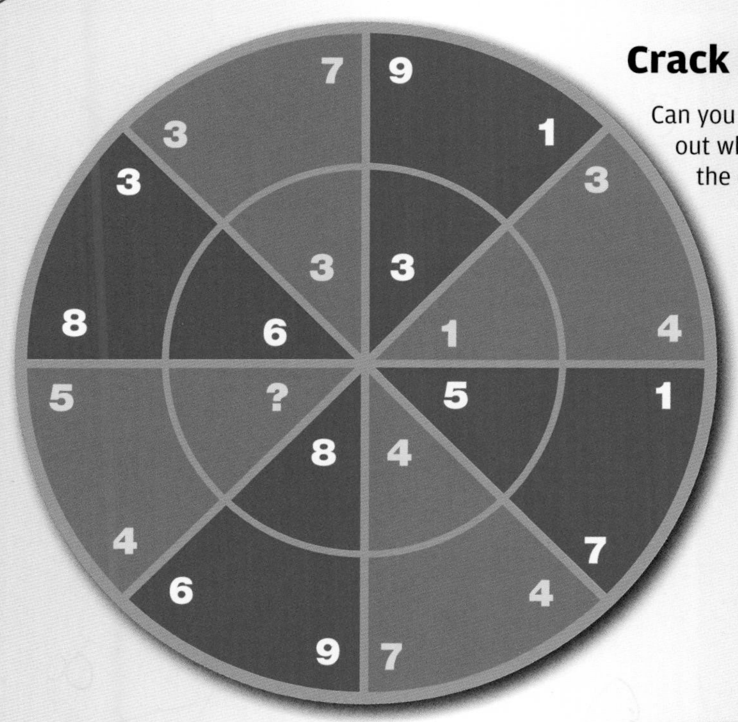

Crack the Code

Can you crack the pie code and work out what number belongs where the question mark is?

"The test of a first-rate intelligence is the ability to hold two opposed ideas in mind at the same time and still retain the ability to function." F. SCOTT FITZGERALD

142

DIFFICULTY

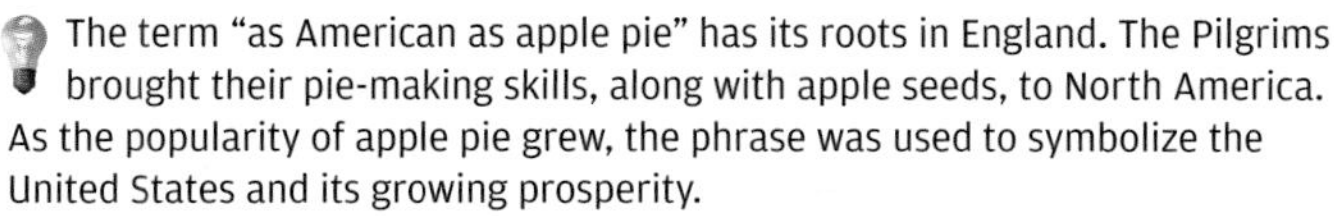

The term "as American as apple pie" has its roots in England. The Pilgrims brought their pie-making skills, along with apple seeds, to North America. As the popularity of apple pie grew, the phrase was used to symbolize the United States and its growing prosperity.

143

DIFFICULTY

Baffling Boxes

The shape below can be folded to make a cube. Which of the four cubes pictured below could it make?

More food is consumed on Superbowl Sunday than on Thanksgiving.

“Some of the most wonderful people are the ones who don't fit into boxes.” Tori Amos

1 2 3 4

144

DIFFICULTY

Logical Locations

Can you crack the logical secret behind the distances to these great cities, and find out how far it is to Melbourne?

“Words are but the signs of ideas.” Samuel Johnson

The 1956 Olympics in Melbourne, Australia, were the first to be held in the southern hemisphere. The equestrian events actually took place in Stockholm, Sweden, because Australia had strict animal quarantine laws.

MOSCOW 78
BRASILIA 16
MELBOURNE ?
TORONTO 140
LAGOS 60

145

DIFFICULTY

Laying It On

What is the logic behind the numbers in these shapes, and the total of A + B + C?

> “The object of art is to give life a shape.”
>
> WILLIAM SHAKESPEARE

Gamophobia is the term for anyone with the fear of marriage, while anuptophobia is the extreme fear of staying single.

146

DIFFICULTY

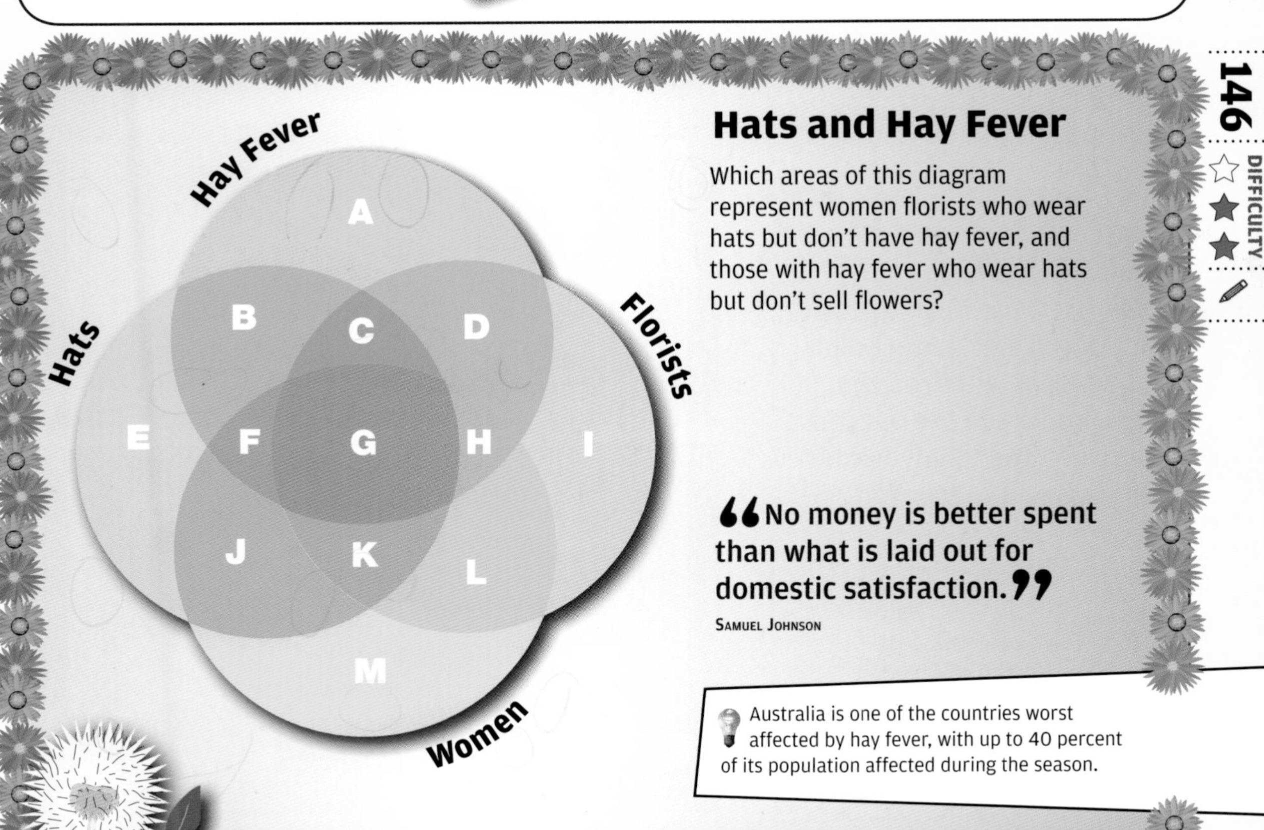

Hats and Hay Fever

Which areas of this diagram represent women florists who wear hats but don't have hay fever, and those with hay fever who wear hats but don't sell flowers?

> “No money is better spent than what is laid out for domestic satisfaction.”
>
> SAMUEL JOHNSON

Australia is one of the countries worst affected by hay fever, with up to 40 percent of its population affected during the season.

147

DIFFICULTY

X and O

The numbers around the edge of the grid describe the number of X's in the vertical, horizontal, and diagonal lines connecting with that square. Complete the grid so that there is an X or O in every square.

3	3	4	2	3	1
4	X	O			2
5	X		O		3
3				O	3
5	O		X	X	3
1	4	4	4	4	3

The safety razor was successfully brought to market by King Gillette in 1901.

“I have friends in overalls whose friendship I would not swap for the favor of the kings of the world.” Thomas A. Edison

148

DIFFICULTY

Look to the Stars

Can you spot the ten differences between these two pictures?

“I don't know whose hand hung Hesperus in the sky, and fixed the Dog Star, and scattered the shining dust of heaven, and fired the sun, and froze the darkness between the lonely worlds that spin in space.”

Gerald Kersh

A basic mix-up between U.S. standard measurements and metric units has been cited as the cause of NASA's 1999 embarrassment, when its $125 million spacecraft, the Mars Climate Orbiter, burned up as it left the earth's atmosphere.

If all the DNA in your body was put end to end, it would reach to the sun and back over 600 times (100 trillion times six feet divided by 92 million miles).

Climb the Mountain

149

DIFFICULTY

Can you reach the summit by replacing the question marks with numbers so that each pair of blocks adds up to the block directly above them?

> **"My dear friend, clear your mind of can't."**
>
> SAMUEL JOHNSON

Make Your Move

150

DIFFICULTY

Can you place a queen, a bishop, a knight, and a rook on this chessboard so that the red squares are attacked by exactly two pieces, the green ones by three pieces, and the yellow ones by four pieces?

St. Adrian Nicomedia is the patron saint of arms dealers, old soldiers, and butchers. He is also a protector against the plague.

Floor Filler

Below is a plan of an apartment, and some very oddly shaped pieces of carpet. Can you arrange them to fill the floor?

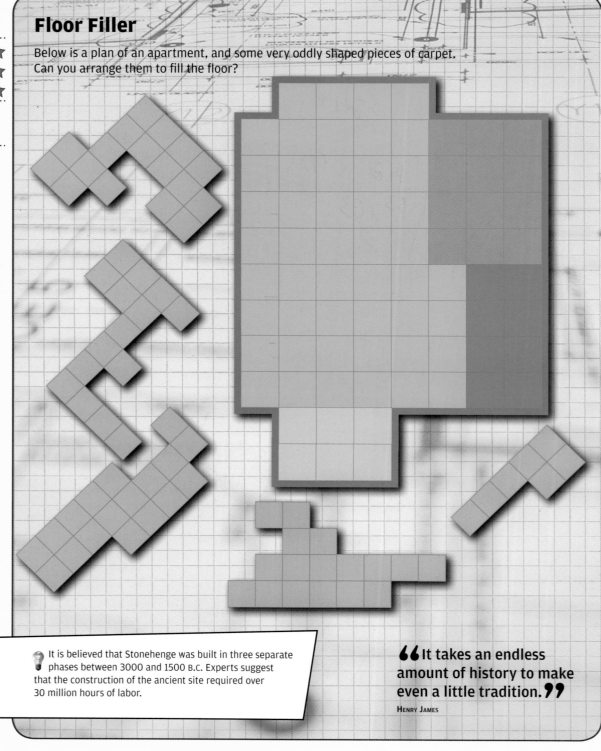

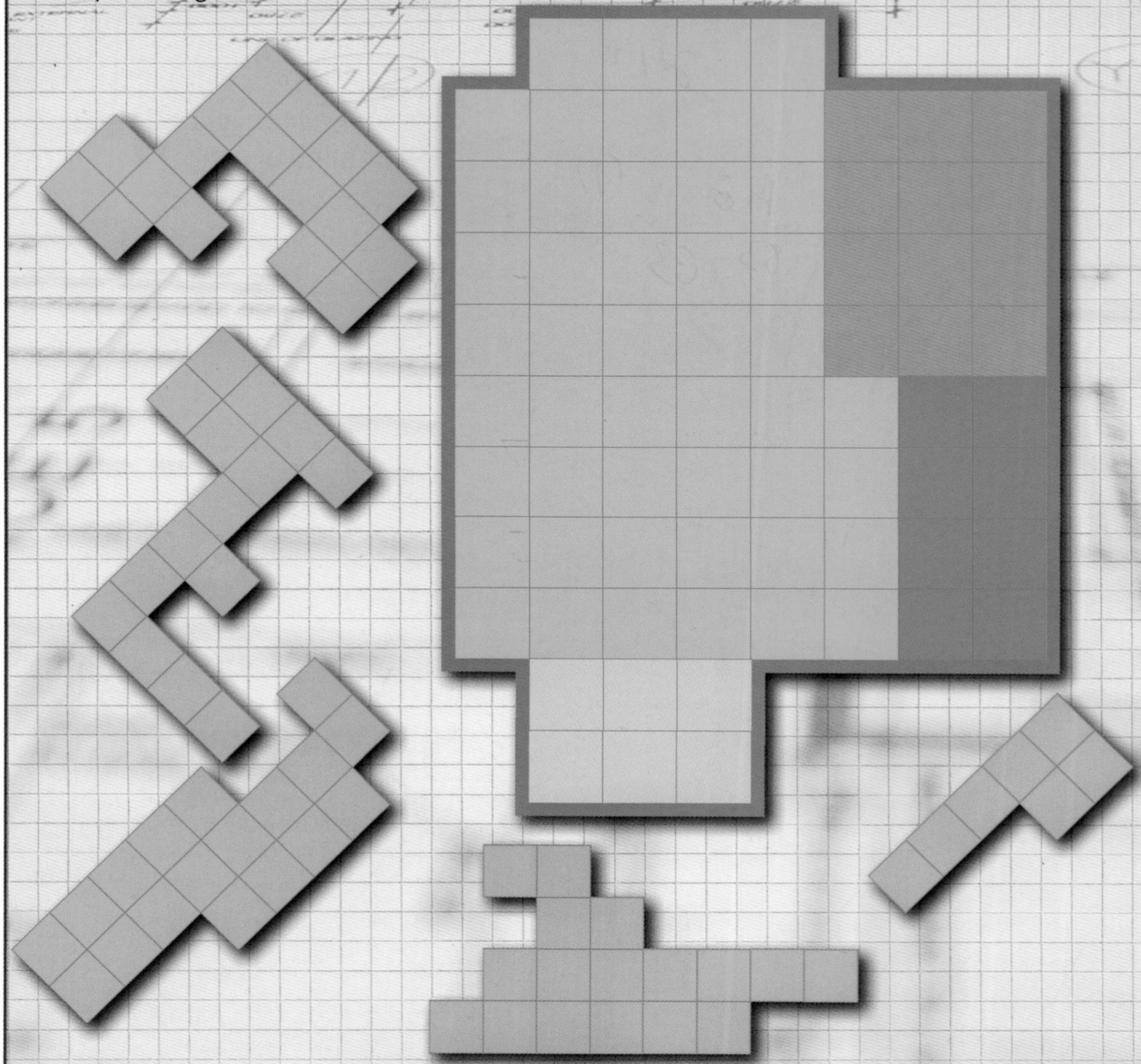

It is believed that Stonehenge was built in three separate phases between 3000 and 1500 B.C. Experts suggest that the construction of the ancient site required over 30 million hours of labor.

"It takes an endless amount of history to make even a little tradition."

HENRY JAMES

8
2 2
2 8 2
2 2 2 4
4 3 8 6 4
2 3 5 1 8 1
1 5 1 7 3
5 1 3 3
8 3 3
9 4
9

Number Chunks

Divide up the grid into four equally sized, equally shaped parts, each containing numbers that add up to 36.

“Mathematics is the only science where one never knows what one is talking about nor whether what is said is true.” Bertrand Russell

152 DIFFICULTY ★★★

Sir Isaac Newton instigated a Royal Society investigation to prove that he invented calculus before German mathematician Gottfried Wilhelm Leibniz, who had, in fact, published the method first.

Biggest to Smallest

Can you put these shapes A, B, C, and D in size order, from biggest to smallest?

“Each generation imagines itself to be more intelligent than the one that went before it, and wiser than the one that comes after it.” George Orwell

153 DIFFICULTY ☆☆★

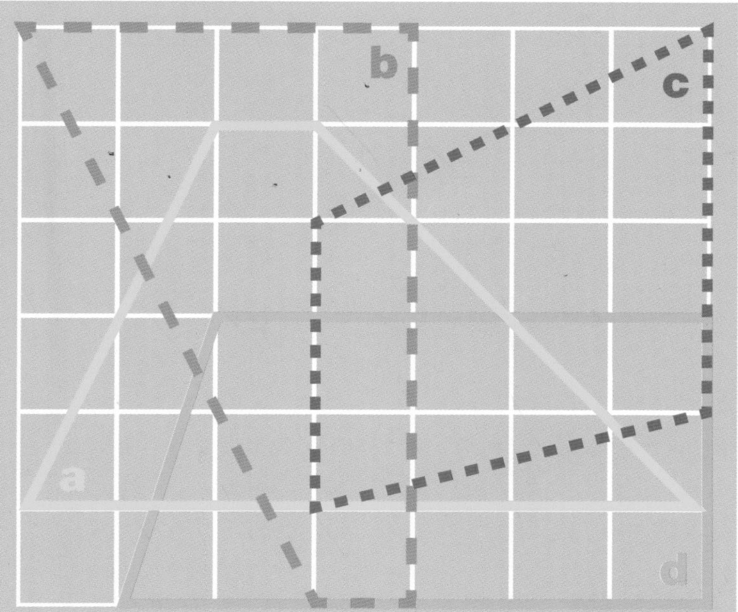

The world's biggest airport is the King Khalid in Riydah, Saudi Arabia, which takes up 81 square miles (143 square kilometers).

154 DIFFICULTY ★★★

Price Puzzle

At a medieval antiquities sale, you took $30,000, bought 18 items, and spent every single cent you had. How many of each item did you buy?

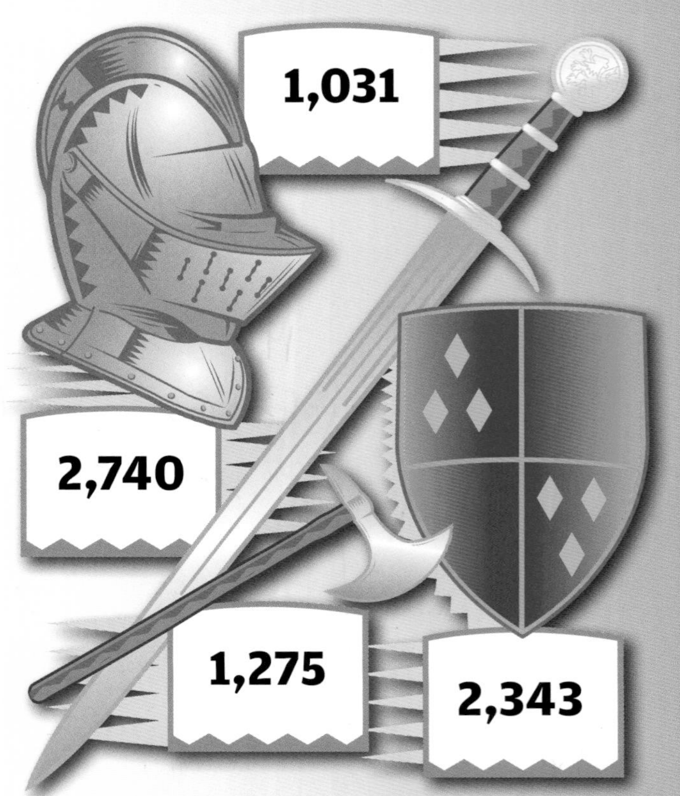

“History is the witness that testifies to the passing of time; it illumines reality, vitalizes memory, provides guidance in daily life, and brings us tidings of antiquity.” MARCUS TULLIUS CICERO

155 DIFFICULTY ☆★★

Destination Unknown

The directions below describe a route that connects two of the five houses below, and passes through every square on the map that isn't occupied by a house. Start at the red house, which two houses does it join?

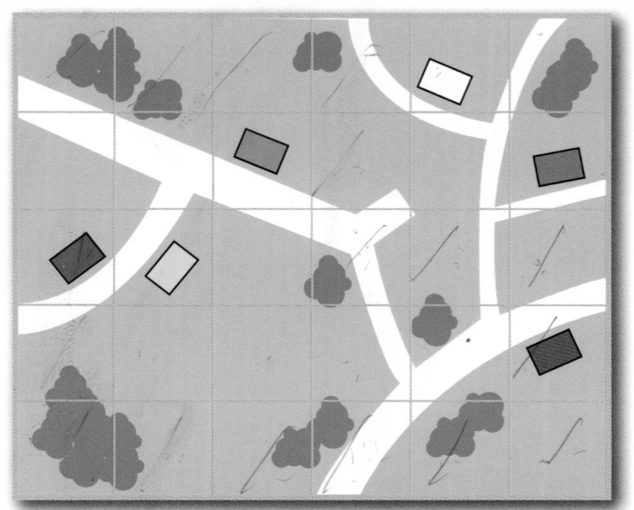

2D 5R 2U 2L 2U 3L 2R 3R 4L 4D 3R 2L 1U 1L 1L 3R 1D 3U 3L 1R 3R 2D 1U 2L 1L

On September 13, 1899, Henry Hale Bliss became the first person to be killed by a traffic accident in the nation. He was struck by an electric-powered taxicab as he stepped down from a streetcar in New York City. The spot at West 74th Street and Central Park West is today marked by a plaque.

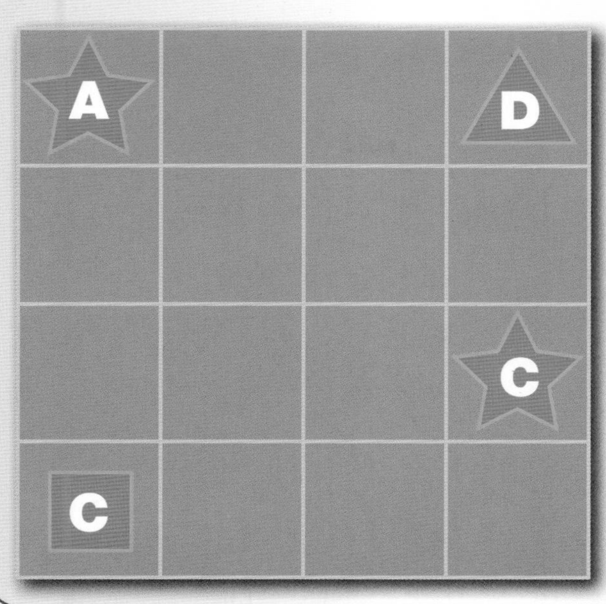

156

DIFFICULTY

Fill Up!

Fill up the shuffle box so that each row, column, and long diagonal contains four different shapes and the letters A, B, C, and D.

"I not only use all the brains that I have, but all that I can borrow." WOODROW WILSON

Wheat is the world's most widely cultivated plant. It is grown on every continent except Antarctica.

157

DIFFICULTY

Fold and Cut

Which of the patterns below is created by this fold and cut?

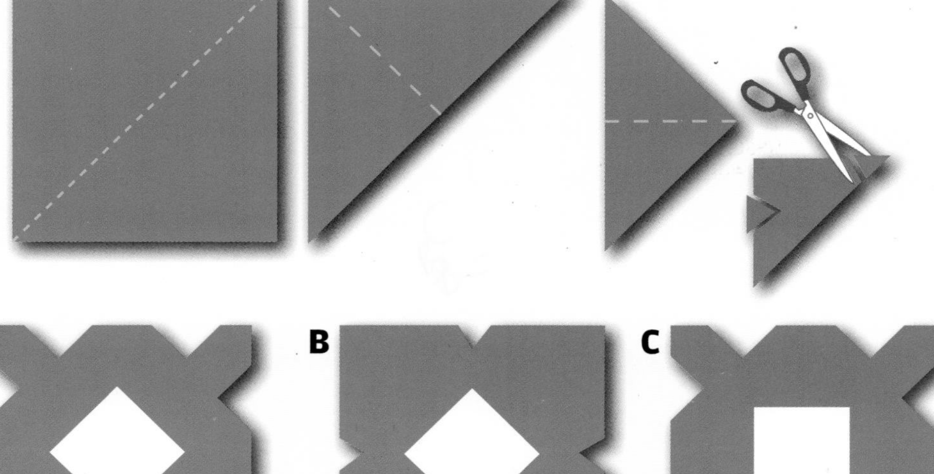

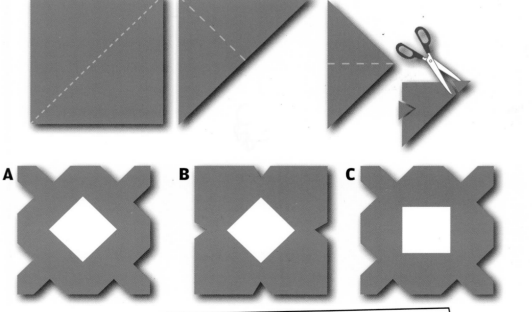

An amateur British astronomer named William Herschel first spied Uranus through his homemade telescope on March 13, 1781. It was the first expansion of the solar system in modern times. His observations helped to double the known size of the solar system and he was honored by King George III.

158

DIFFICULTY ★★★

Missing Dots

How many dots should there be in the hole in this pattern?

"We should take care not to make the intellect our god; it has, of course, powerful muscles, but no personality."

Albert Einstein

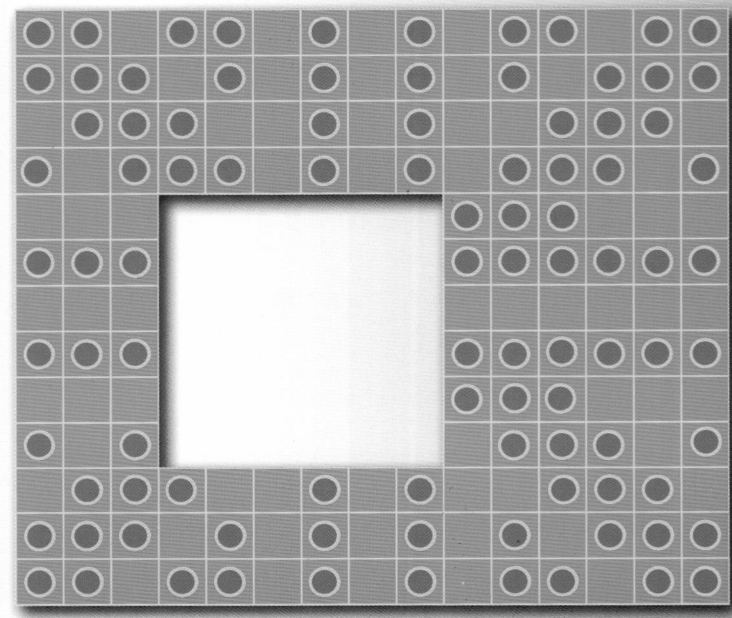

There is an estimated 13-14 species of animal on the earth; 1.75 million have been recorded.

159

DIFFICULTY ☆★★

Tricky Trucks

Which toy box contains exactly the right parts to make the truck?

A

B

C

The U.S. Postal Service operates the largest civilian vehicle fleet in the world, with more than 216,000 vehicles driving more than 1.2 billion miles (1.9 billion kilometers) each year and using nearly 121 million gallons (458 million liters) of fuel.

Perfect Symmetry

160

DIFFICULTY ★

This picture, when finished, is symmetrical along a vertical line up the middle. Can you color in the missing squares to see what the picture is?

The peregrine falcon is the world's fastest animal. It has been known to reach speeds of 200 mph (322 kph) during near vertical dives in pursuit of prey.

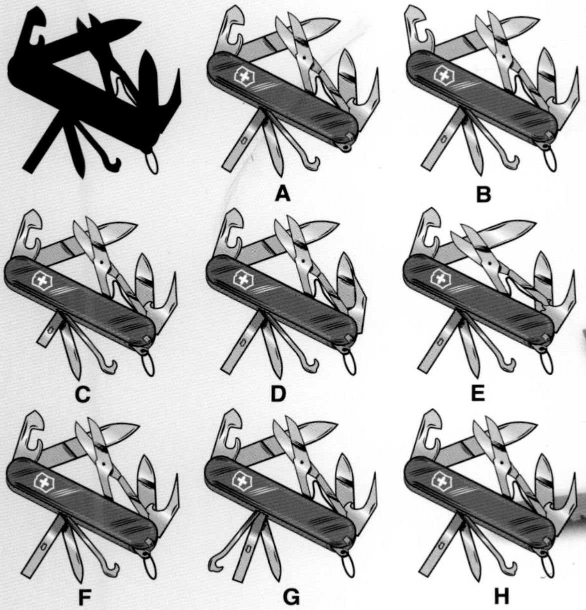

Silhouette

161

DIFFICULTY ★

A B C D E F G H

Which of the colored-in images matches the silhouette?

"History will be kind to me for I intend to write it."

WINSTON CHURCHILL

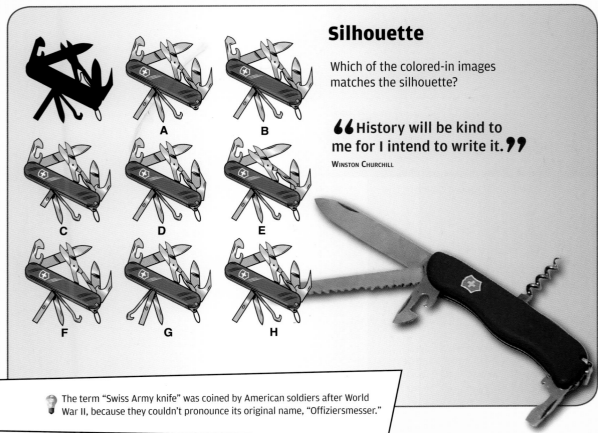

The term "Swiss Army knife" was coined by American soldiers after World War II, because they couldn't pronounce its original name, "Offiziersmesser."

162 DIFFICULTY ★★★

Seeing Stars

Believe it or not, none of these stars is exactly alike. They represent every single combination of five colors, except one. What is the color placements on the missing star?

Sirius is the brightest star in the night sky. Aptly named, the word comes from the Greek *seirius*, meaning, "searing" or "scorching". Blazing at a visual magnitude of -1.42, it is twice as bright as any other star in the sky.

163 DIFFICULTY ☆★★

Easy as Pie

Can you crack the pie code and work out what number belongs where the question mark is?

"Love conquers all things—except poverty and toothache." Mae West

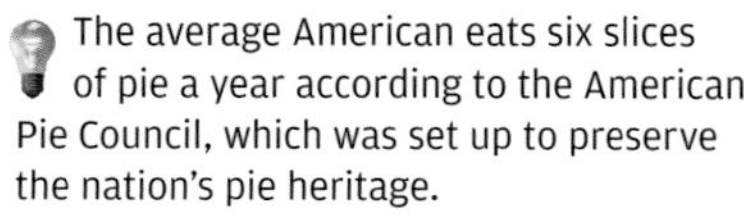

The average American eats six slices of pie a year according to the American Pie Council, which was set up to preserve the nation's pie heritage.

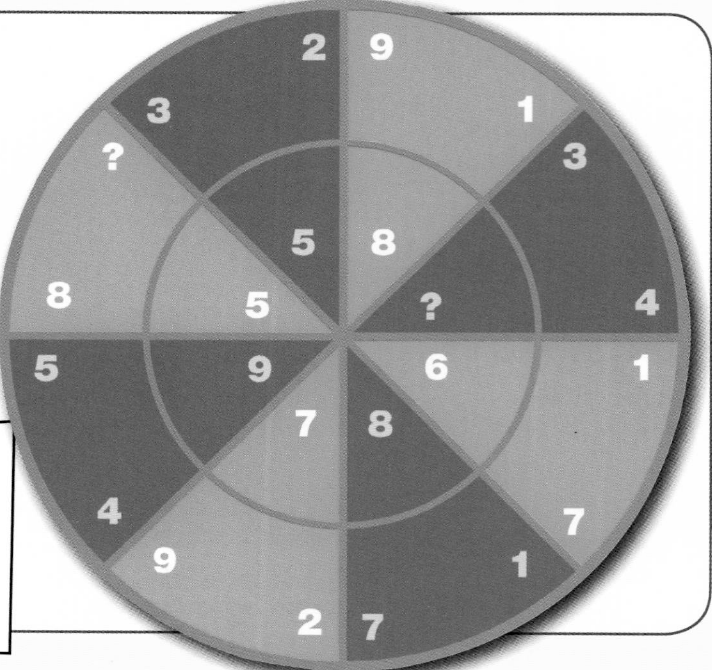

164

DIFFICULTY

Symbol Sums

These symbols represent the numbers 1 to 4. If the green phone represents the number 3, what do the other color phones represent? Finish the equation.

The two key innovators of the Cubist art movement were Pablo Picasso and Georges Braque. Both were residents of Montmartre, a district of Paris.

165

DIFFICULTY

Hubble Bubble

What numbers should appear in the hubs of these number wheels?

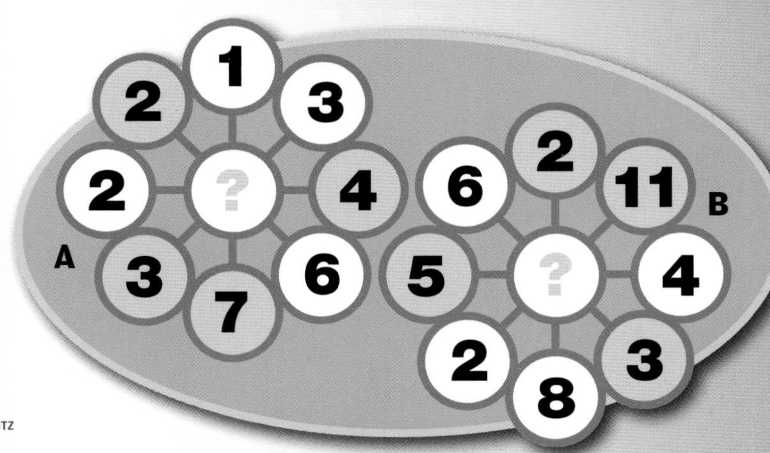

“Wealth and power are much more likely to be the result of breeding than they are of reading.” Fran Lebowitz

Galaxies are classified using Edwin Hubble’s scheme, describing spiral, barred spiral, elliptical, peculiar, and irregular shapes.

166

DIFFICULTY ★★★

Going in Circles

Draw a single continuous line around the grid that passes through all the circles. The line must enter and leave each box in the center of one of its four sides.

Black Circle: Turn left or right in the box, and the line must pass straight through the next and previous boxes.
White Circle: Travel straight through the box, and the line must turn in the next and/or previous box.

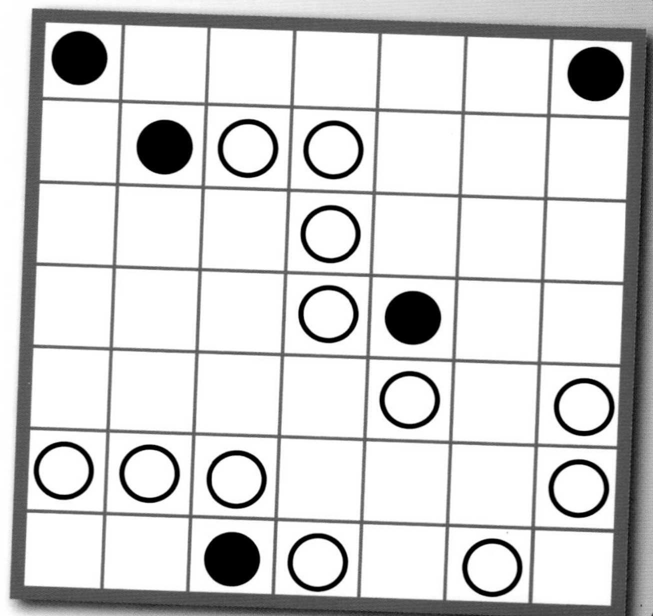

In the late 1980s, scientists developed a checkers-playing computer program. In 2007, they announced that the program had improved to the point where it was unbeatable.

167

DIFFICULTY ★★★

Compass Capers

Complete the grid by drawing an arrow in each box that points in any one of the eight compass directions (N, E, S, W, NE, NW, SE, and SW). The numbers in the outside boxes in the finished puzzle will reflect the number of arrows pointing in their direction.

"Conscience is a man's compass." VINCENT VAN GOGH

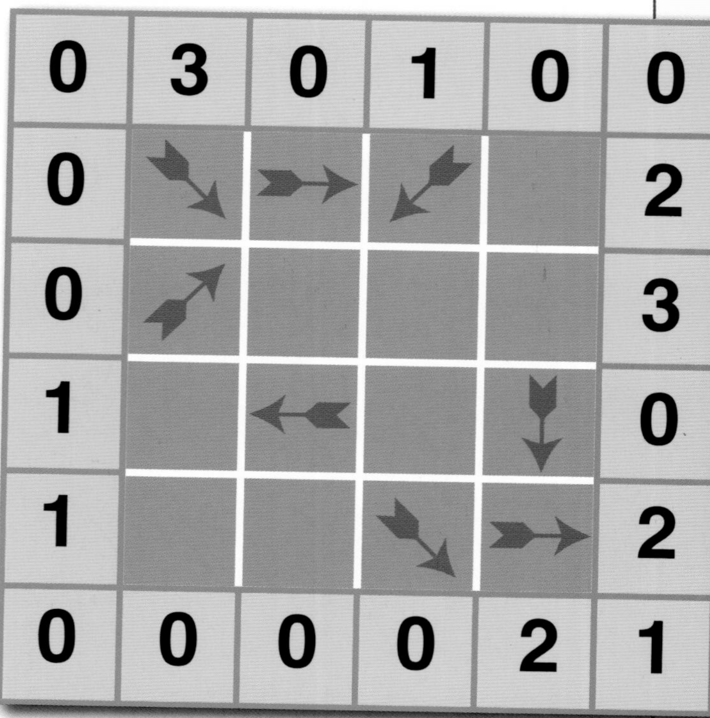

The first magnetic compass was made in China during the Qin dynasty (221-206 B.C.). Fortune-tellers used lodestones (a mineral composed of an iron oxide, which aligns itself in a north-south direction) to construct their fortune-telling boards. Eventually, someone noticed that the lodestones were better at pointing out real directions, leading to the first compasses.

168

DIFFICULTY ★★☆

Fish Tank Thinker

Divide up the grid into four equally sized, equally shaped parts, each containing one of the five colored fish.

"If you want to catch more fish, use more hooks." George Allen

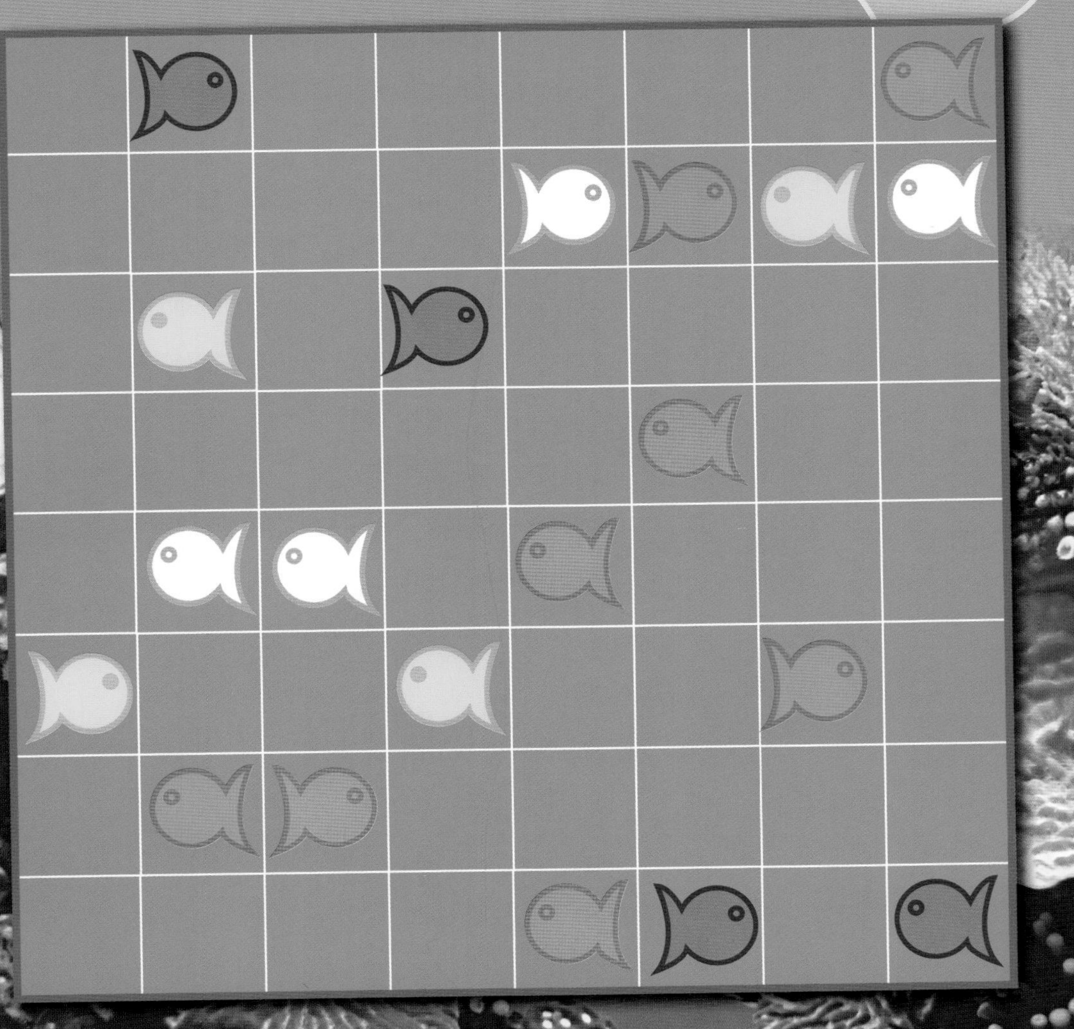

Japan boasts 15 percent of the world's global fishing catch, which explains why sushi is so popular there.

169

DIFFICULTY ★★☆

Off the Wall

Three of the sections below can be found in the main grid, one cannot. Which section doesn't belong? Beware: The sections might not be the same way around!

At the time it came down in 1989, the Berlin Wall covered a 27 mile (43 kilometer) distance. There were 302 watchtowers along the wall and between its erection in 1961 and 1989, 192 people were killed trying to cross the border.

170

DIFFICULTY

In the Area

Can you work out the approximate area that this elephant head is taking up?

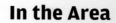

“Nature’s great masterpiece, an elephant—the only harmless great thing.” John Donne

171

Pack It In

Fill up the shuffle box so that each row, column, and long diagonal contains four different shapes and the letters A, B, C, and D.

“As human beings, we are endowed with freedom of choice, and we cannot shuffle off our responsibility upon the shoulders of God or nature. We must shoulder it ourselves. It is our responsibility.” Arnold J. Toynbee

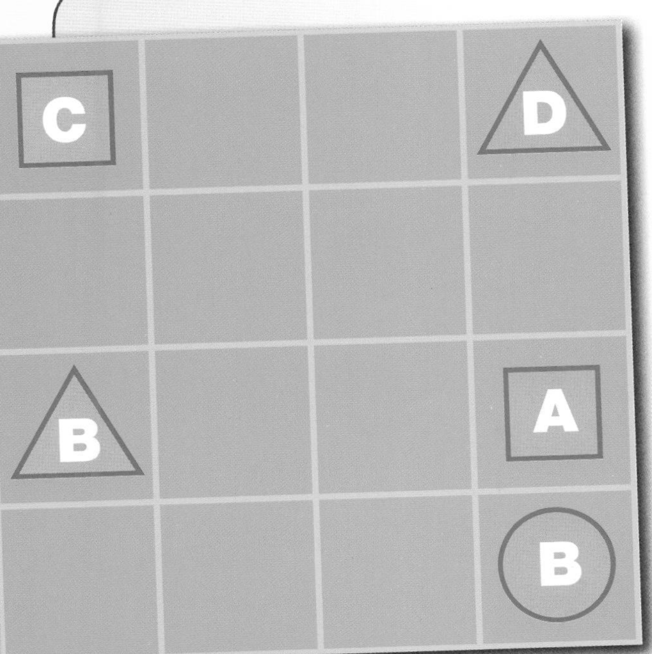

In 1993, the world’s first bicycle elevator opened in Trondheim, Norway, to help cyclists negotiate the city’s steep Brubakken Hill.

172

DIFFICULTY

Gridlock

Look at the pattern to the right; which of the squares shown below correctly completes the grid?

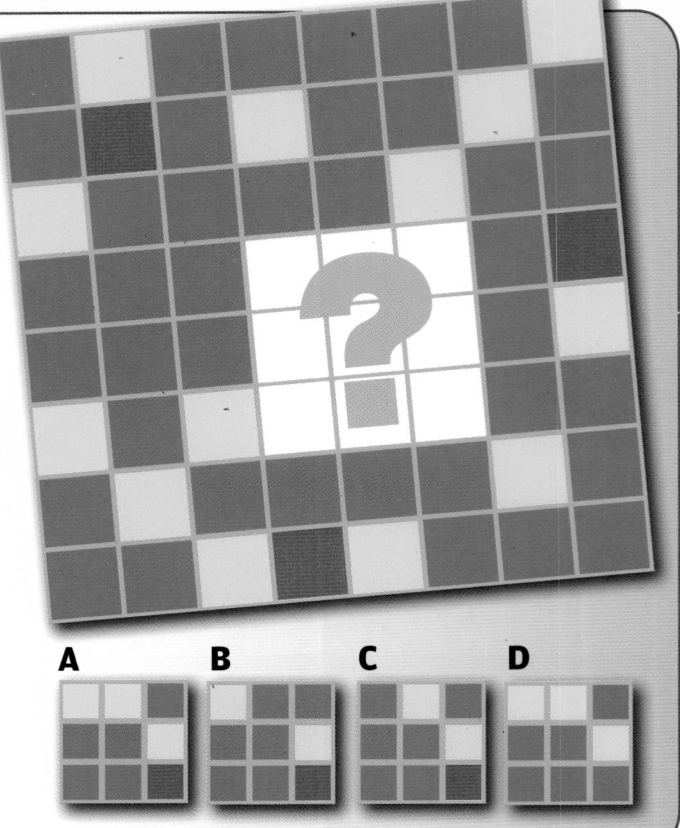

“My wife and I, we like to ride where there’s not much traffic.” EVEL KNIEVEL

As of October 2007, the five most gridlocked cities in the nation are: New York City, San Francisco, Seattle, Minneapolis, and Miami.

173

DIFFICULTY

Thinking Box

The value of each shape is the number of sides each shape has, multiplied by the number within it. So a square containing the number 4 has a value of 16. Find a block of four squares (two squares wide by two squares high) with a total value of exactly 70.

When a hurricane has had a major impact, any country affected by the storm can request that the name of the hurricane be “retired.” It cannot be reused for at least ten years, to facilitate historic references, legal actions, insurance claims, and to avoid public confusion.

The sapphire blue blood of the horseshoe crab is the world's only known substance that can be used to test for contaminants in every drug and every vaccine in the world. The crabs are "bled" by a fast and painless process. They are then returned to the ocean 24 hours later.

174

DIFFICULTY ☆★★

Secret Color Code

The pattern on the left gives you all the clues you need to color in the pattern on the right. Can you discover the secret of the color code?

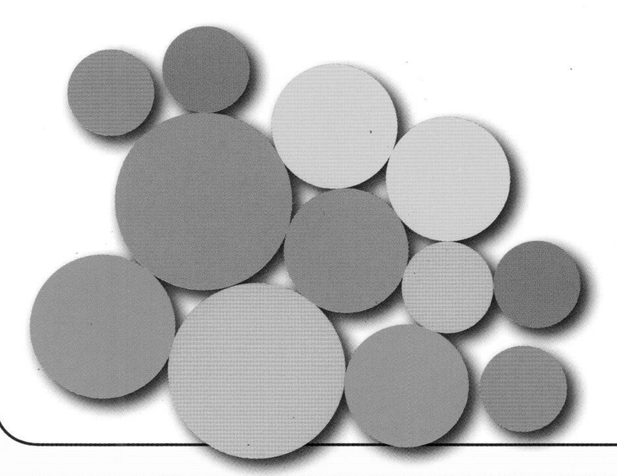

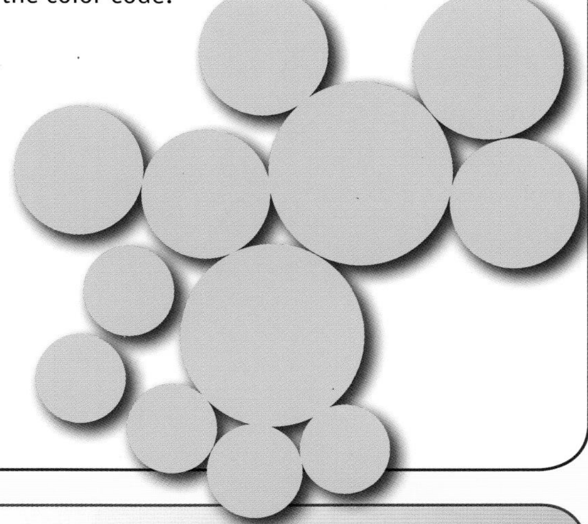

175

DIFFICULTY ☆★★

Dicey Directions

Each color represents a direction—up, down, left, and right. Starting in the middle die of the grid, follow the instructions correctly and you will visit every die in turn only once. What's the last die you visit on your trip?

Blue = Left
Green = Right
Yellow = Up
Red = Down

"Thinking is the hardest work there is, which is probably the reason why so few engage in it." Henry Ford

The Venetian Casino, which opened in Macau, China, in October 2007, claims to have 10.5 million square feet (3.2 million square meters) of floor space—making it the world's biggest building.

176

DIFFICULTY ★★★

Find the Pirate's Plunder

The numbers on the side and bottom of the grid indicate occupied squares or groups of consecutive occupied squares in each row or column. Can you complete the grid so that it contains two amulets, two cutlasses, two bars of gold, and two keys, and the numbers tally?

> **"Why join the navy if you can be a pirate?"**
>
> STEVE JOBS

Blackbeard, perhaps the most notorious pirate in history, was eventually tracked down to Ocracoke Inlet, North Carolina, by the British Royal Navy and killed in a brief but bloody battle on November 22, 1718.

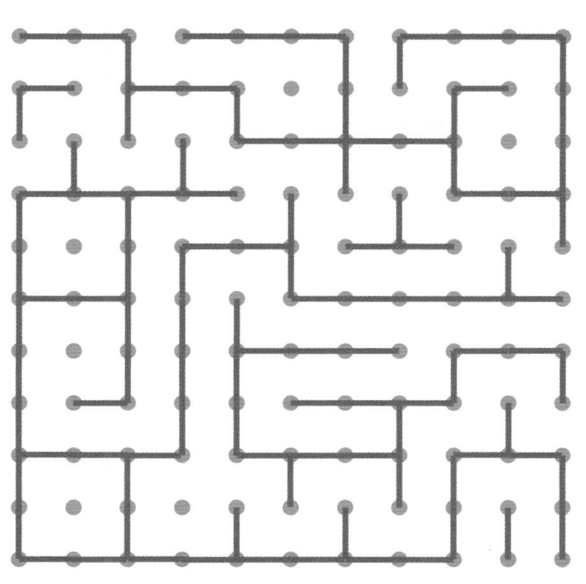

It's Your Turn!

177

DIFFICULTY

Playing the game of boxes, each player takes it in turn to join two adjacent dots with a line. If a player's line completes a box, the player wins the box and has another turn. It's your turn in the game below. To avoid giving your opponent a lot of boxes, what's your best move?

The oldest living thing is a box huckleberry bush growing in Pennsylvania. It is 13,000 years old.

Shaping Relations

178

DIFFICULTY

By examining the relationships of the following shapes, can you identify the next shape?

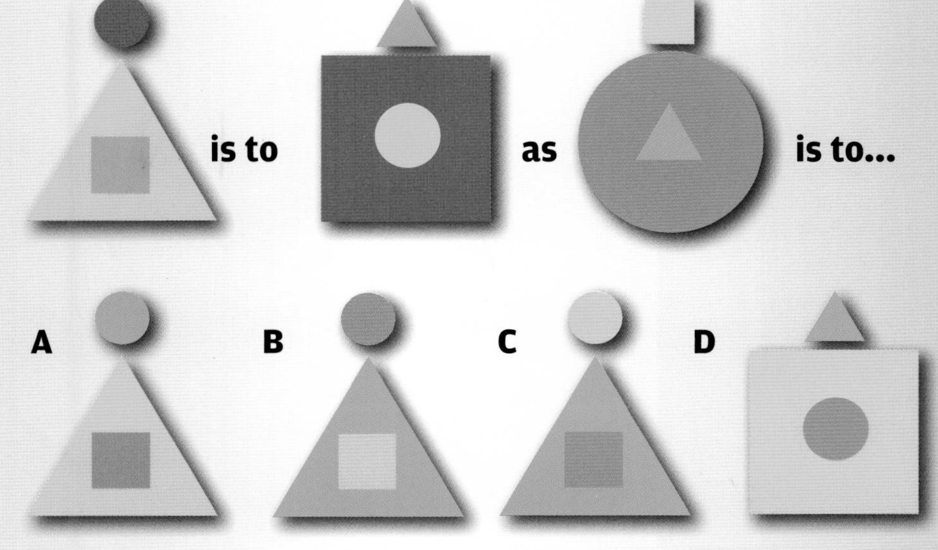

Amsterdam is the most bicycle friendly city in the world with 40 percent of all journeys undertaken in the Dutch capital on two wheels.

179

DIFFICULTY ★★★

Points to Remember

An arrow in the blue scores one, in the white, two, in the red, five. Study these images for a minute, then cover up the targets and answer the following five questions:

The Hundred Years' War between France and England started in 1337 and ended in 1453. So it actually spanned 116 years. English archers played a key role in the war. They could unleash 12 arrows a minute and shoot through a thick oak door from a great distance.

A

B

C D

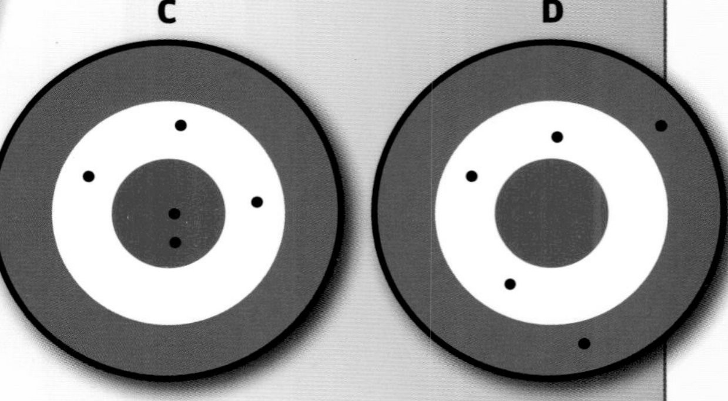

"Every great man nowadays has his disciples, and it is always Judas who writes the biography." Oscar Wilde

Questions:

1. How many of the scores were even numbers?
2. How many arrows were in the blue in target C?
3. What was the total score of all four targets?
4. How many total hits in the red on targets A and B?
5. How many total hits in the white on all targets?

180

DIFFICULTY ☆☆★

Circle Solutions

Can you work out which areas of this diagram represent Swedish people who are blond and have Volvos but don't like meatballs, and Swedish people who like meatballs and have Volvos but aren't blond?

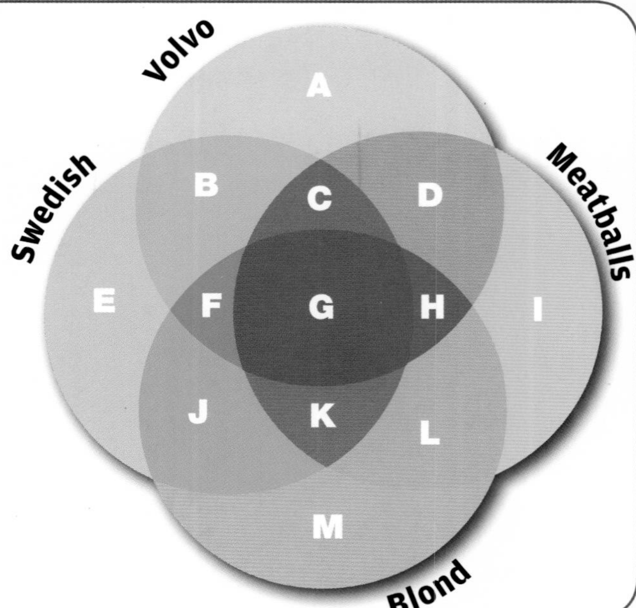

Drivers in Sweden drove on the left-hand side of the road until 1967, when the government literally changed the rules overnight.

181

DIFFICULTY

Spare Wheel

Which of the wheels—A, B, C, or D—is missing from the set above?

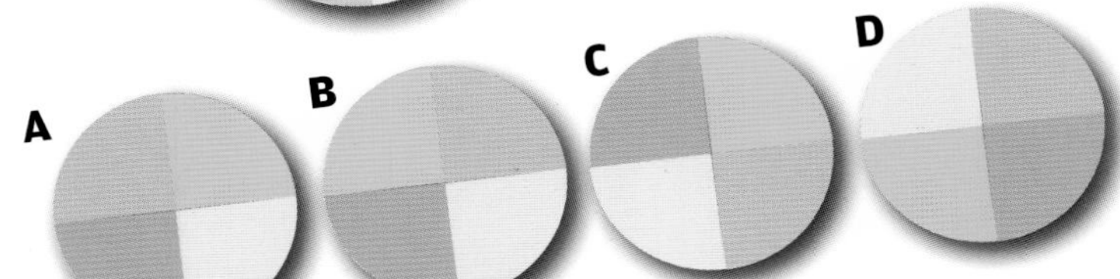

A B C D

“On their own merits modest men are dumb.”

George Colman

The world's fastest jet-powered aircraft is the SR-71 Blackbird, which has been officially recorded as reaching Mach 3.3. The X-43 Hyper-X, an unmanned experimental aircraft, has recorded speeds ranging from Mach 7 to Mach 10.

182

DIFFICULTY

Matrix Matters

Which of the four boxed figures completes the set?

“I love everything that's old—old friends, old times, old manners, old books, old wine.”

Oliver Goldsmith

Mozart was an avid billiards player, often playing the game all through the night to help his musical compositions.

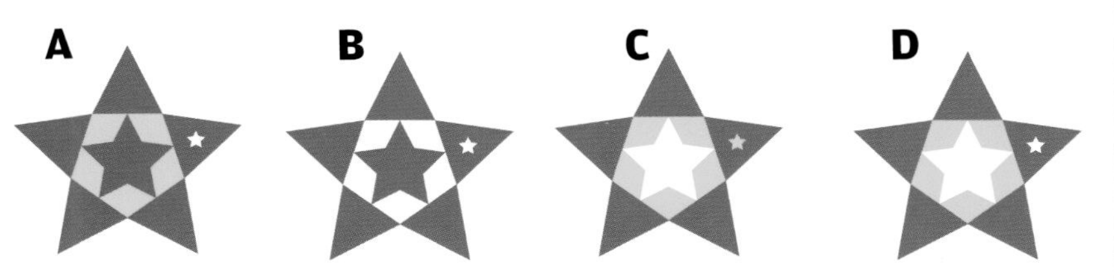

A B C D

183

DIFFICULTY ☆★★

Bees and Blooms

Every bloom has one bee found horizontally or vertically adjacent to it. No bee can be in an adjacent square to another bee (even diagonally). The numbers by each row and column tell you how many bees are there. Can you locate all the bees?

BLOOM

BEE

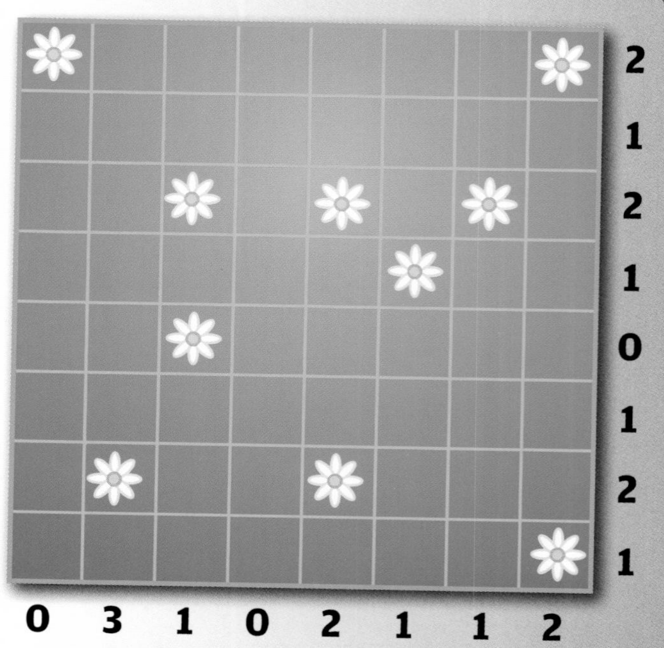

A productive queen bee surrounded by efficient drones can lay between 2,000–3,000 eggs every day.

184

DIFFICULTY ☆★★

Beautiful Boxes

Which of the four boxed figures completes the set?

“If I keep a green bough in my heart, then the singing bird will come.” CHINESE PROVERB

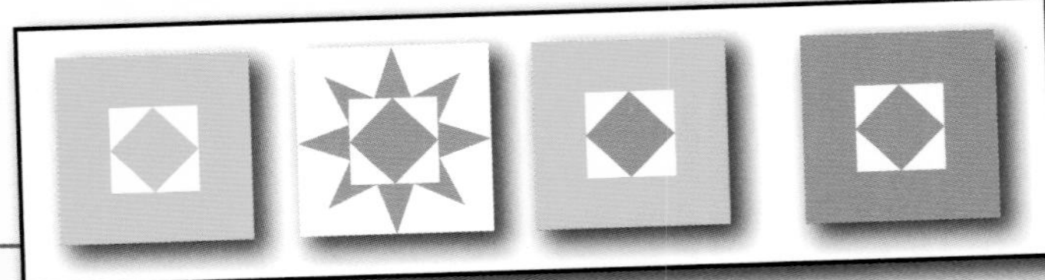

A hummingbird feeds up to 15 times every hour in order to remain active enough to maintain a body temperature of 105-109˚F (40.5-42.7˚C).

185

DIFFICULTY

Gone to the Dogs

What is the approximate area of the dog in this picture?

"Scratch a dog and you'll find a permanent job."

Franklin P. Jones

According to Herodotus, when a dog died in an Egyptian household the entire family went into mourning and shaved their heads and bodies in memory of the animal.

186

DIFFICULTY

Play the Cards

Fill up the shuffle box so that each row, column, and long diagonal contains a jack, queen, king, and ace of each suit.

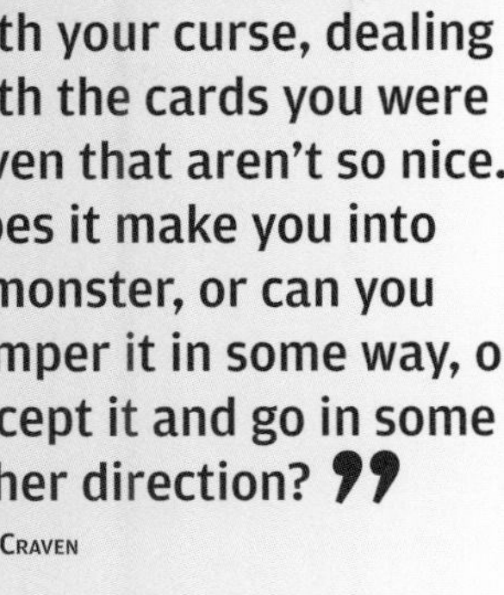

"A lot of life is dealing with your curse, dealing with the cards you were given that aren't so nice. Does it make you into a monster, or can you temper it in some way, or accept it and go in some other direction?"

Wes Craven

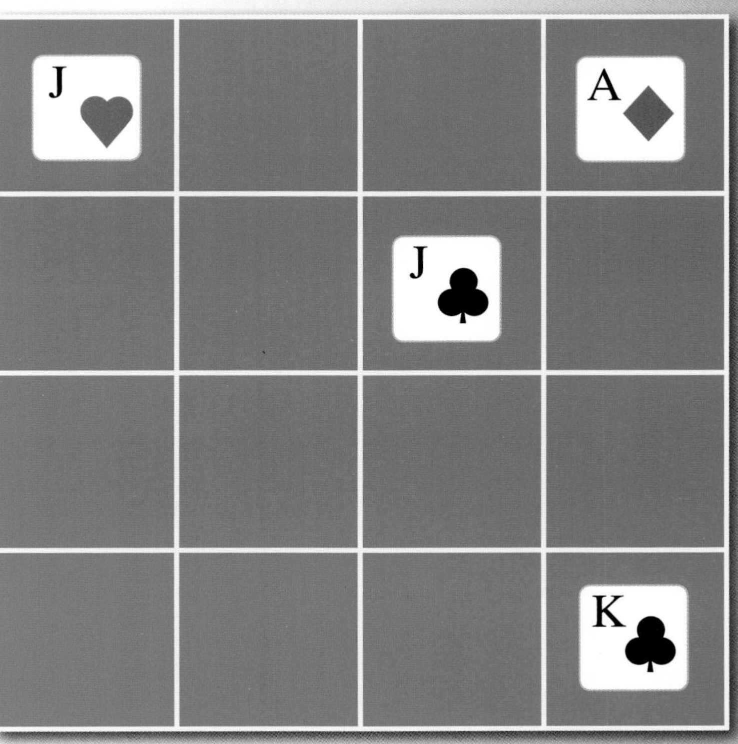

187

DIFFICULTY ☆☆★

Pack It In

Fill up the shuffle box so that each row, column, and long diagonal contains four different shapes and the letters A, B, C, and D.

“Too many people are thinking of security instead of opportunity. They seem to be more afraid of life than death.” James F. Bymes

Russian playwright Anton Chekov died in the German town Badenweiler. His body was returned to Moscow for burial by train in a refrigerated box marked “Oysters”—actually the title of one of his short stories.

188

DIFFICULTY ☆★★

Wallpaper Poser

Stan is wallpapering his cousin Claire's apartment but he has been given more paper than he needs. Three of the paper strips shown below can be found in our main grid, one can't. Can you find the section that doesn't belong? Beware: The sections might not be the same way around!

A B C D

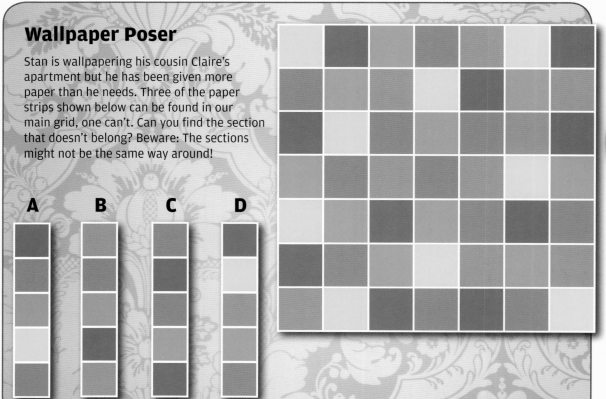

189

DIFFICULTY

Roulette Returns

This roulette wheel pays 14 to 1 for every number successfully bet on. If the number 7 came up three times in a row, and you bet $10 on it initially and reinvested half your return each time, how much would you end up with?

“In Vegas, I got into a long argument with the man at the roulette wheel over what I considered to be an odd number.”

STEVEN WRIGHT

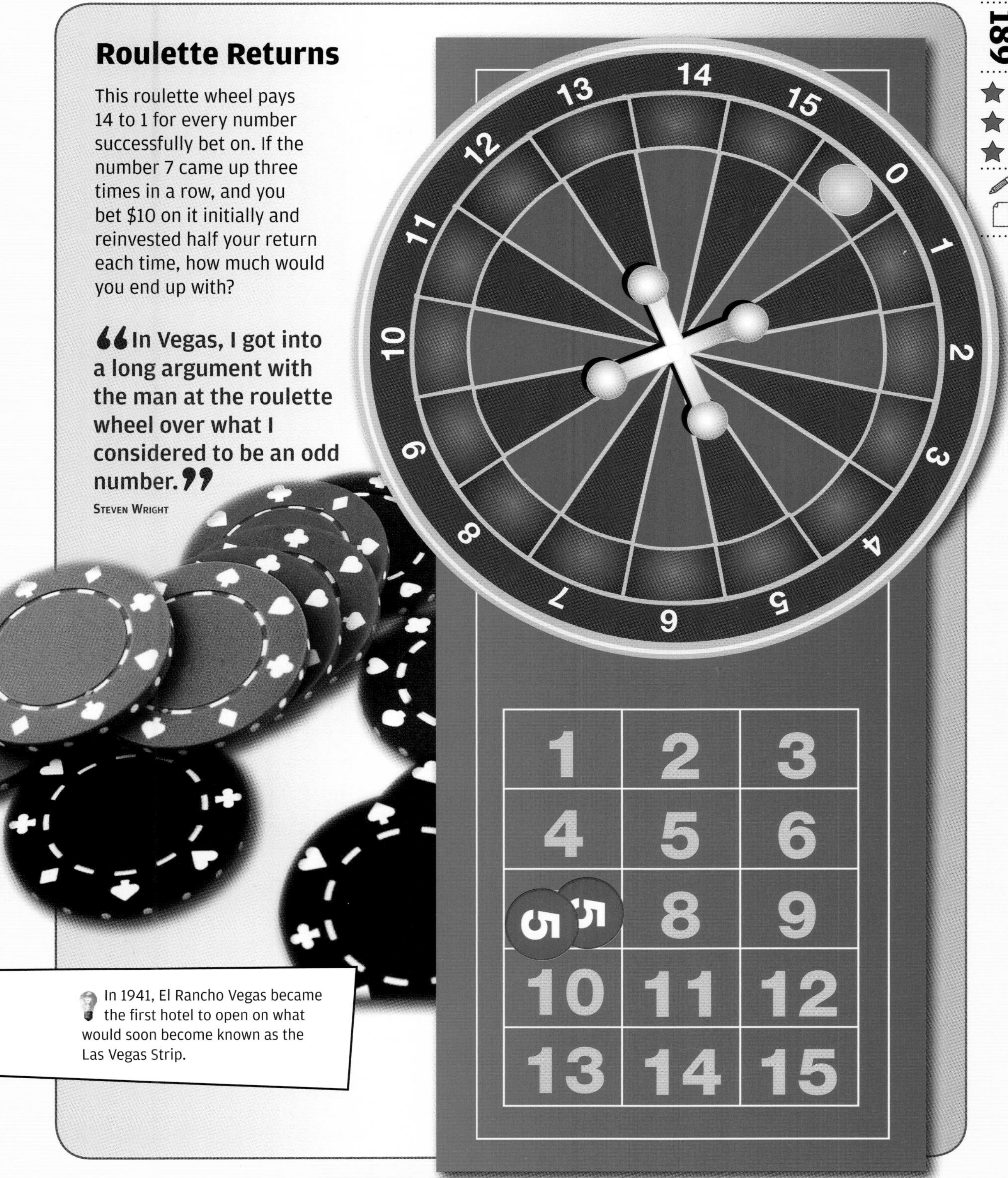

In 1941, El Rancho Vegas became the first hotel to open on what would soon become known as the Las Vegas Strip.

190

DIFFICULTY ★★★

Galaxy of Stars

In 1958, Perry Como received the first official Gold Record for his recording of "Catch a Falling Star."

Believe it or not, none of these stars are exactly alike. They represent every single combination of five colors, except one. What is the color placements on the missing star?

191

DIFFICULTY ☆★★

Color to Come

There are exactly 24 different ways to arrange four colors next to each other in a line. 23 are shown here, can you work out the order the colors should be in the missing swatch?

"The only place where success comes before work is in the dictionary." DONALD KENDALL

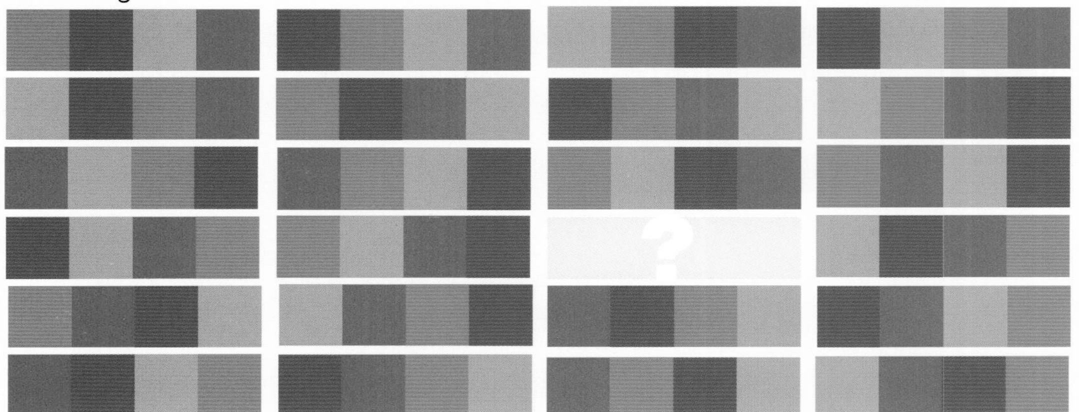

Romantic Riddle

192

DIFFICULTY ★★★

Princess Penelope fell in love with a lowly woodcutter called Frank.
The people were delighted that the princess had chosen one of them for her beau. Her father the king, on the other hand, was distraught at his daughter's terrible choice in eligible boys, and he cooked up a plan to get Frank out of the picture.
"We must let fate decide," he said, "whether this commoner can claim my daughter and my crown. If the gods smile on him, I will do the same."
The people thought this was fair enough, and the test of fate was designed thus: On two pieces of paper were drawn a cross and a checkmark. The pieces of paper would be placed in a bag and Frank would pick. If he chose the checkmark, Penelope was his. If he chose the cross, he must leave the kingdom forever. The test was set for Saturday morning at 11 o'clock, and the whole kingdom would come to watch.
On Friday night, very late, Frank answered his door to a friend, Bob, who worked in the Palace kitchens. Bob, taking the queen her nightly cocoa, had overheard the King telling her that both pieces of paper would have crosses on them!
"What am I going to do?" said Frank. "If I do the test I'll lose and be banished. If I don't I'll never marry Penelope. And if I expose the king in front of everyone he'll surely have me killed!" Exactly what did Frank do to keep his head, and his bride?

"At the touch of love everyone becomes a poet."
Plato

The Brothers Grimm, Jakob and Wilhelm, began collecting and writing fairy tales from 1807. They were depicted on the German 100 Deutsche Mark from 1990 until the introduction of the Euro in 2000.

193

DIFFICULTY ★★★

Shape Stacker

What is the logic behind the numbers in these shapes, and what number should replace the question mark?

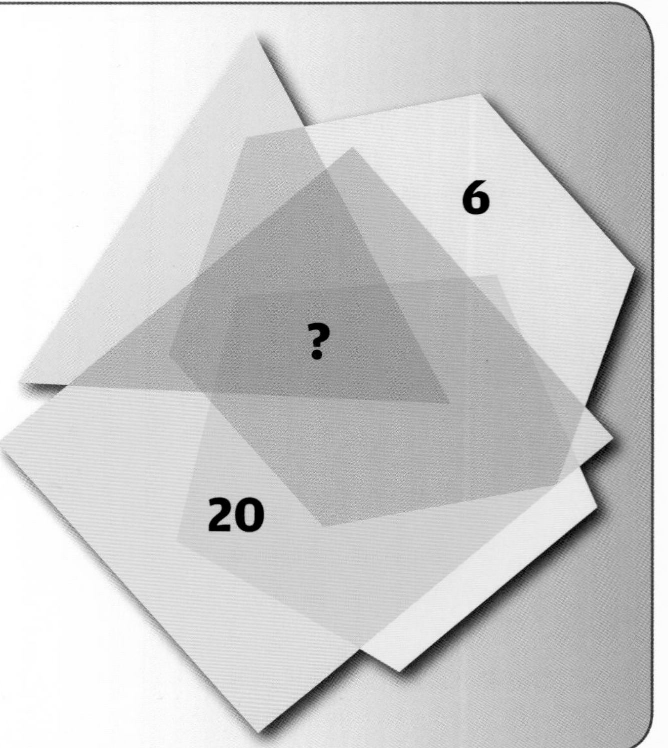

“How can a woman be expected to be happy with a man who insists on treating her as if she were a perfectly normal human being.” OSCAR WILDE

In 2004, scientists in Arizona discovered that women are capable of seeing more subtle shades of red than men.

194

DIFFICULTY ☆☆★

The One and Only

Only one of the tiles below is unique, the other 14 all have an exact double. Can you find it?

The Catalan architect Antoni Gaudí transformed Barcelona, Spain, into a mosaic city in the early 1990s. He used recycled tiles to create his outdoor works of art.

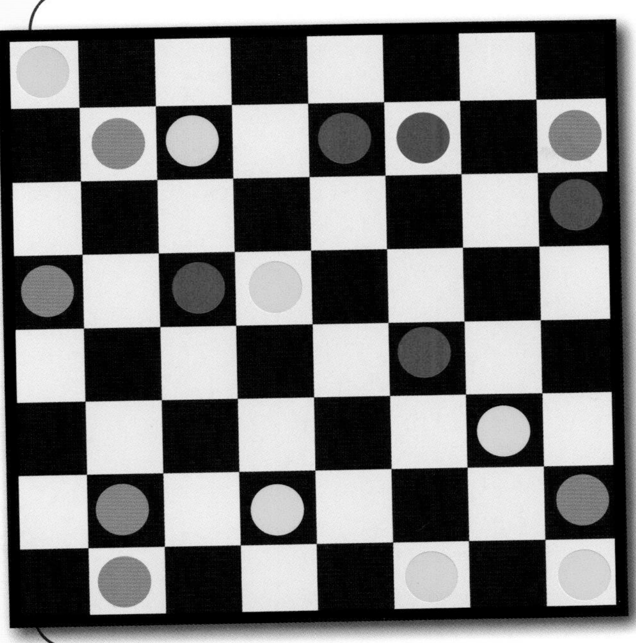

Knight's Move

195

DIFFICULTY

Find an empty square in the grid that is one chess knight's move away from a blue, red, and yellow circle. A knight's move is an "L" shape—two squares sideways, up or down in any direction, followed by one square to the left or right.

"Architecture begins where engineering ends."

WALTER GROPIUS

Excavation work on the 51-mile (82-kilometer) long Panama Canal began in 1904. The first ship entered the waterway ten years later in 1914.

Shaping Relations

196

DIFFICULTY

By examining the relationships of the following shapes, can you identify the next shape?

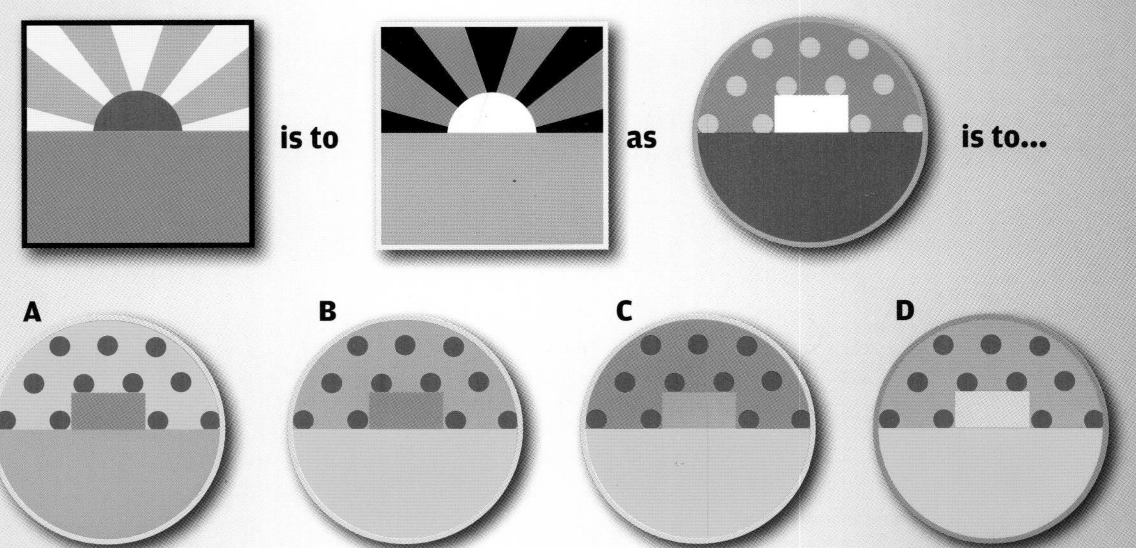

Andy Warhol was actually born Andrew Warhola in Pittsburgh, Pennsylvania, in 1928.

197

DIFFICULTY ★★★

Love is in the Area

What is the approximate area in inches that the happy couple are occupying?

"To love is to find pleasure in the happiness of the person loved."
ANONYMOUS

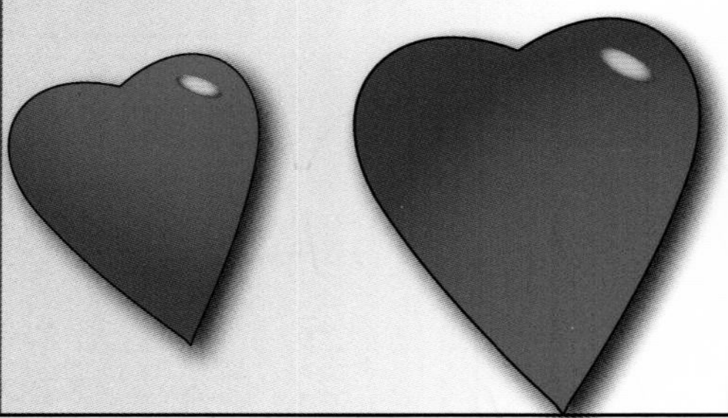

Las Vegas, Nevada, is known as the "Wedding Capital of the World" with an average of 150 couples getting married there every day.

198

DIFFICULTY ☆★★

Row of Houses

The sequence of houses below follows a logical pattern. Can you work out what color house follows, and whether the light should be on?

The Kremlin in Moscow has been the official residence of the Russian ruler since the capital was reestablished there in 1918 by Lenin. The word means "fortress."

"Houses are built to live in, and not to look on: therefore let use be preferred before uniformity." FRANCIS BACON

199
DIFFICULTY

Flag Flummox

Study these flags for a minute, then cover with a sheet of paper and answer the five questions below.

> **"If you want a symbolic gesture, don't burn the flag; wash it."**
> NORMAN THOMAS

Questions:
1. How many flags contain the color blue? 2. How many flags do not contain the color red? 3. Which flag is between two crosses? 4. How many colors make up the three top row flags? 5. Which two colors only feature on one flag each?

200
DIFFICULTY

Spiderweb

	2		2			
	3	3				
	3			4	2	
2	3	2				1
				5		
3	3	3				
			2			

The numbers in some cells in the spiderweb indicate the exact number of black cells that should border it. Shade these black, until all the numbers are surrounded by the correct number of black cells.

> **"The bird a nest, the spider a web, man friendship."**
> WILLIAM BLAKE

The Brazilian wandering spider is thought to be the most venomous in the world. It is native to South and Central America but was first discovered in the Pantanal, Brazil.

201

DIFFICULTY ★★☆

Park Life

Jack and Sadie met at the snack stand by the fountain before taking a long rambling walk around the park, the directions of which are below. Eventually, they stopped to rest on a bench. Which bench? And what is the only square on the map they didn't visit?

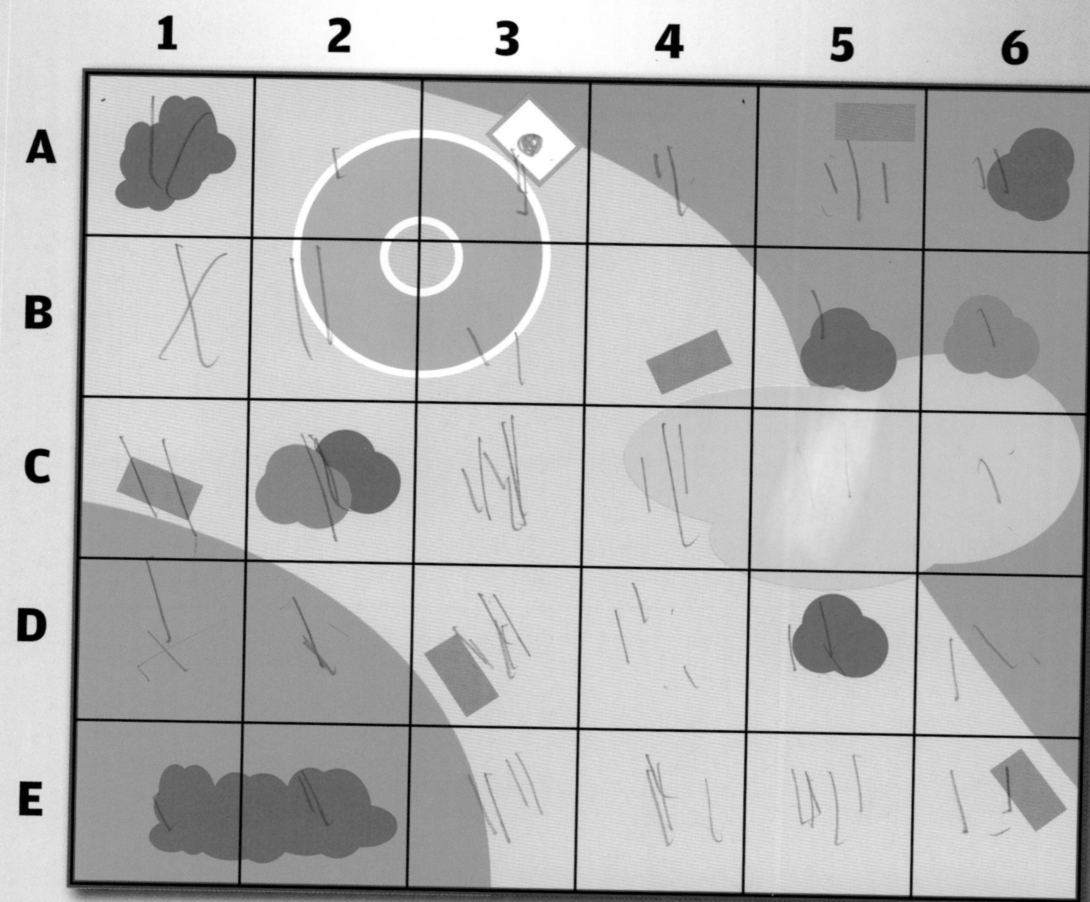

3E, 3S, 5W, 2E, 2N, 1S, 2S, 2W, 5E, 4W, 4N, 1W, 4E, 1W, 4S, 1E, 1N, 3W, 2E, 1N, 2W, 1W, 3E, 1N, 3W, 4E, 1W, 3W, 1S.

Rome's Trevi fountain was designed by Nicola Salvi, who died in 1751 when the project was only half complete. It was finally finished in 1762.

202

DIFFICULTY ★★

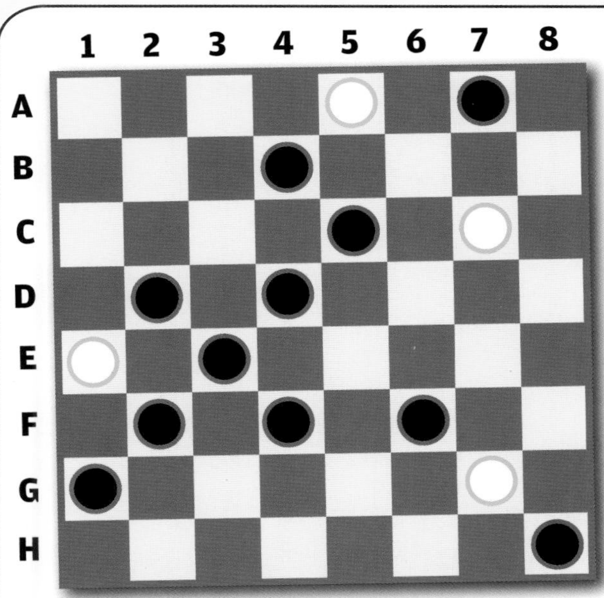

Checkers

Make a move for white so that eight black pieces are left, none of which are in the same column or row.

“Courage is like love; it must have hope for nourishment.”

NAPOLEON BONAPARTE

In 1937, Austria became the first country to issue a special commemorative stamp for the Christmas season.

203

DIFFICULTY ★★★

Number Knights

These symbols represent the numbers 1 to 4. What color knights represent which numbers? Finish the equation.

“A true knight is fuller of bravery in the midst, than in the beginning of danger.”

SIR PHILIP SIDNEY

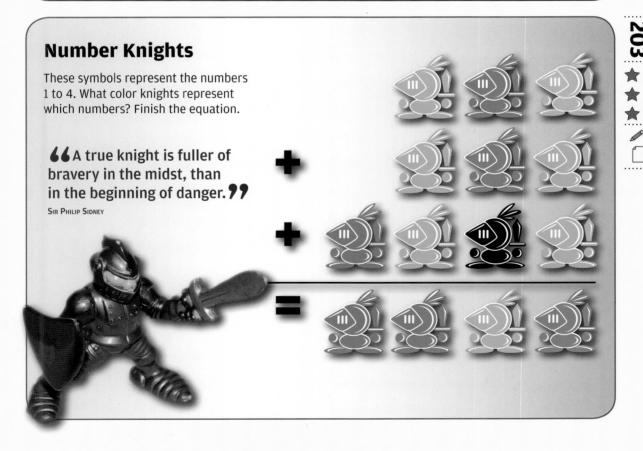

+

+

=

204

DIFFICULTY ☆★★

Color Amaze

Find a path from one white cell to the other the shortest way. You may only pass from a red cell to a blue one, a blue to a yellow, a yellow to a green, or a green to a red.

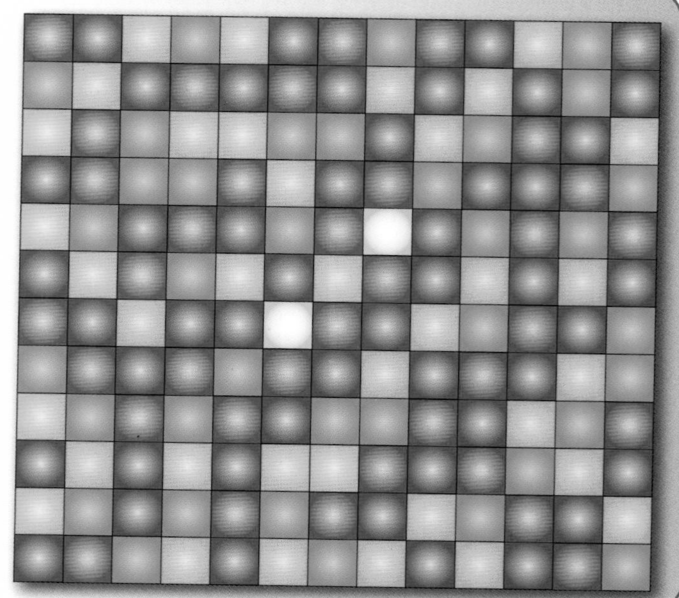

“It is the artist’s business to create sunshine when the sun fails.” ROMAIN ROLLAND

205

DIFFICULTY ☆★★

Pond and Patio

Below is a fishpond, with a surround waiting to be paved. Can you fit the pieces together and finish the job?

“Fish say, they have their stream and pond; But is there anything beyond?” RUPERT BROOKE

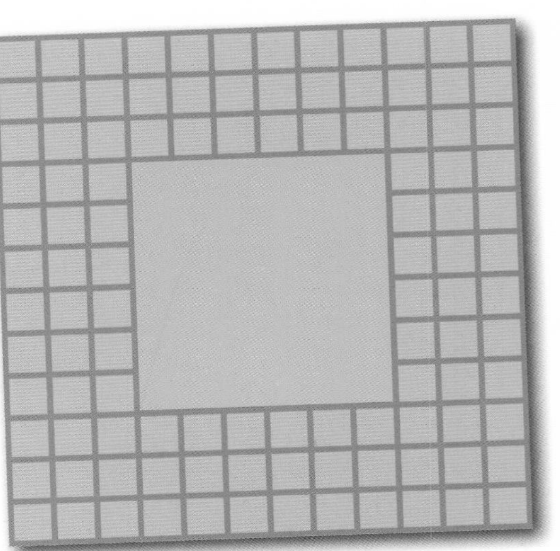

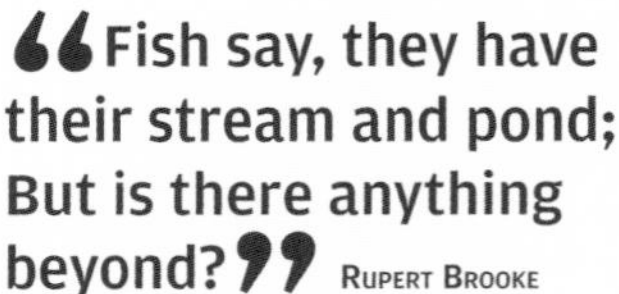

206 DIFFICULTY

Number Chunks

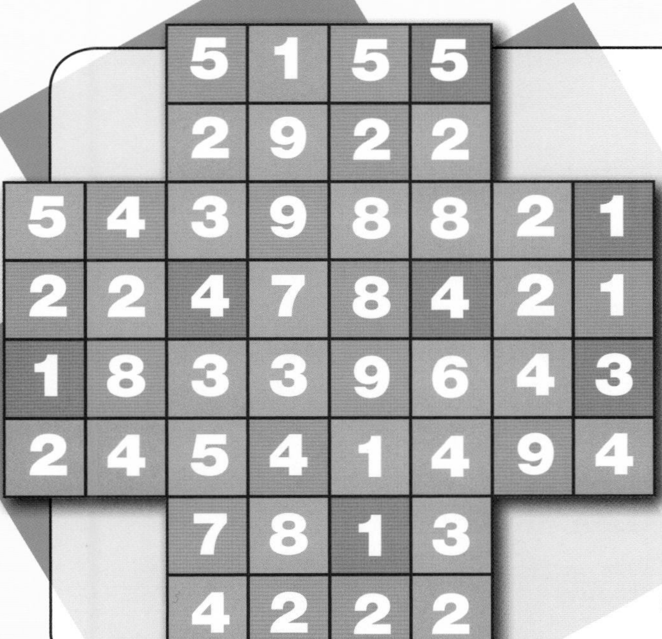

Divide up the grid into four equally sized, equally shaped parts, each containing numbers that add up to 50.

“Anyone who thinks there’s safety in numbers hasn’t looked at the stock market pages.”

IRENE PETER

Two dogs survived the sinking of the *Titanic* in 1912—a Pomeranian belonging to a Margaret Hays of New York is listed in lifeboat 7, while a Pekingese accompanied Henry Sleeper Harper in number 3.

207 DIFFICULTY

Precious Puzzler

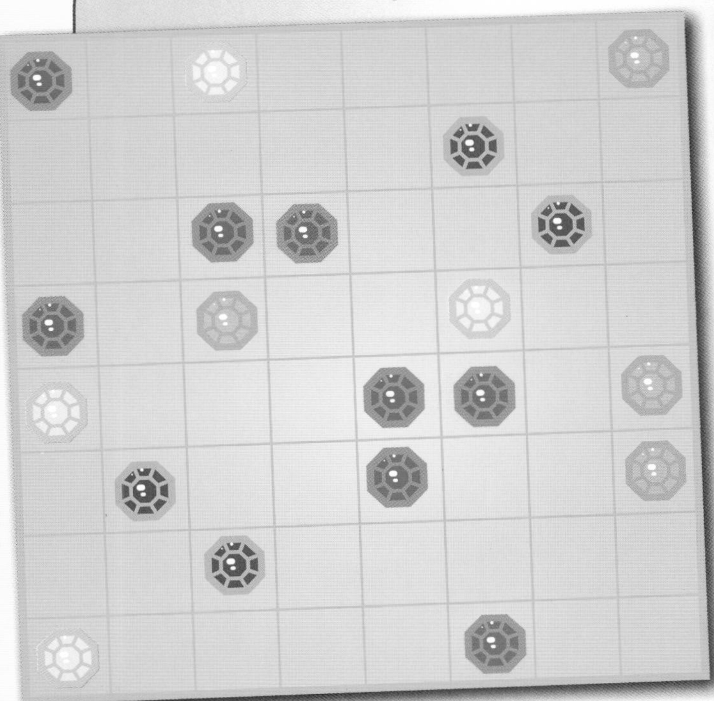

Divide up the grid into four equally sized, equally shaped parts, each containing one of the five colored precious gems.

“The soul is placed in the body like a rough diamond, and must be polished, or the luster of it will never appear.”

DANIEL DEFOE

The Cullinan Diamond was discovered in 1905 and, at 3,106 carats, was the largest gem-quality rough diamond ever found. Cullinan I, or the Great Star of Africa—at 530 carats, formerly the largest cut diamond—was one of the 105 gems cut from it.

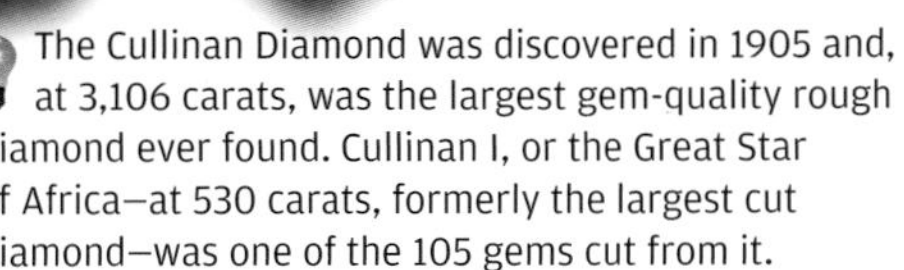

208

DIFFICULTY ★

Back Together

These ten pieces can be arranged to spell out the name of a famous painter, but who?

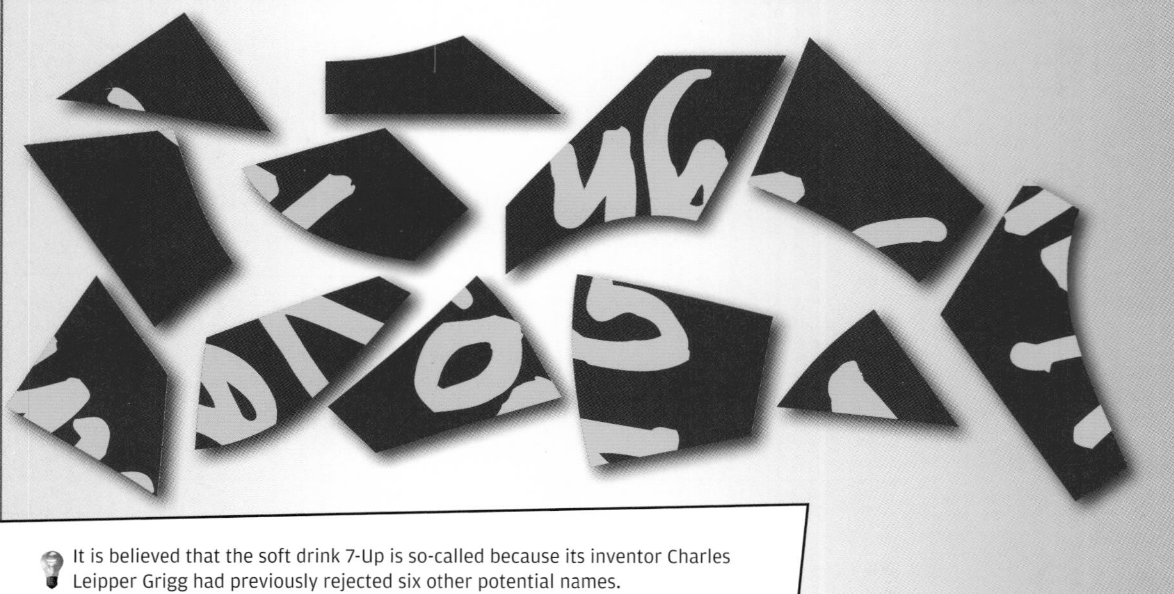

It is believed that the soft drink 7-Up is so-called because its inventor Charles Leipper Grigg had previously rejected six other potential names.

209

DIFFICULTY ★

Coming Together

Which two shapes below will pair up to create the top shape?

“Our life is composed greatly from dreams, from the unconscious, and they must be brought into connection with action. They must be woven together.” Anaïs Nin

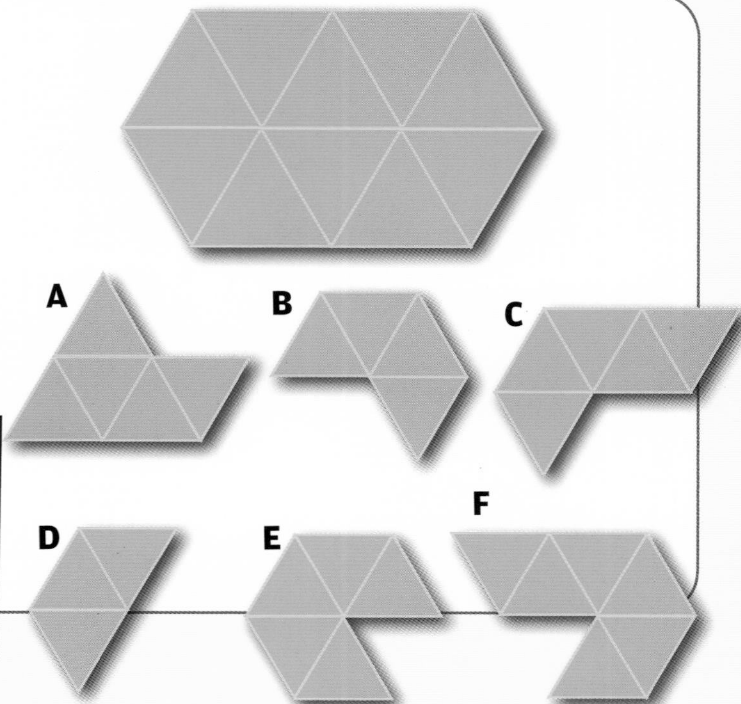

D. H. Lawrence's controversial 1928 novel *Lady Chatterley's Lover* was one of the top-selling books in the United States upon its eventual publication in 1959. It was published in Great Britain. in the following year. It had previously been banned in both countries because it was considered obscene.

210 DIFFICULTY

Work of Art

This wall is to be painted in green, blue, and lilac, with no adjacent bricks to be in the same color. Can you work out what color the bottom right-hand corner should be?

211 DIFFICULTY

Petal Parts

Which box has exactly the right parts to make the model of the flower?

"Life is the flower for which love is the honey." Victor Hugo

A

B

C

By law, all buildings in the Moroccan city of Marrakech are painted red.

212

DIFFICULTY ★

Singled Out

All the shapes in this box appear twice except one. Can you find it?

“In questions of science, the authority of a thousand is not worth the humble reasoning of a single individual.” Galileo Galilei

Pablo Picasso appeared as an extra in a crowd scene during Jean Cocteau's 1962 film *The Testament of Orpheus.*

213

DIFFICULTY ★★

Ship Shape

Only two of these naval ships are exactly the same. Can you find the matching pair?

“We joined the Navy to see the world . . . And what did we see? We saw the sea.” Irving Berlin

On February 15, 1898, the USS *Maine* sank in Havana harbor after a mystery explosion, sparking the Spanish-American War. It is the origin of the phrase “Remember the Maine!”

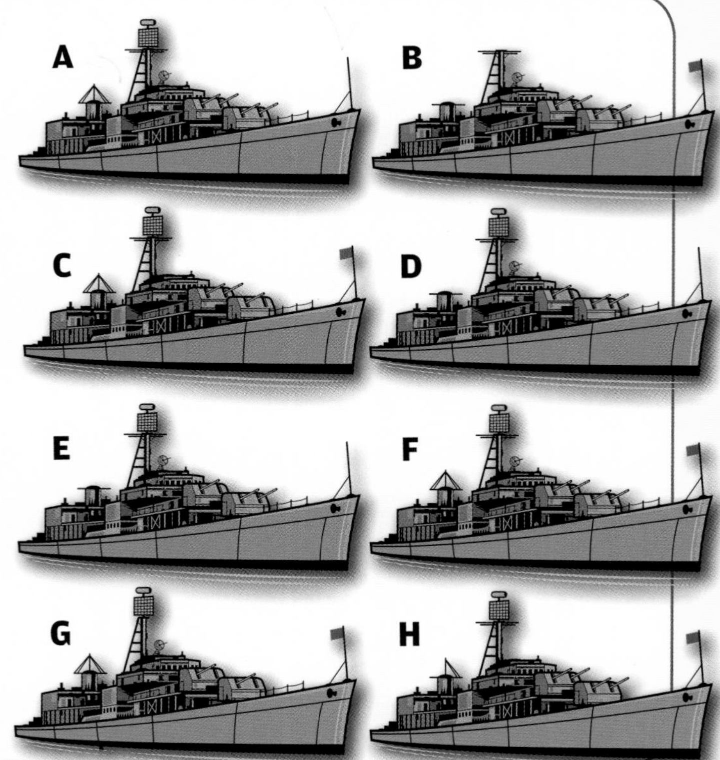

214

DIFFICULTY

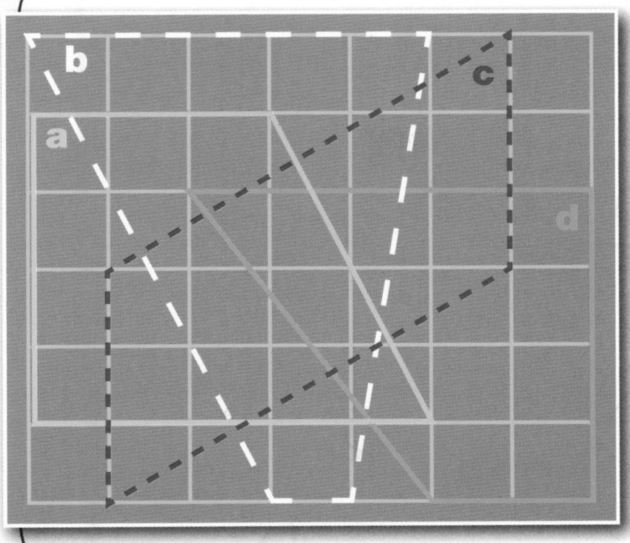

Blueprint Baffler

Look at this blueprint. Can you put these shapes in order, from biggest to smallest?

"Happiness serves hardly any other purpose than to make unhappiness possible."
MARCEL PROUST

The promotional video clip that accompanied Bob Dylan's 1965 release 'Subterranean Homesick Blues' was actually shot in an alleyway that runs behind the Savoy Hotel in London, England, where Dylan was staying.

215

DIFFICULTY

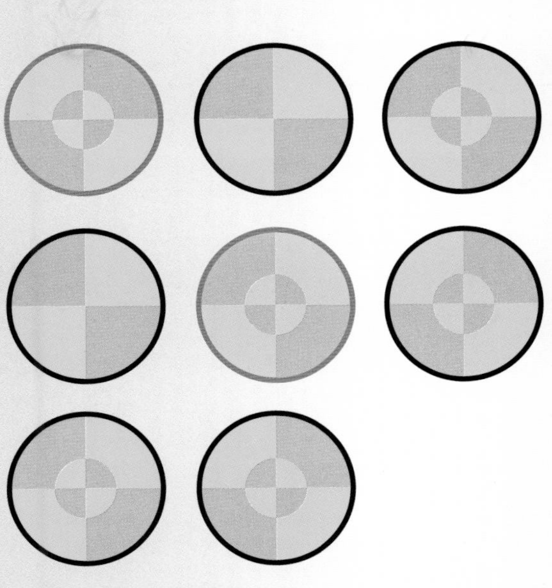

Complete the Set

Which of the four boxed figures completes the set?

"Being deeply learned and skilled, being well trained and using well spoken words; this is good luck." HINDU PRINCE GAUTAMA SIDDHARTHA

Car giant Cadillac was named after the French explorer Antoine Laumet de La Mothe, sieur de Cadillac, who founded Detroit, Michigan, in 1701. Cadillac is a small town in the South of France near to where he was born.

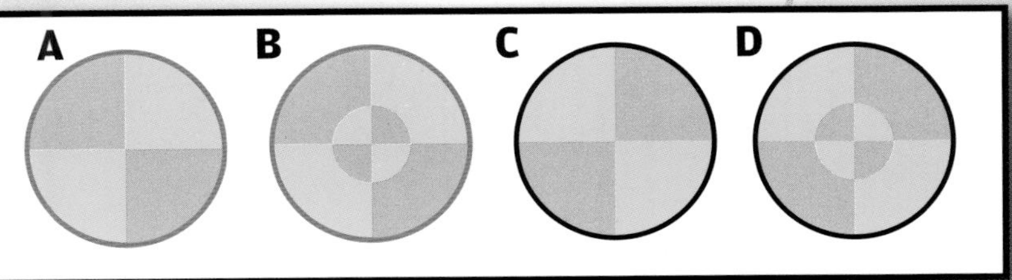

216

DIFFICULTY ☆★★

Scene It!

The four squares below can all be found in this jungle scene—can you track them down?

> “He that does good for good's sake seeks neither paradise nor reward, but he is sure of both in the end.”
>
> William Penn

Batavia was the old Dutch name for the modern Indonesian capital of Jakarta.

217

DIFFICULTY ★★★

Codoku Composer

Complete the first grid so that every row and column contains all the letters G, L, M, R, W, and Y. Do the same with grid 2 and the numbers 1, 2, 3, 4, 5, and 6. To decode the finished grid, add the numbers in the shaded squares to the letters in the matching squares in the second (A + 3 = D, Y + 4 = C) to get six new letters, which can be arranged to spell the name of a famous composer.

L			W	R	
Y		G		W	R
				L	
W		M			
	L			Y	G
G		L	R		W

4			1	3	
	1	6			4
	4			2	
6		1		4	
			3		6
1	3	5			2

A single manuscript page from the unpublished novella *Clisson and Eugenie,* written by Napoleon Bonaparte in 1795, fetched $35,000 at an auction in 2007.

218 DIFFICULTY ☆★★

Pentagon Puzzles

The numbers on these pentagons follow a pattern. Your task is to uncover the secret to the pattern and fill in the question marks to complete the puzzle.

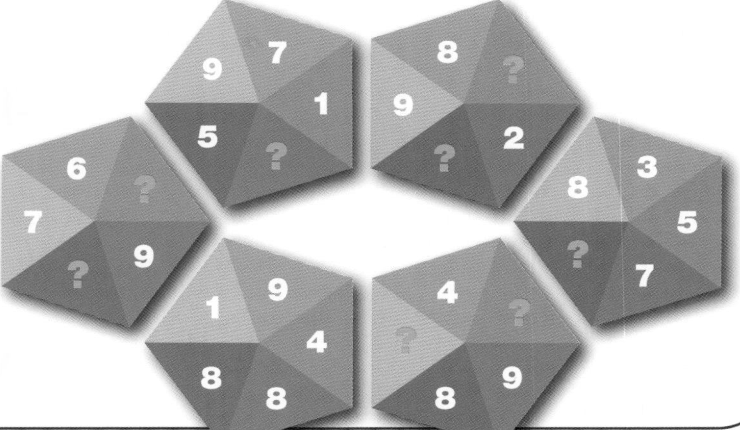

In February 2004. the *New York Times* reported that 62 percent of all e-mail traffic could be described as "spam."

219 DIFFICULTY ★★★

Center of Attention

What numbers should replace the question mark at the center of the second hub?

"The greatest gift you can give another is the purity of your attention." Richard Moss

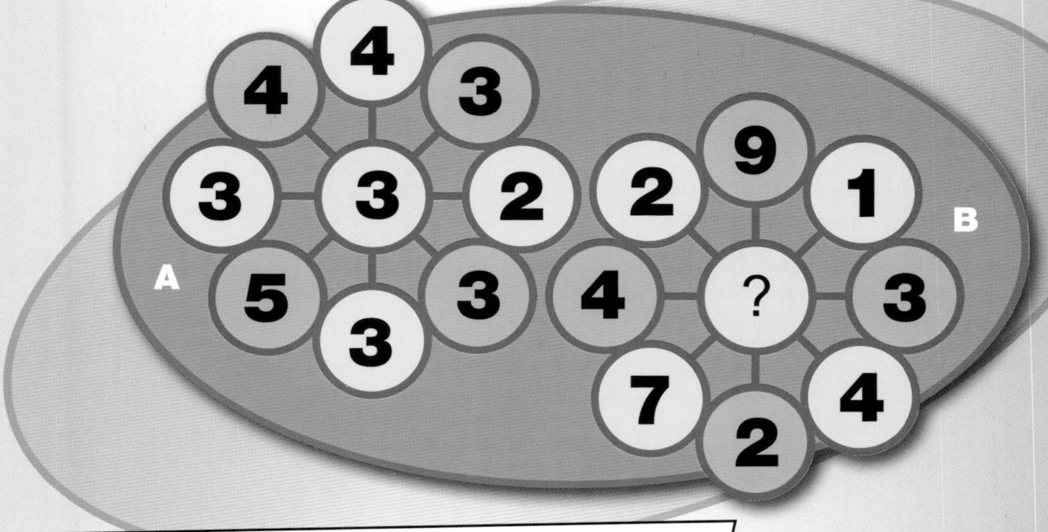

Someone who collects money or medals is known as a numismatist.

220

DIFFICULTY

Barnyard Balance

The pig, piglet, chicken, chick, and egg each weigh an exact number between one and ten. Can you work out which number represents which, and how many chicks are required to balance the final scale?

Because the animals kept outgrowing the role, 30 different piglets were used during the filming of the movie *Babe* in 1995.

“I like pigs. Dogs look up to us. Cats look down on us. Pigs treat us as equals.” WINSTON CHURCHILL

221

DIFFICULTY

Cool Question

Which areas of this diagram represent skaters that wear gloves and hats but not scarves, and people who wear gloves, hats, and scarves but who don't skate?

“Constant kindness can accomplish much. As the sun makes ice melt, kindness causes misunderstanding, mistrust, and hostility to evaporate.” ALBERT SCHWEITZER

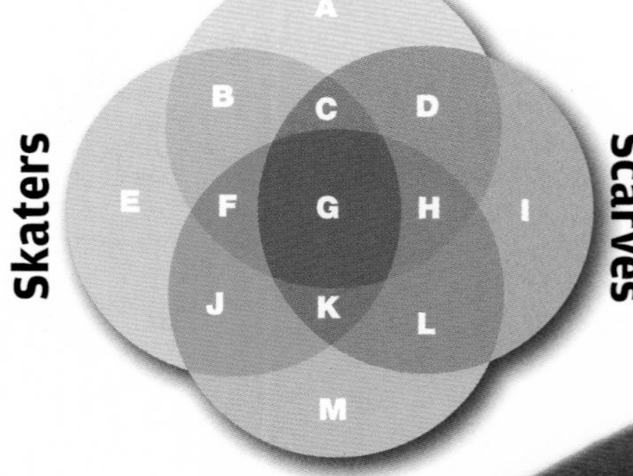

St. Lidwina is the patron saint of ice skaters. Born in 1380, she lived in Holland and had a severe injury while skating as a child, from which she never recovered. She is said to have had religious visions.

222

DIFFICULTY ☆☆★

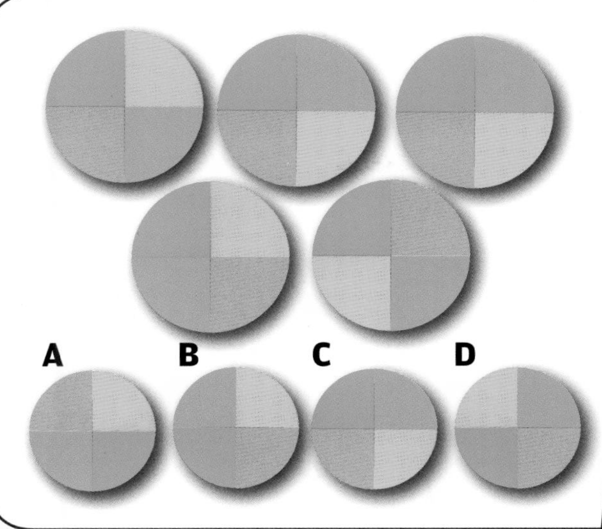

Which Wheel?

Which of the wheels—A, B, C, or D—is missing from the set above?

“I want to die in my sleep like my grandfather . . . Not screaming and yelling like the passengers in his car.” WILL SHRINER

By 1918, 55 percent of cars in the United States were Model T Fords, which had been introduced just ten years earlier.

223

DIFFICULTY ★★★

“The best way to predict the future is to invent it.”
ALAN KAY

Next in Sequence!

In the sequence below, which of the numbered alternatives, A, B, C, or D, should replace the question mark?

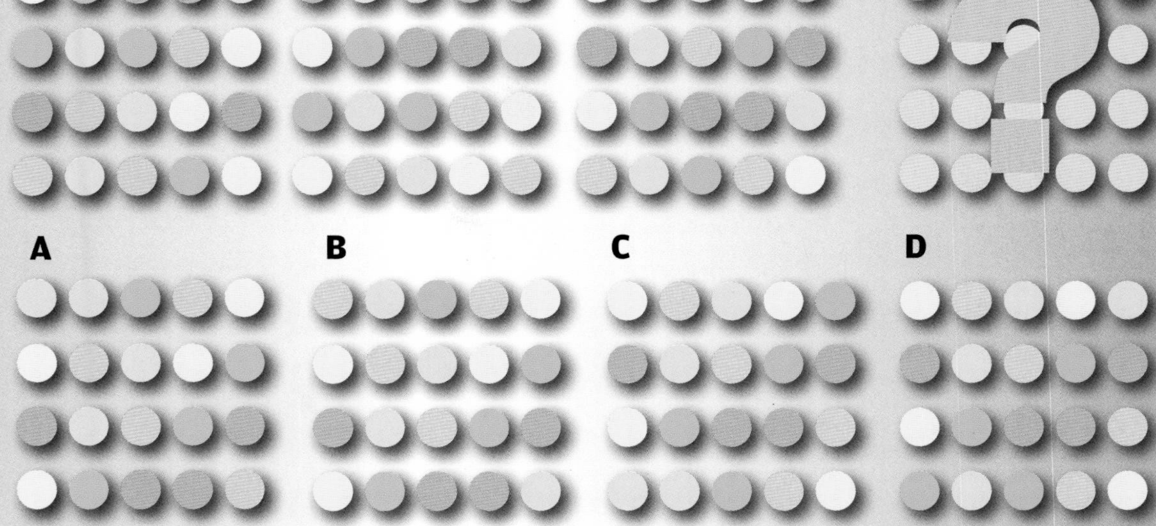

Monrovia in Liberia is the only non-American capital city to be named after a U.S. president—in this case, James Monroe.

224

DIFFICULTY ☆★★

So Much to Remember

Study these images for a minute, cover with a sheet of paper, and then answer the five questions shown below.

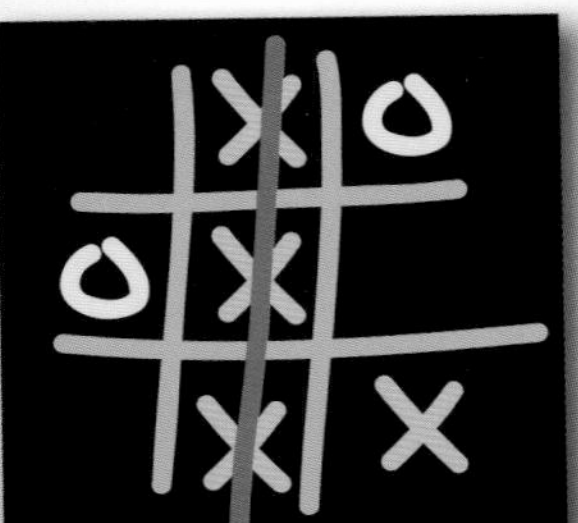

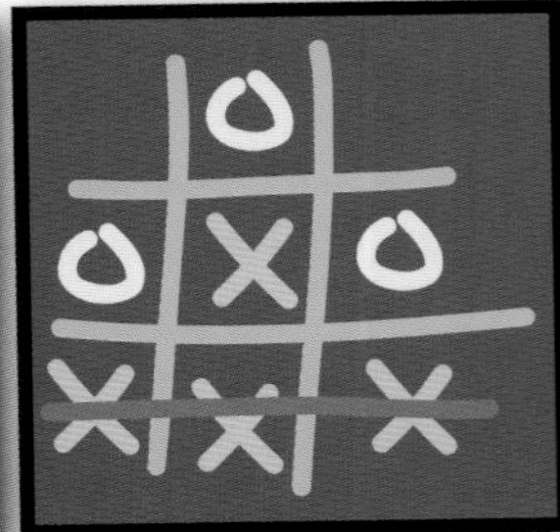

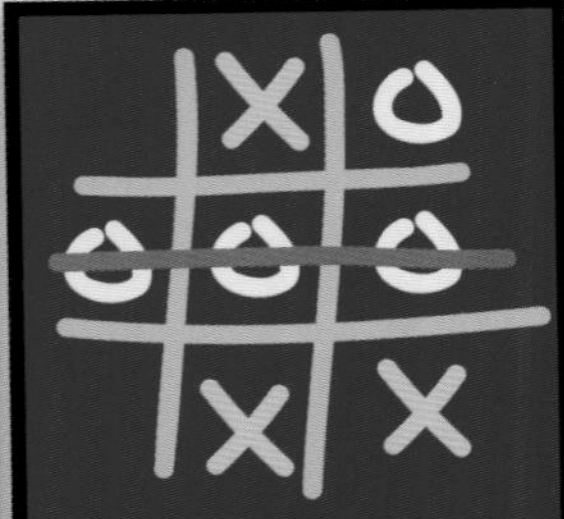

In his experimental novel *Rayuela* or *Hopscotch*, Julio Cortazar begins by inviting readers to choose between reading the proceeding chapters in a linear or nonlinear form.

Questions:
1. How many winning lines included the middle square?
2. Which section of the game grid was always empty?
3. Did X or O win the game with the black background?
4. How many bottom right-hand corners featured an "X"?
5. How many "O" were there in total?

225

DIFFICULTY ☆★★

Letter Values

Which number is represented by which letter? Fill in the question mark.

“I wonder if illiterate people get the full effect of alphabet soup?” Jerry Seinfeld

The Ottoman Empire once had seven emperors in seven months. They died of (in order): burning, choking, drowning, stabbing, heart failure, poisoning, and being thrown from a horse.

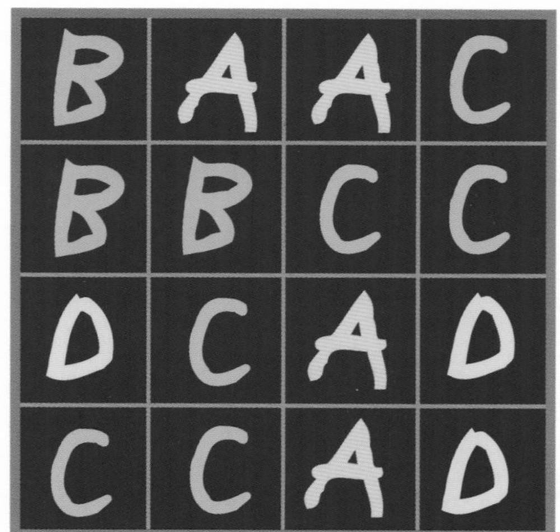

B	A	A	C	14
B	B	C	C	20
D	C	A	D	26
C	C	A	D	23
?	18	12	30	

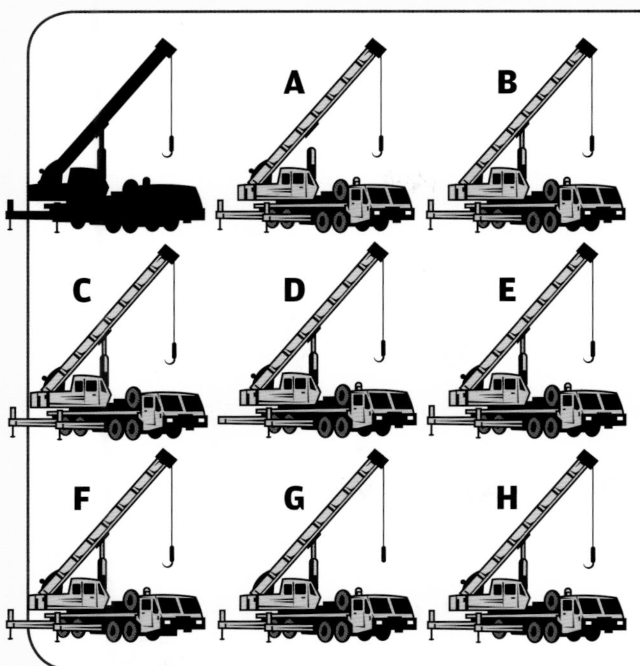

Being Constructive

Which of the colored-in construction cranes matches the silhouette?

“When I say artist I mean the man who is building things—creating, molding the earth—whether it be the plains of the West—or the iron ore of Penn. It’s all a big game of construction—some with a brush—some with a shovel, some choose a pen.”

JACKSON POLLOCK

226 DIFFICULTY

Apple of the Eye

Can you spot the ten differences between these pictures?

“Goodness comes out of people who bask in the sun, as it does out of a sweet apple roasted before the fire.”

CHARLES DUDLEY WARNER

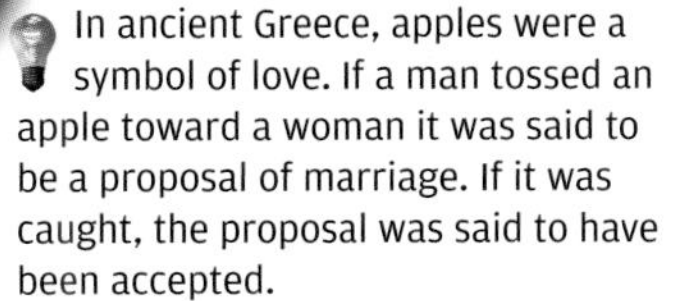

In ancient Greece, apples were a symbol of love. If a man tossed an apple toward a woman it was said to be a proposal of marriage. If it was caught, the proposal was said to have been accepted.

227 DIFFICULTY

228

DIFFICULTY ★

Tic-Tac-Toe

The numbers around the edge of the grid describe the number of X's in the vertical, horizontal, and diagonal lines connecting with that square. Complete the grid so that there is an X or O in every square.

"Beauty is power; a smile is its sword."

JOHN RAY

4	2	3	3	2	0
3					3
4					3
2					2
4					3
0	4	3	4	3	4

In humans, type O is the most common blood type.

229

DIFFICULTY ★★

Patch of the Day

Place the shape over the grid so that no color appears twice in the same row or column. Beware: The shape may not be the right way up!

Of the 40 million e-mails generated by his administration, Bill Clinton sent only two while president—one to test his e-mail address, the second to astronaut John Glenn while he was orbiting the earth.

45c

$2.28

42c

$4.85

230

DIFFICULTY

Gone Shopping

You're in a fruit market buying ingredients for a giant fruit salad. You bought 11 pieces of fruit, paid $15, and got 25 cents change. What did you buy?

"If men liked shopping, they'd call it research."

CYNTHIA NELMS

The pineapple was named because of its resemblance to a pinecone by the English in 1664. The native tribes of Central America called it *nana,* meaning "flavor."

231

DIFFICULTY

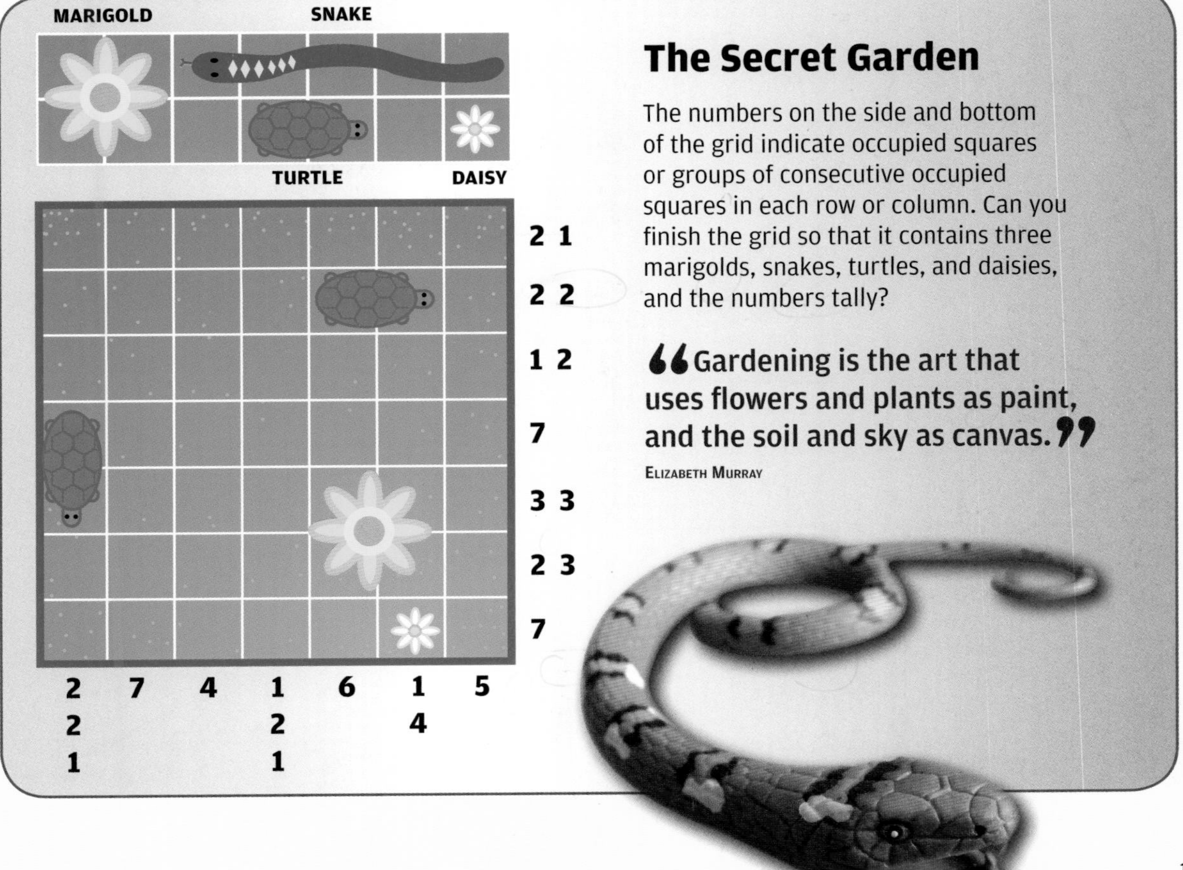

The Secret Garden

The numbers on the side and bottom of the grid indicate occupied squares or groups of consecutive occupied squares in each row or column. Can you finish the grid so that it contains three marigolds, snakes, turtles, and daisies, and the numbers tally?

"Gardening is the art that uses flowers and plants as paint, and the soil and sky as canvas."

ELIZABETH MURRAY

232 DIFFICULTY ★★☆

Same Difference

In 1978, Princess Margaret became only the second member of the British Royal Family to divorce. The first was Henry VIII in 1533.

By examining the relationships of the following shapes, can you identify the next shape?

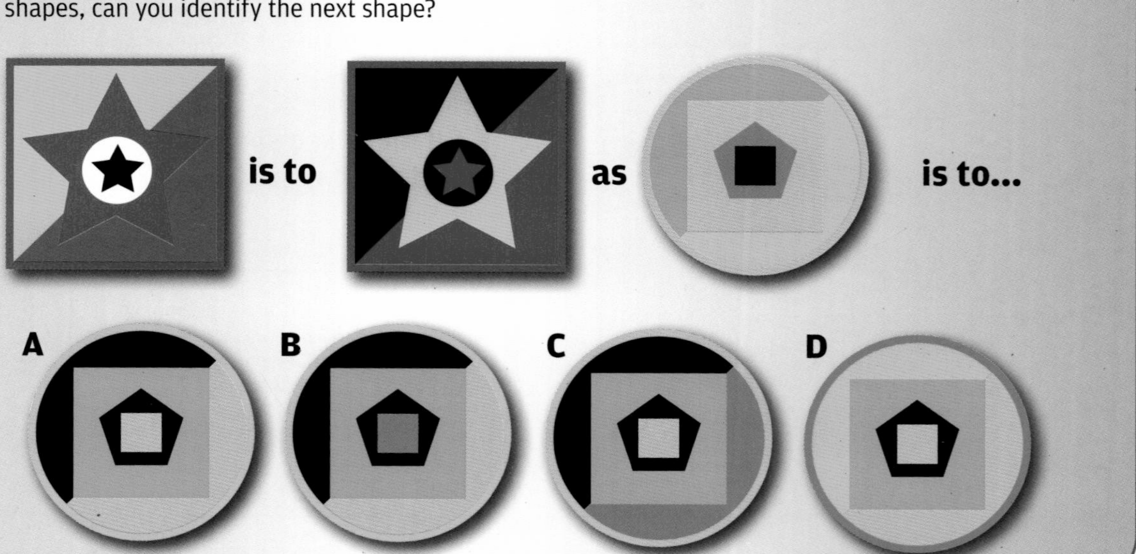

233 DIFFICULTY ★★☆

T-Shirt Teaser

This new T-shirt design features the colors red, white, and blue in the outlined areas. No area borders another area of the same color. What color is the collar?

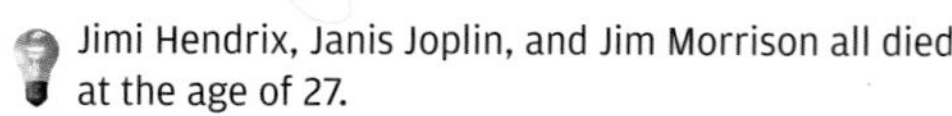

Jimi Hendrix, Janis Joplin, and Jim Morrison all died at the age of 27.

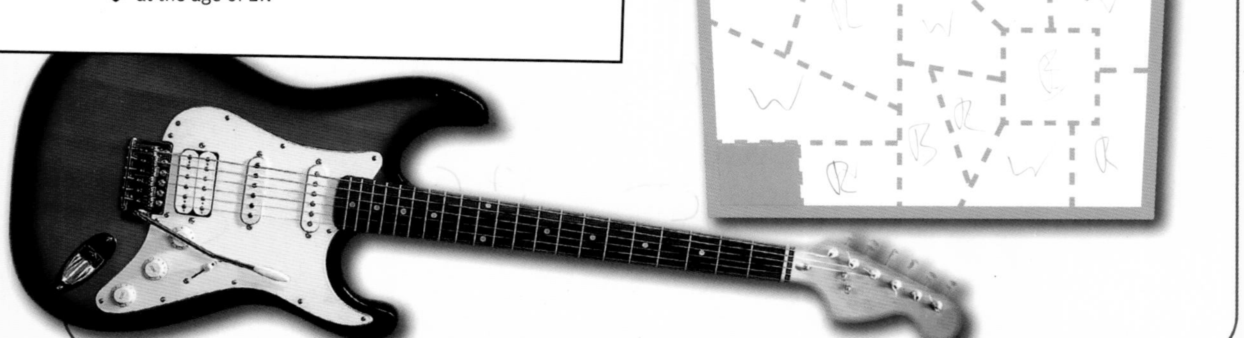

234

DIFFICULTY

Making Sense

The word "utopia" actually translates from the original Greek as "no place" or "the place that does not exist."

The tiles below have been rearranged. Can you work out the new sequence from the clues given below?

- The two numbers in the middle total 6.
- The number 5 is immediately to the left of the number 6.
- The two left-hand numbers total the same as the bottom row.

235

DIFFICULTY

Knight's Move

Find an empty square in the grid that is one chess knight's move away from a blue, red, and yellow circle. A knight's move is an "L" shape—two squares sideways, up or down in any direction, followed by one square to the left or right.

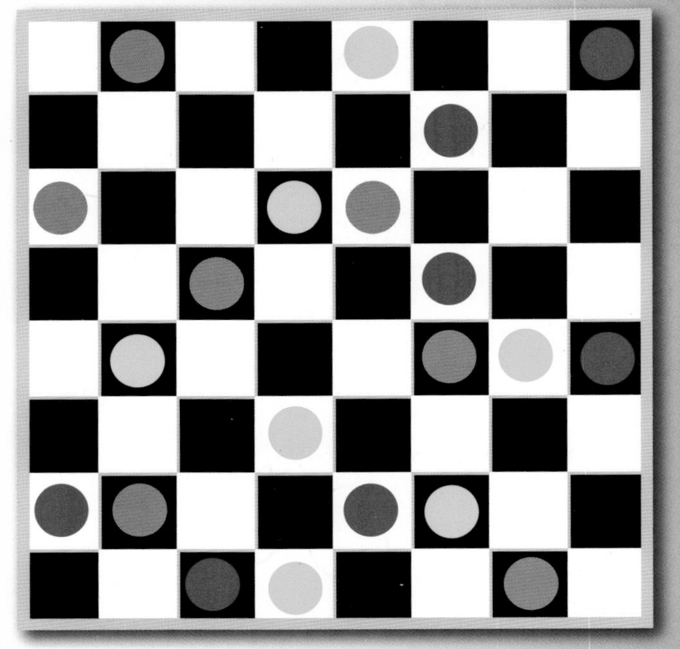

Although widely thought to be the birthplace of chess, Iran actually banned the game for a little under ten years after the Islamic revolution of 1979. Ayatollah Khomeini said that the game "hurts memory and may cause brain damage."

236

DIFFICULTY ★☆☆

Find the Spies!

A Morse code transmission containing the identity of some of the enemy's top female spies has been intercepted. Unfortunately, spaces between the letters and words are missing. Using the Morse code key below can you find the names of the ten femme fatales?

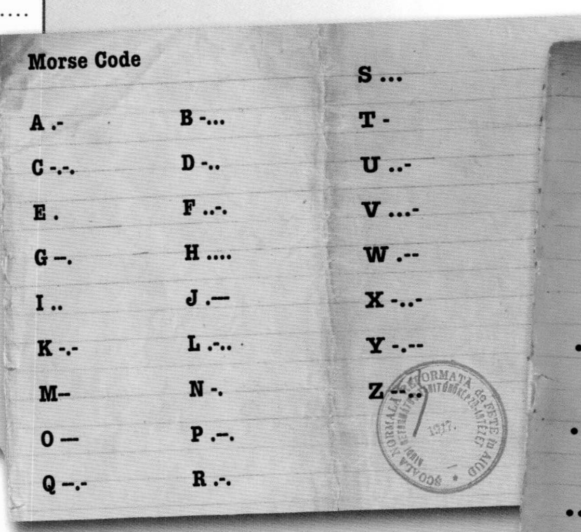

Morse Code
A .-
B -...
C -.-.
D -..
E .
F ..-.
G --.
H ....
I ..
J .---
K -.-
L .-..
M --
N -.
O ---
P .--.
Q --.-
R .-.
S ...
T -
U ..-
V ...-
W .--
X -..-
Y -.--
Z --..

TOP SECRET

....---.--.-.....-

.---.........-.-..-

.....--.-..-....

.---..-.-.....-

.--.--...-...-

.---.-.-.....-...-.

..-....--...--....-....

--..-.-.......-...-...

--..-..--.-..

------...-.-..-

TOP SECRET

In 1995, the U.S. Coastguard officially stopped using Morse code communications because the majority of vessels were by then fitted with a global maritime distress safety system.

> "And in the end, it's not the years in your life that count. It's the life in your years."
>
> ABRAHAM LINCOLN

237 DIFFICULTY ★★★

Police Percentages

Officers Kaplutski and Wojowitz were arguing about how good they both were as cops. It turned out that of the cases they had worked on together, Kaplutski had solved 48 percent, while Wojowitz had solved 52 percent. What is the lowest number of cases they could have worked on?

The "blood" in the famous shower scene in Alfred Hitchcock's *Psycho* is actually chocolate syrup.

238 DIFFICULTY ☆★★

Peculiar Percentages

What percentage of this shape is blue and what percentage is orange?

"Security is not the meaning of my life. Great opportunities are worth the risks."

SHIRLEY HUFSTEDLER

Over 200,000 telephone calls are made daily in the Pentagon through phones connected by 100,000 miles (170 kilometers) of telephone cable.

239

DIFFICULTY ★★☆

Picture Logic Puzzle

The numbers by each row and column describe black squares and groups of black squares that are adjoining. Color in all the black squares and a six-number combination will be revealed.

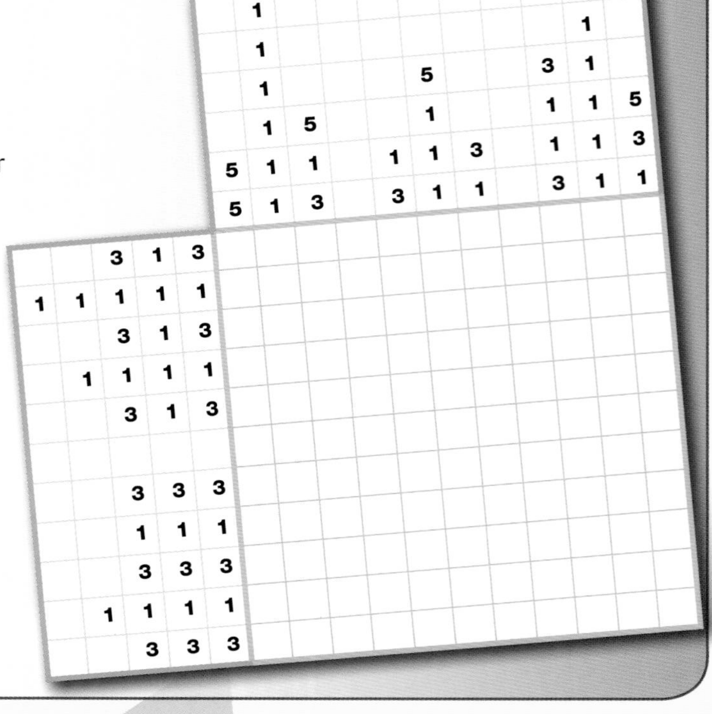

Don Quixote, by Miguel de Cervantes Saavedra, has been translated into more languages than any book other than the Bible.

> **“Books are divided into two classes: the books of the hour and the books of all time.”**
>
> John Ruskin

240

DIFFICULTY ★★★

Layered Logic

Can you work out the logic behind the numbers in these shapes, and what A + B totals?

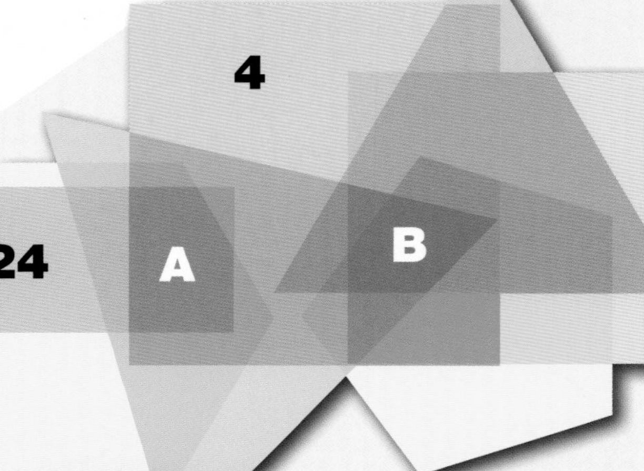

> **“No stream rises higher than its source. What ever man might build could never express or reflect more than he was. He could record neither more nor less than he had learned of life when the buildings were built.”**
>
> Frank Lloyd Wright

In 1978, James Dyson realized the domestic vacuum cleaner needed to be improved. The first generation Dyson arrived five years and 5,127 prototypes later. The company has to date sold over $10 billion of units worldwide.

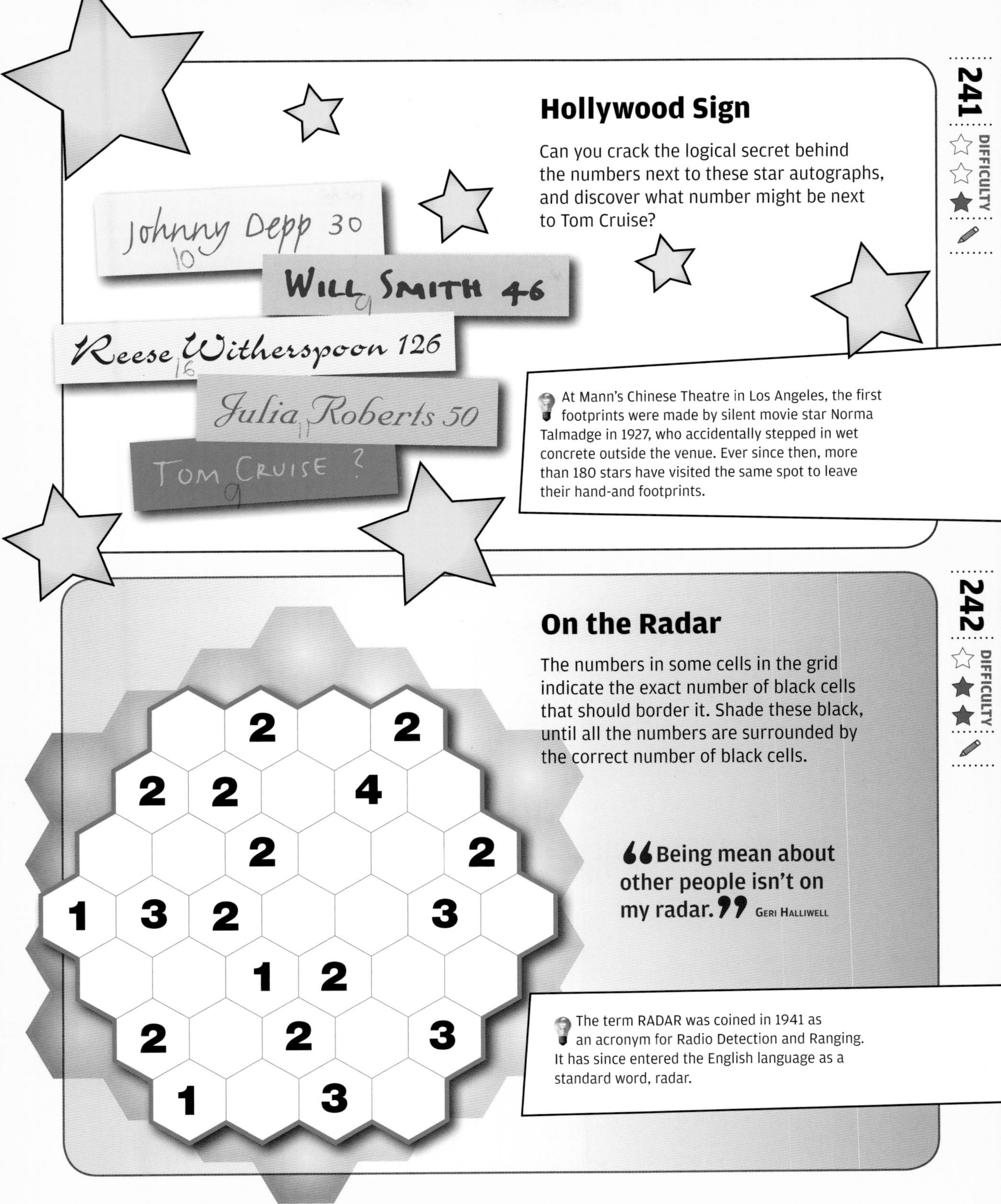

241

DIFFICULTY

Hollywood Sign

Can you crack the logical secret behind the numbers next to these star autographs, and discover what number might be next to Tom Cruise?

At Mann's Chinese Theatre in Los Angeles, the first footprints were made by silent movie star Norma Talmadge in 1927, who accidentally stepped in wet concrete outside the venue. Ever since then, more than 180 stars have visited the same spot to leave their hand-and footprints.

242

DIFFICULTY

On the Radar

The numbers in some cells in the grid indicate the exact number of black cells that should border it. Shade these black, until all the numbers are surrounded by the correct number of black cells.

> "Being mean about other people isn't on my radar." Geri Halliwell

The term RADAR was coined in 1941 as an acronym for Radio Detection and Ranging. It has since entered the English language as a standard word, radar.

243

DIFFICULTY ★★★

Cocktail Mixer

Which box has exactly the right pieces to make the cocktail?

The Sazerac is one of the oldest known cocktails. It is based on a combination of cognac and bitters, and absinthe is used in the preparation of the glass. It was created by Antoine Amédée Peychaud in New Orleans, Louisiana, and given its name by John Schiller in 1859 upon the opening of his Sazerac Coffee House in the same city.

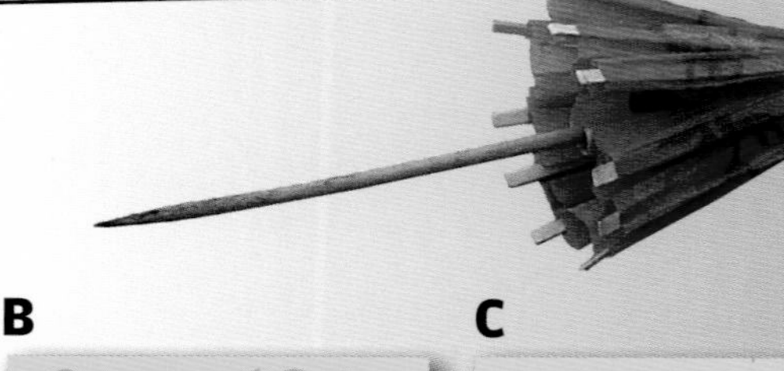

“If you want an interesting party sometime, combine cocktails and a fresh box of crayons for everyone.” Robert Fulghum

A

B

C

244

DIFFICULTY ☆★★

Patio Percentage

What percentage of this yard is grass and what percentage is stone?

“People’s backyards are much more interesting than their front gardens, and houses that back onto railways are public benefactors.” John Betjeman

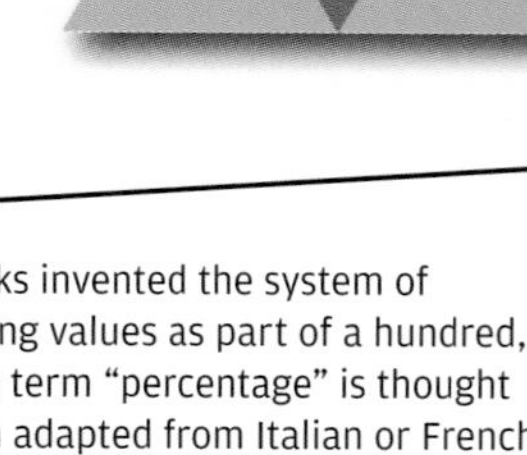

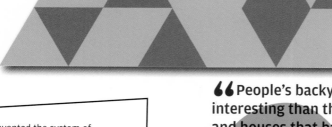

The Greeks invented the system of considering values as part of a hundred, although the term “percentage” is thought to have been adapted from Italian or French with the % symbol deriving from the Italian abbreviation for “per cento”.

245

DIFFICULTY ★★★

Dice Puzzler

What's the missing number?

"God may not play dice but he enjoys a good round of Trivial Pursuit every now and again." FEDERICO FELLINI

Brunei and the United Arab Emirates are the only two countries where there is no right to vote.

246

DIFFICULTY ☆☆★

Card Shuffle

Fill up the shuffle box so that each row, column, and long diagonal contains a jack, queen, king, and ace of each suit.

	K♥		Q♣
			A♦

"A great social success is a pretty girl who plays her cards as carefully as if she were plain."

F. SCOTT FITZGERALD

There are over 1,000 variations of the perennially popular game solitaire, all deriving from around a dozen "base" games.

247

DIFFICULTY ☆★★

Shooting Stars

Divide up the grid into four equally sized, equally shaped parts, each containing four different colored stars.

David Wolf was the first person to cast an absentee ballot from space. In November 1997, he cast a vote via e-mail for the mayor of Houston while onboard the space station *Mir*.

"If you shoot for the stars and hit the moon, it's OK. But you've got to shoot for something. A lot of people don't even shoot." CONFUCIUS

248

DIFFICULTY

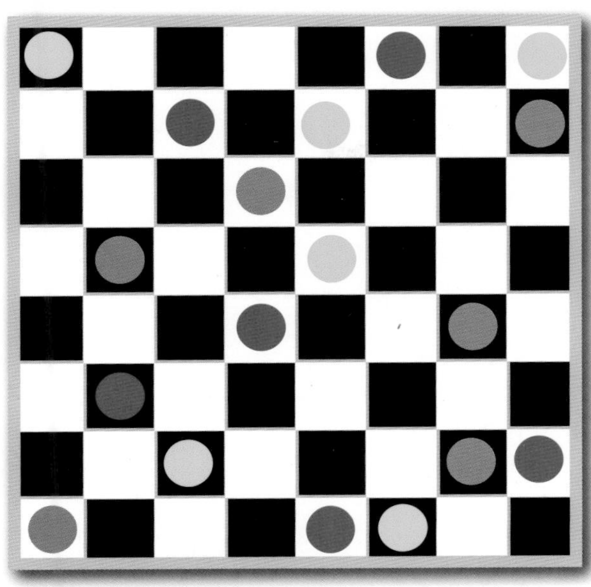

Knight's Move

Find an empty square in the grid that is one chess knight's move away from a blue, red, and yellow circle. A knight's move is an "L" shape—two squares sideways, up or down in any direction, followed by one square to the left or right.

Avalon is a mythical island located somewhere in Great Britain. Mentioned in Arthurian legend it was, as early as the 12th century, linked to Glastonbury Tor in Somerset, England, where the bones of King Arthur and his queen were supposedly uncovered. It remains associated with present-day Glastonbury.

249

DIFFICULTY

	>	4			<			
		^				v		^
		5	>					
v								
	<				>			
					>	2	<	
v		^		^				
1							>	3

Tough Going

The arrows indicate whether a number in a box is greater or smaller than an adjacent number. Complete the grid so that all rows and columns contain the numbers 1 to 5.

“The story is more important to me than the part.”

Catherine Deneuve

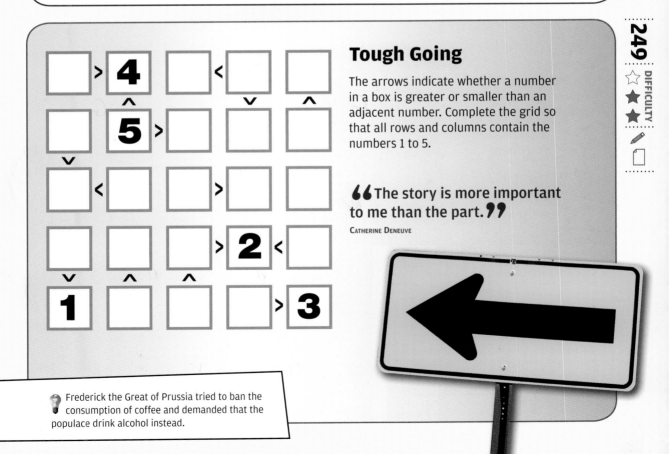

Frederick the Great of Prussia tried to ban the consumption of coffee and demanded that the populace drink alcohol instead.

250 DIFFICULTY ☆★★

Around the Block

Can you crack the color code and make your way from one yellow square to the other, moving one square at a time? The blue arrow tells you which way is up.

"Happiness is not being pained in body or troubled in mind." THOMAS JEFFERSON

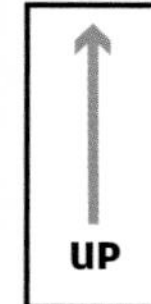

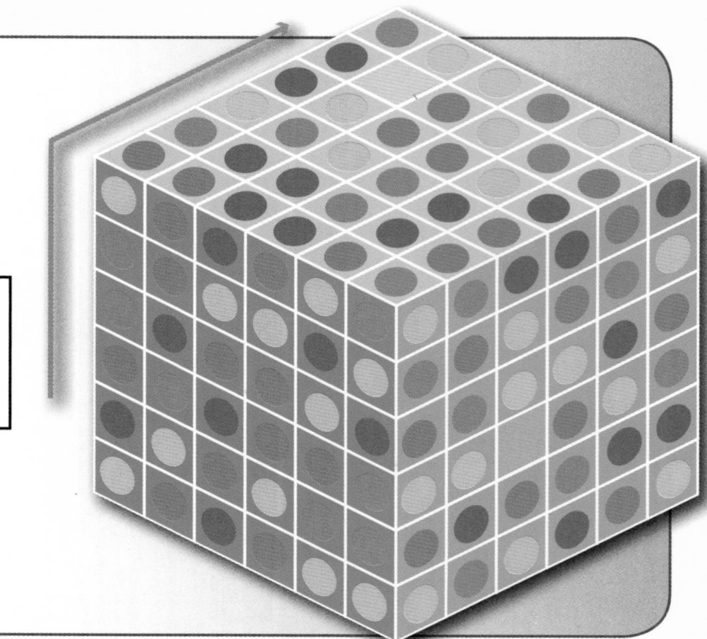

The Atlantic giant squid has larger eyes than any other animal, either alive or extinct. One specimen had eyes with an estimated diameter of 20 inches (0.5 meters).

251 DIFFICULTY ☆★★

Priceless Pottery

The areas outlined on this vase will be painted blue, red, and green, and no two areas that touch each other can be the same color. What color should the handle be?

"You can only mend the vase so many times before you have to chuck it away." CHRISTINE MCVIE

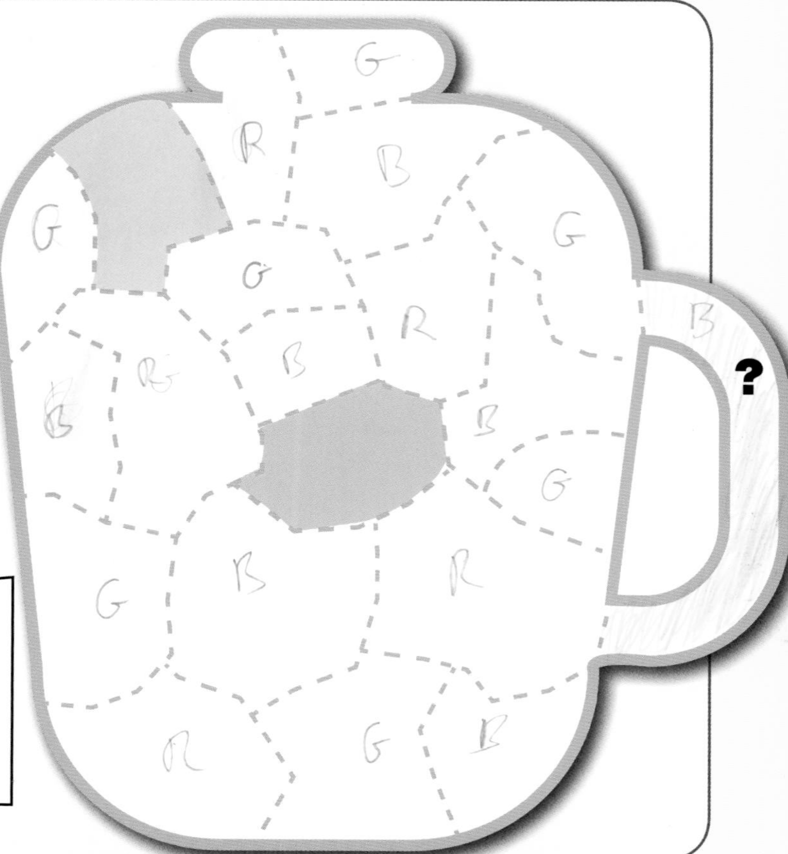

Josiah Wedgwood, one of the most innovative figures in the history of pottery, was elected a fellow of the Royal Society in 1783, primarily for inventing the pyrometer to measure oven temperatures. He had been the appointed "Queen's Potter" since 1762.

252

DIFFICULTY

Lost Swatch

There are exactly 24 different ways to arrange four colors next to each other in a line. 23 are shown here, can you work out the order the colors should be in the missing swatch?

“The purest and most thoughtful minds are those which love color the most.”
JOHN RUSKIN

253

DIFFICULTY

Find the Treasure

The numbers on the side and bottom of the grid indicate occupied squares or groups of consecutive occupied squares in each row or column. Can you finish the grid so that it contains two amulets, two cutlasses, three bars of gold, and two keys, and the numbers tally?

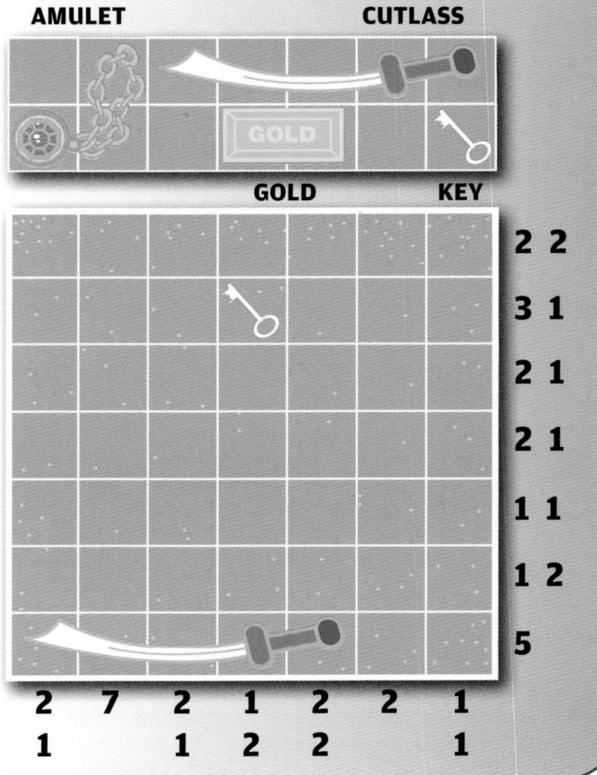

It was Plutarch, the Greek historian, who gave the first definition of piracy as an illegal attack on a ship or coastal city.

“The average man will bristle if you say his father was dishonest, but he will brag a little if he discovers that his great-grandfather was a pirate.”
BERN WILLIAMS

254

DIFFICULTY ★★☆

Making Shapes

Which of the pictures below represents the correct overhead view of this scene?

“A cynic is a man who knows the price of everything but the value of nothing.” OSCAR WILDE

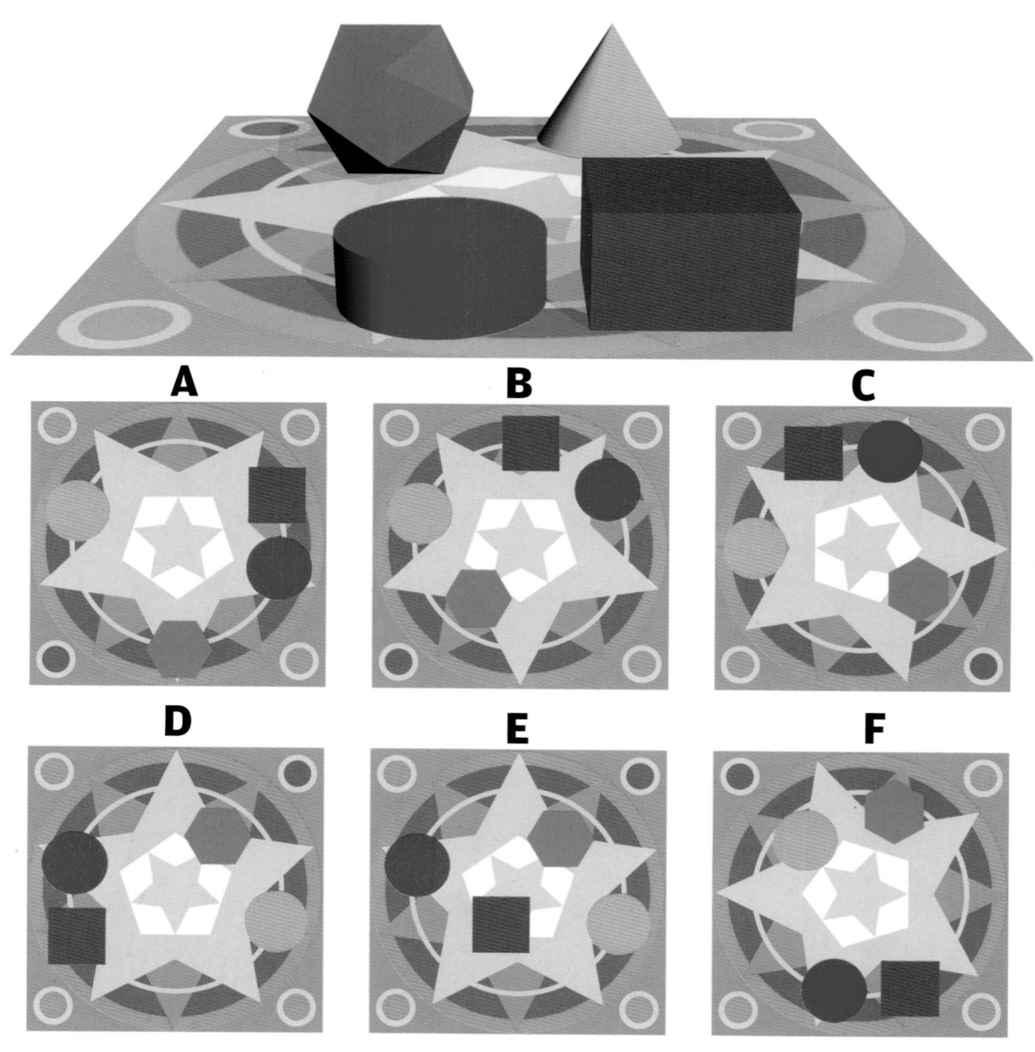

The botanical gardens in the Argentine capital Buenos Aires were designed in 1898 by the French landscaper Carlos Thays, and occupy 83,388 square yards (76,250 meters) of the city's northern district of Palermo. Today, they are best known for the huge number of feral cats that call the garden home.

255

DIFFICULTY

Amounting to Something

F. Scott Fitzgerald was named after a distant relative, Francis Scott Key, who wrote the words to the "Star Spangled Banner" in 1814.

Use the white numbers to make the central number the same way in all three cases. What number should replace the question mark?

256

DIFFICULTY

"A man of genius has been seldom ruined but by himself."
SAMUEL JOHNSON

In a Spin

What numbers should appear in the hubs of these number tornadoes?

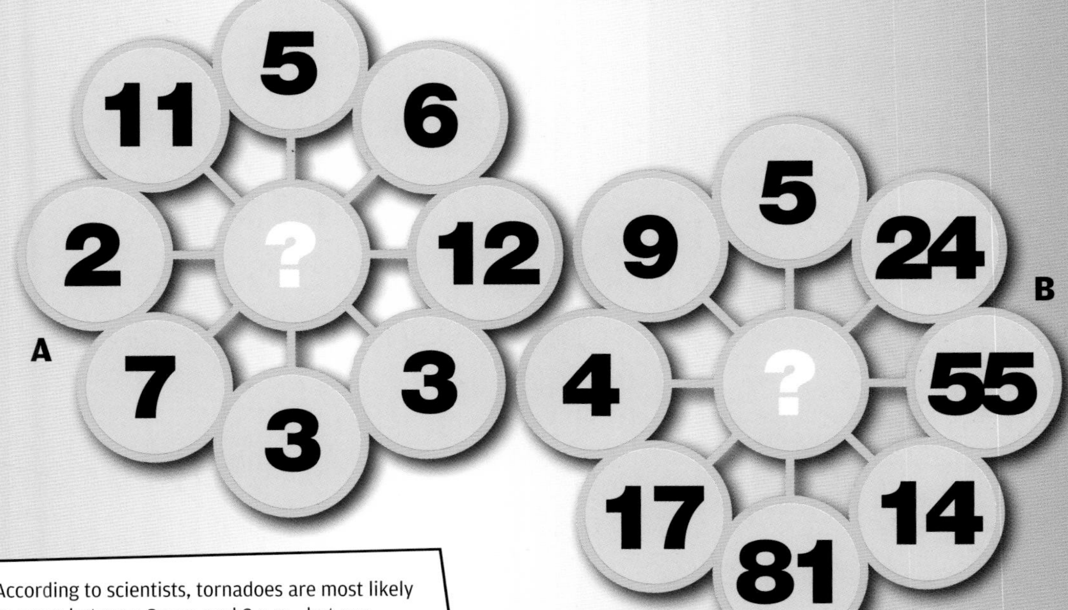

According to scientists, tornadoes are most likely to occur between 3 p.m. and 9 p.m., but can occur at any time.

257

DIFFICULTY ★★★

Reach the Top

Replace the question marks with numbers so that each pair of blocks adds up to the block directly above them.

"I'll love you, dear, I'll love you till China and Africa meet and the river jumps over the mountain and the salmon sing in the street." W. H. Auden

98

? 39

38 ? ?

? 15 ? ?

? ? ? 4 ?

258

DIFFICULTY ☆★★

Mine Sweeper

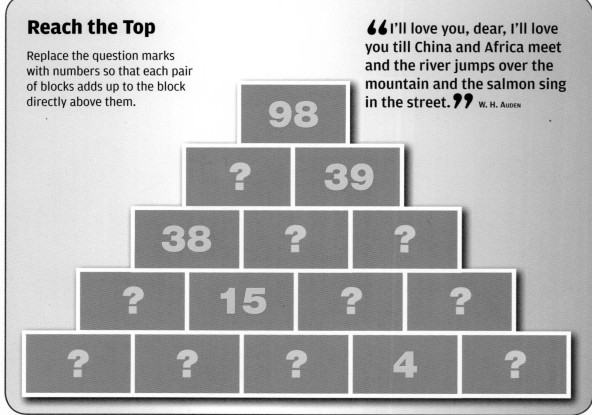

The numbered squares in the grid indicate the exact number of shaded squares that should surround them. The puzzle is solved when all these squares are surrounded by the correct number of shaded squares.

1	2			2	2		
3					3	4	
			4	2	4		3
4		5	3		4		
				2	3		3
	2	3	2	3		4	
2				3			
1		2			2	3	

Near the confessionals in the Cattedrale di San Lorenzo in Genoa, Italy, lies an unexploded World War II bomb.

259

DIFFICULTY

Exactly the Same

Only two of the shapes below are exactly the same; can you find the matching pair?

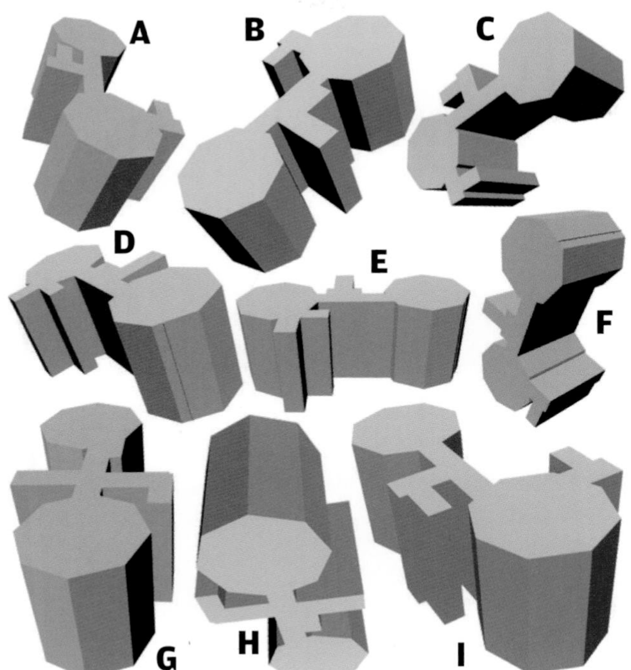

“There are two things in life for which we are never truly prepared: twins.”

Josh Billings

It is believed that the alcoholic drink gin originated in the Netherlands during the 17th century and that it was the invention of Dr. Slyvuis, a Professor of Medicine who used it to treat kidney ailments. He called it “genever,” after the French *genièvre*, or “juniper.”

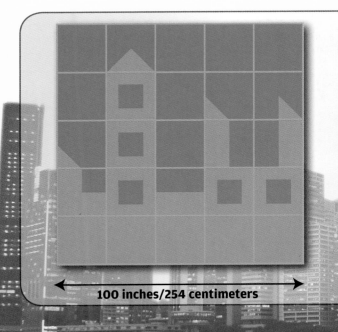

260

DIFFICULTY

City Scrape

Luke is considering buying a loft apartment but is concerned that it does not receive enough natural light. Can you work out the approximate area that this cityscape is occupying?

100 inches/254 centimeters

“A great city is not to be confounded with a populous one.”

Aristotle

One of the most famous cityscape paintings is Jan Vermeer’s *View of Delft*, which he composed between 1659 and 1660. It currently hangs in the Mauritshuis in the Hague.

261 DIFFICULTY ★

Arrow Escape

Complete the grid by drawing an arrow in each box that points in any one of the eight compass directions (N, E, S, W, NE, NW, SE, SW). The numbers in the outside boxes in the finished puzzle will reflect the number of arrows pointing in their direction.

“Learning is finding out what you already know. Doing is demonstrating that you know it.” Richard Bach

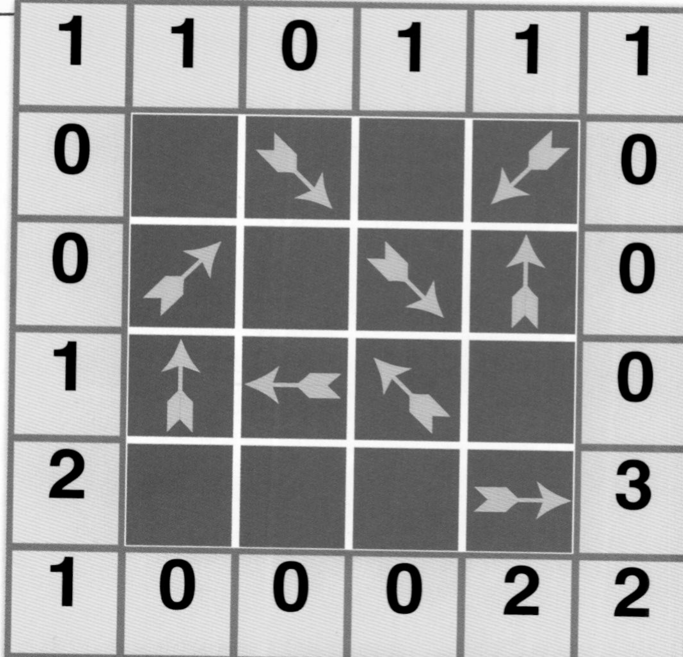

The compass plant was given its name because during midsummer its leaves point precisely north and south.

262 DIFFICULTY ★★

Acting Parts

These ten pieces can be assembled to spell the name of a movie star. Who?

In 2001, the American Film Institute released a list of the “Most Thrilling Movies in American Cinema.” In reverse order the top three were *The Exorcist* (1973), *Jaws* (1975), and *Psycho* (1960).

263 DIFFICULTY

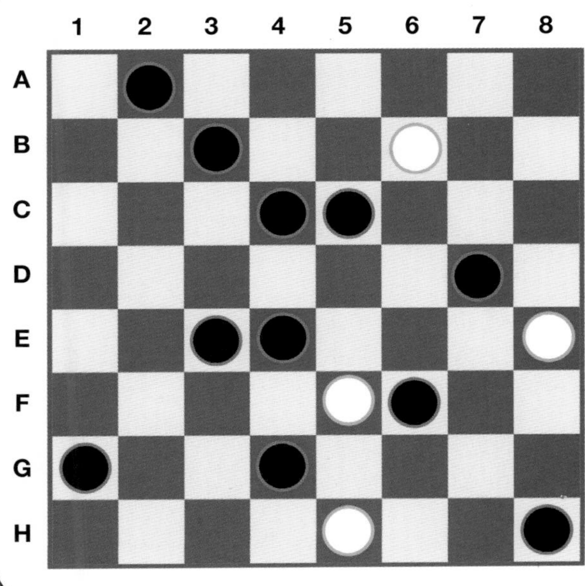

Check This Out

Make a move for white so that eight black pieces are left, none of which are in the same column or row.

“If life doesn’t offer a game worth playing, then invent a new one.”

ANTHONY J. D’ANGELO

It would take a person typing 60 words per minute, eight hours a day, around 50 years to type the human genome.

264 DIFFICULTY

Place the Shapes

Place the two shapes over the grid so that no color appears twice in the same row or column. Beware, the shapes may not be the right way up!

“Think in the morning. Act in the noon. Eat in the evening. Sleep in the night.”

WILLIAM BLAKE

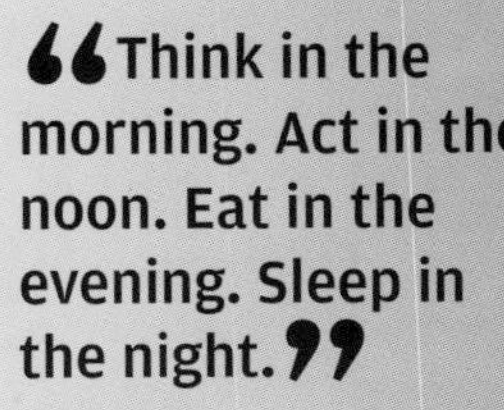

 Only one national flag is a solid color—the green flag of Libya.

265

DIFFICULTY ★★★

Make It Up

Divide up the grid into four equally sized, equally shaped parts, each containing numbers that add up to 36.

		1	1	1	1		
	4	2	2	2	2	6	
1	2	3	3	3	3	2	2
2	3	4	7	4	4	3	1
3	4	0	3	9	5	4	2
2	1	0	4	1	3	1	2
	1	7	6	1	4	1	
		1	8	2	0		

“If a man’s wit be wandering, let him study the mathematics.”

Francis Bacon

Did you know that 111,111,111 x 111,111,111 = 12,345,678,987,654,321?

Gramo-Phonies

Which box has exactly the right parts to build the gramophone?

A

B

C

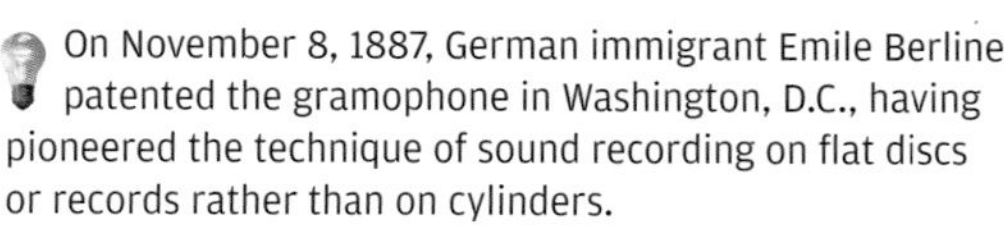

On November 8, 1887, German immigrant Emile Berliner patented the gramophone in Washington, D.C., having pioneered the technique of sound recording on flat discs or records rather than on cylinders.

Follow That Taxi!

The jewel thieves have left their loot in a yellow taxi in New York City. They have left directions on how to find the taxi in the black car. Can you track down the taxi and rescue the rocks?

"The great thieves lead away the little thief." DIOGENES

267

DIFFICULTY

	1	2	3	4	5	6
A						
B						
C						
D						
E						

2e, 4s, 2w, 1n, 1w,
1s, 4n, 1s, 1w, 4e,
1w, 3s, 2e, 5w, 4n,
3s, 1n, 5e, 4w, 1e,
1n, 3e, 2s, 3n, 2w,
2s, 1s, 1e, 1n

In June, 1926, Spanish architect Antoni Gaudí was run over by a tram in Barcelona. Poorly dressed, he was not recognized and taxi drivers refused to take a "vagabond" to the hospital (they were later fined by the police). His greatest work, the Sagrada Familia, on which he had been working for nearly 30 years, remains unfinished and he is buried in its crypt.

268

DIFFICULTY

Dice Puzzle

What's the missing number?

Elvis Presley was a black belt in karate. He took up martial arts under the shotokan sensei Jürgen Seydal, while fulfilling his military duties in Germany in 1958.

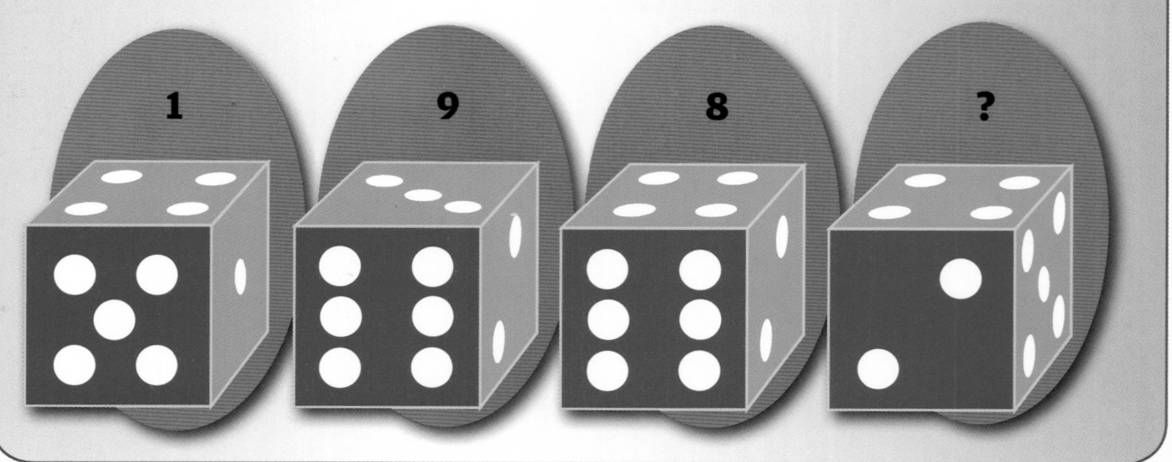

269

DIFFICULTY

The Perfect Pair

Which two shapes below will pair up to create the top shape?

A

B

C

D

E

F

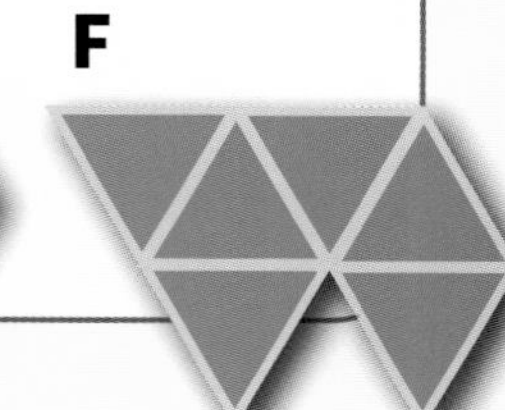

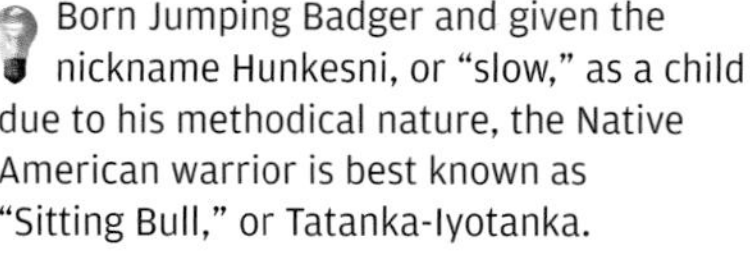

Born Jumping Badger and given the nickname Hunkesni, or "slow," as a child due to his methodical nature, the Native American warrior is best known as "Sitting Bull," or Tatanka-Iyotanka.

Tabletopper

270

DIFFICULTY

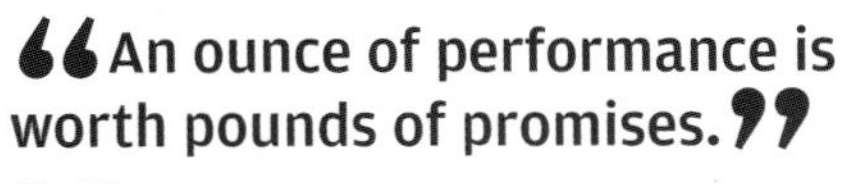

“An ounce of performance is worth pounds of promises.”

Mae West

Below is a table, ready for mosaic tiles. Can you arrange the groups of tiles to finish it?

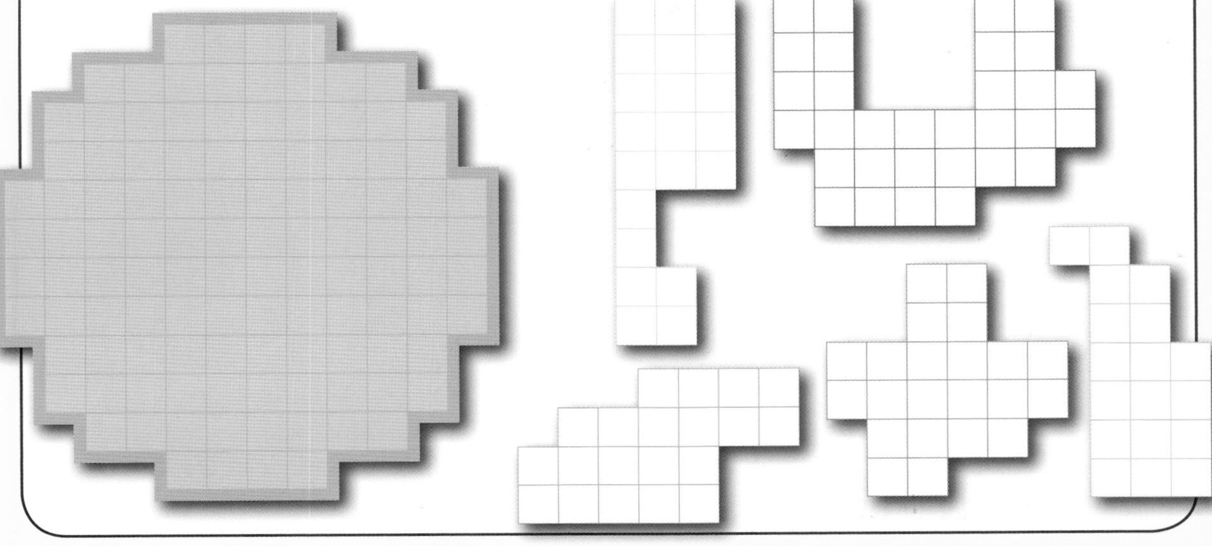

Cube Route

271

DIFFICULTY

Can you crack the color code and make your way from one purple square to the other? The blue arrow tells you which way is up.

UP

“The mind can make a heaven out of hell or a hell out of heaven.” John Milton

John Milton was blinded by glaucoma in middle age and he composed his epic works *Paradise Lost* (1667) and *Paradise Regained* (1671) through dictation. It is believed that fellow poet Andrew Marvell was one of those who wrote down Milton’s words.

272

DIFFICULTY

A Different View

Of the plan views below, only one of them is a true overhead representation of the scene shown here; can you find it?

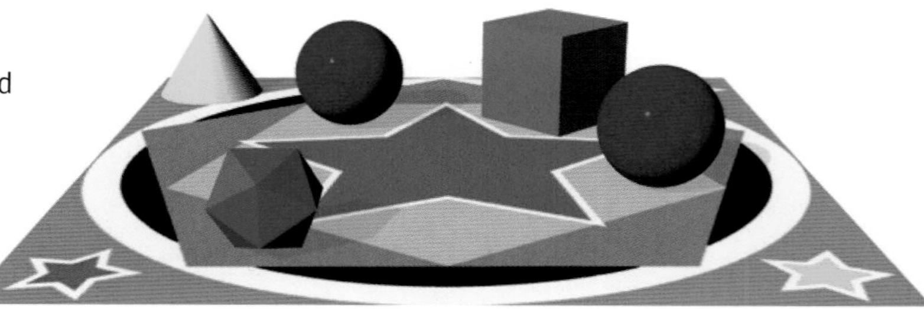

A

B

C

D

E

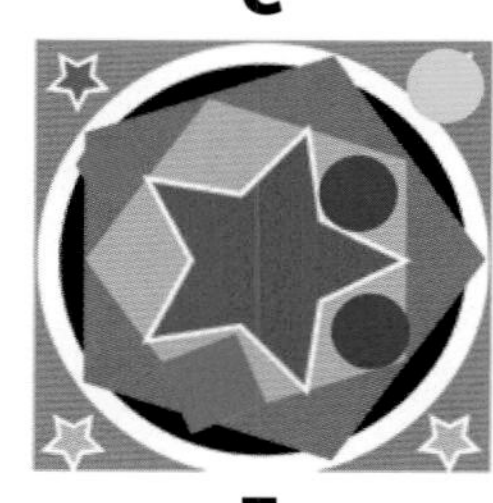

F

In 1873, the Mauch Chunk Switchback Railway in the Pennsylvania mountains began to carry passengers instead of coal. It is considered to be the first American roller coaster, though some believe LaMarcus Thompson's Switchback roller coaster, which opened at Coney Island in 1874, to be the first.

273

DIFFICULTY

Hard Cell

The numbers in some cells in the grid indicate the exact number of black cells that should border it. Shade these black, until all the numbers are surrounded by the correct number of black cells.

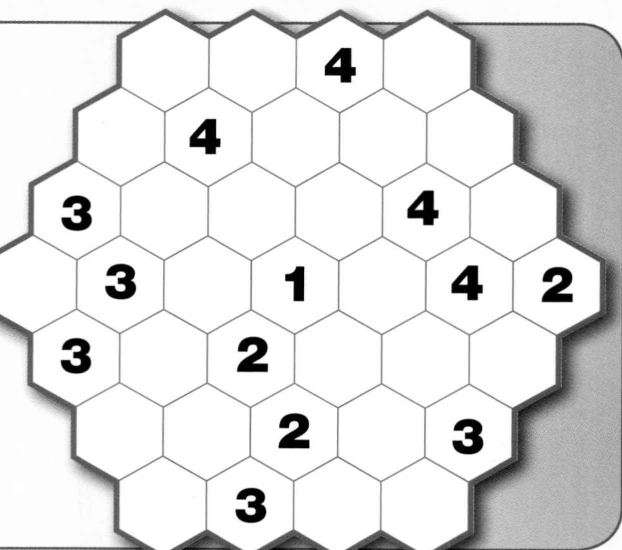

The first known contraceptive was crocodile dung. It was used by the Ancient Egyptians in 2000 B.C.

274

DIFFICULTY ★★★ (1 of 3 filled)

Duck Hunt

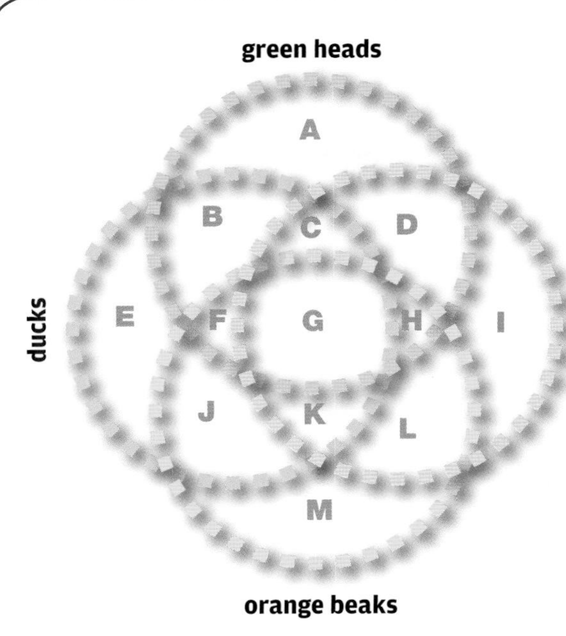

Can you work out which areas of this diagram represent ducks with orange beaks that don't have black feet or green heads, and green-headed, black-footed birds that aren't ducks and don't have orange beaks?

"If it looks like a duck, and quacks like a duck, we have at least to consider the possibility that we have a small aquatic bird of the family anatidae on our hands." Douglas Adams

All of the Peking ducks in the United States are direct descendants of nine ducks imported to Long Island in 1873.

275

DIFFICULTY ★★★ (2 of 3 filled)

Make the Shape

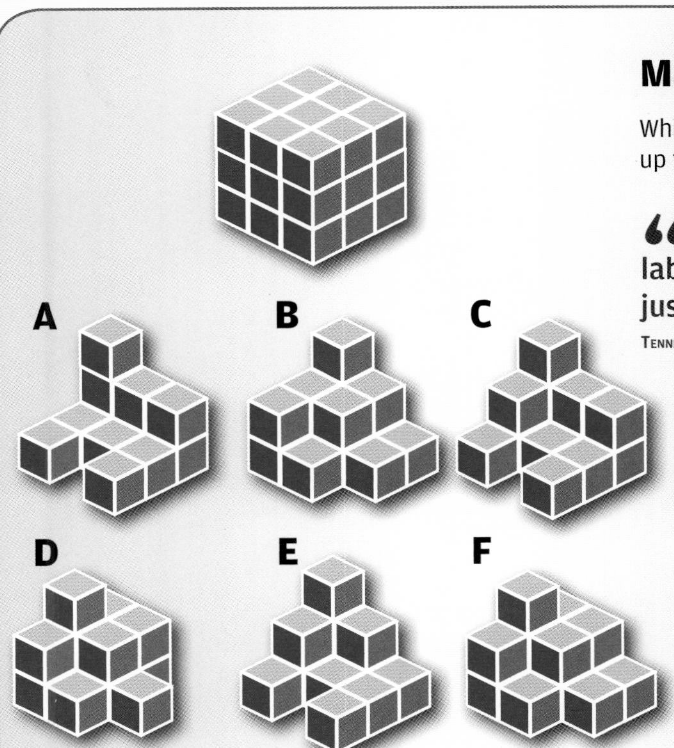

Which two shapes below will pair up to create the top shape?

"All of us are guinea pigs in the laboratory of God. Humanity is just a work in progress." Tennessee Williams

In 1895, the Swedish chemist Svante Arrhenius discovered that humans could enhance the greenhouse effect by making carbon dioxide, a greenhouse gas.

276

DIFFICULTY

Ball Logic

The balls below have been rearranged. Can you work out the new sequence of the balls from the clues given below?

- The 2 ball isn't touching the 5 or the 4.
- The 4 ball is touching the 10 but not the 6.
- The 8 ball is immediately to the left of the 6.
- The bottom row totals 16.

"It's good sportsmanship not to pick up lost balls while they are still rolling." Mark Twain

277

DIFFICULTY

Chess Move

Can you place a queen, a bishop, a knight, and a rook on this chessboard so that the blue squares are attacked by exactly two pieces, the green ones by three pieces, and the red ones by four pieces?

278

DIFFICULTY

Double Drat

All these shapes appear twice in the box except one. Can you spot it?

“Anybody can be pope; the proof of this is that I have become one.”

Pope John XXIII

In 1624, Pope Urban VIII threatened to excommunicate snuff tobacco users.

279

DIFFICULTY

Fisherman’s Riddle

Jose the Fisherman passed away, leaving his fleet of 17 fishing boats to his three daughters. He stipulated in his will that his eldest daughter, Manuela, should get half the boats, his second daughter, Maria, should get one-third of them, and his youngest, Monica, should get one-ninth of the fleet. The girls were at a loss as to how they were supposed to carry out their father’s last wish, until another fisherman offered to help them. What did he do?

“The fishermen know that the sea is dangerous and the storm terrible, but they have never found these dangers sufficient reason for remaining ashore.” Vincent van Gogh

280

DIFFICULTY ☆★★

Island Spy

The four squares below can all be found in the picture grid; can you track them down? Beware: They may not be the right way up!

“True friendship multiplies the good in life and divides its evils. Strive to have friends, for life without friends is like life on a desert island . . . to find one real friend in a lifetime is good fortune; to keep him is a blessing.” Baltasar Gracian

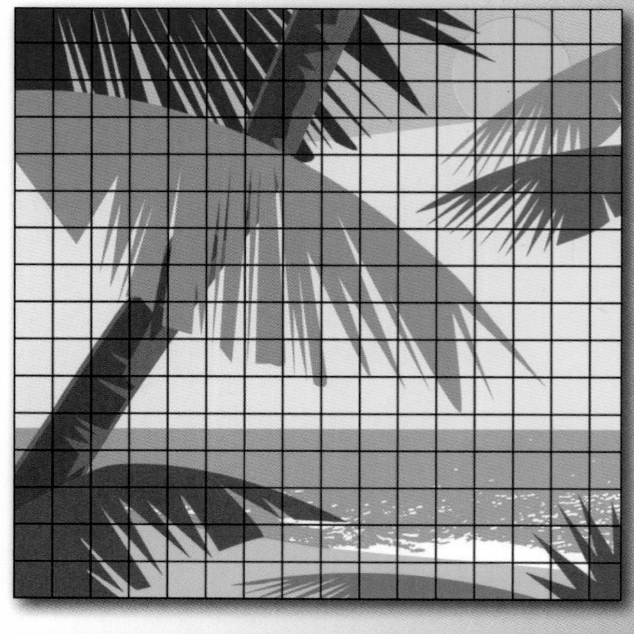

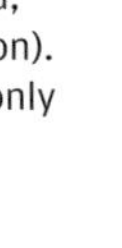

Of the 6 billion plus people in the world, one in ten lives on an island (600 million). Some 60 million live in Great Britain, the only island connected to a continent (through the Channel Tunnel).

281

DIFFICULTY ☆★★

Mystery Symmetry

This picture, when finished, is symmetrical along a vertical line up the middle. Can you color in the missing squares and see the picture?

“We build statues out of snow, and weep to see them melt.” Sir Walter Scott

The Inuit language has more than 20 words for snow, and Inuit women have a tradition of never combing their hair on the day a polar bear is to be killed.

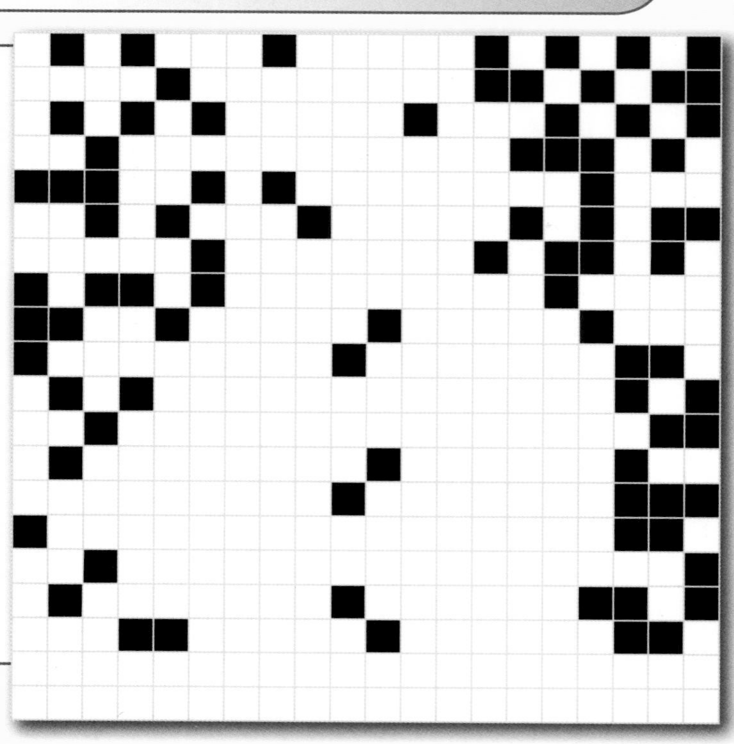

282

DIFFICULTY

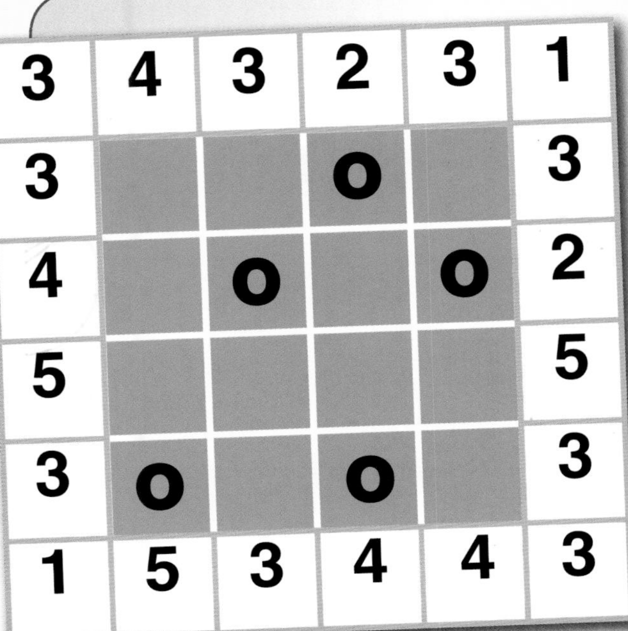

3 4 3 2 3 1
3 O 3
4 O O 2
5 5
3 O O 3
1 5 3 4 4 3

Tic-Tac-Toe

The numbers around the edge of the grid describe the number of Xs in the vertical, horizontal, and diagonal lines connecting with that square. Complete the grid so that there is an X or O in every square.

“Who in the world am I? Ah, that’s the great puzzle.”
LEWIS CARROLL

The head of a woodpecker striking a tree is traveling at more than 1,300 miles mph (2,092 kph)—twice the speed of a bullet.

283

DIFFICULTY

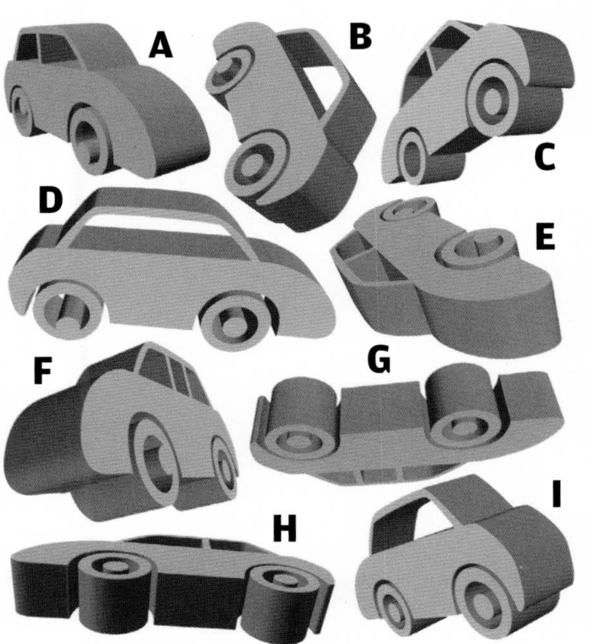

Matching Motor Cars

Only two of these cars are exactly the same; can you find the matching pair?

“A suburban mother’s role is to deliver children obstetrically once, and by car for ever after.” PETER DE VRIES

The Indianapolis Speedway Stadium built in 1909 can claim to be the biggest in the world. It has a capacity of 250,000 in its all-seater complex.

284

DIFFICULTY

Corkscrew Caper

Which of the colored-in corkscrews matches the silhouette?

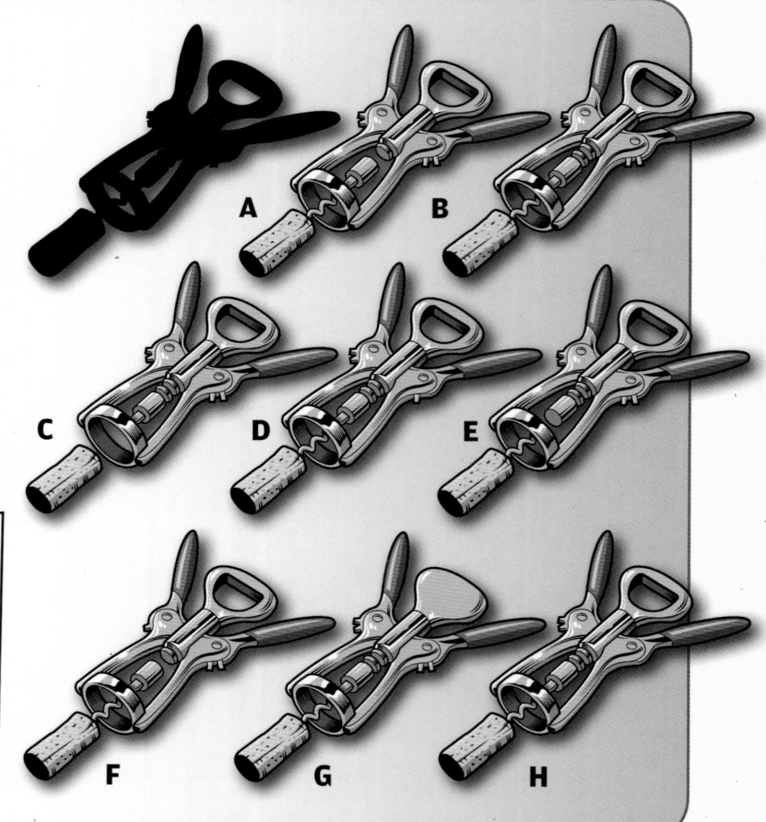

“What though youth gave love and roses, Age still leaves us friends and wine.”

THOMAS MORE

There are about 3,000 wineries in the United States–1,300 of these are in California. The state is the fourth ranked wine producer by volume in the world, after Italy, France, and Spain.

285

DIFFICULTY

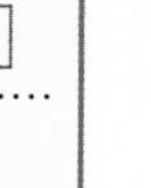

Tents and Trees

Every tree has one tent found horizontally or vertically adjacent to it. No tent can be in an adjacent square to another tent (even diagonally). The numbers by each row and column tell you how many tents are there. Can you locate all the tents?

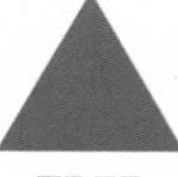

TREE

TENT

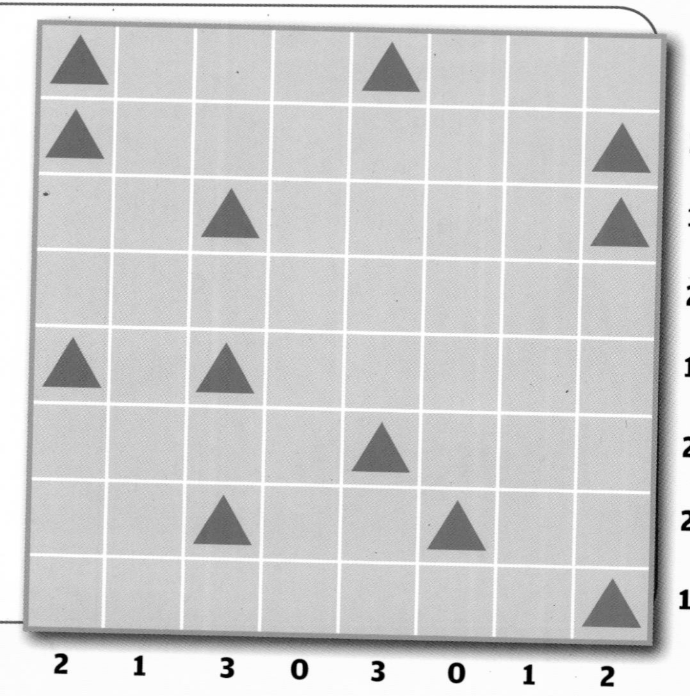

The Smoky Mountains Natural Park in North Carolina and Tennessee is the most visited park in the United States with 9 million visitors a year. There are ten campsites to choose from in the park.

286

DIFFICULTY

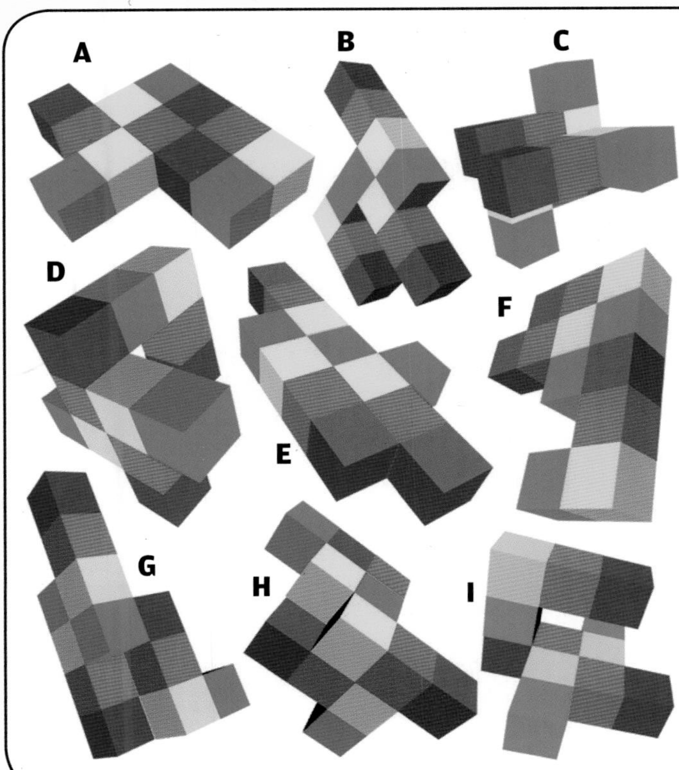

Spare Part

All these pictures below show constructions built from three of the spare part. Except one! Can you find the different design?

In 1869, Russian chemist Dimitry Ivanovich Mendeleyev developed the Periodic Table of the Elements—a chart that reflected their properties and that went on to become a common sight in chemistry classrooms the world over.

287

DIFFICULTY

Paint Planning

This wall is to be painted in green, blue, and lilac, with no adjacent bricks to be in the same color. What color should the window frame be?

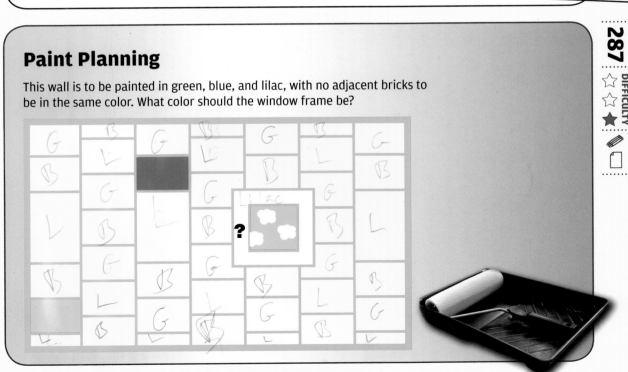

?

288 DIFFICULTY

A Piece of Pie

Can you crack the pie code and fill in the missing numbers?

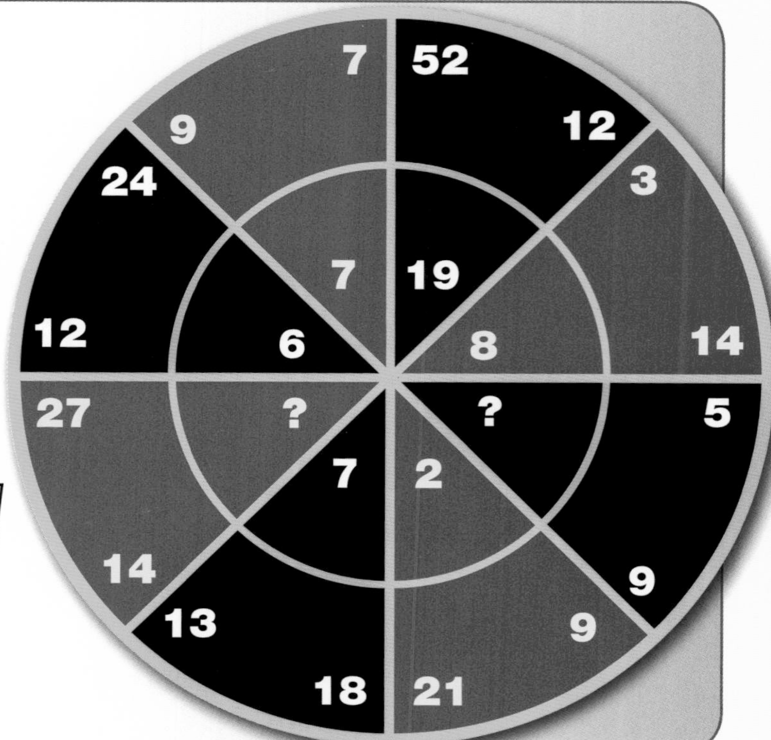

“If you want to make an apple pie from scratch, you must first create the universe.” DR. CARL SAGAN

Brasília, the modern capital of Brazil, was officially opened on April 22, 1960. It was a federal decision to build a new rigidly planned city away from the country's sea border so it would be less susceptible to sea invasion.

289 DIFFICULTY

Five Point Problem

The numbers on these pentagons follow a pattern. Your task is to uncover the secret to the pattern and fill in the blanks to complete the puzzle.

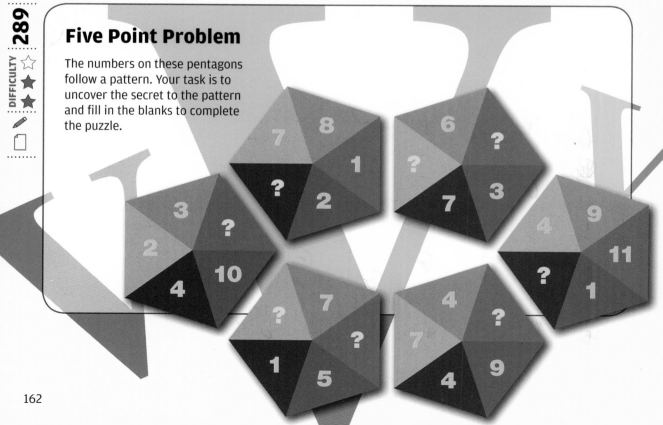

290

DIFFICULTY

Beethoven 40

Mozart 16

Schubert 24

Bach 6

Vivaldi ?

Composer Poser

Can you crack the logical secret behind the numbers by these famous composers, and discover what's Vivaldi number?

"I pay no attention whatever to anybody's praise or blame. I simply follow my own feelings." WOLFGANG AMADEUS MOZART

In 1762, the two prodigiously talented Mozart children, which included Wolfgang Amadeus at the age of just six, embarked on the first of a series of concert tours across Europe.

291

DIFFICULTY

"Too many have dispensed with generosity in order to practice charity." ALBERT CAMUS

Shaping Relations

By examining the relationships of the following shapes, can you identify the next shape?

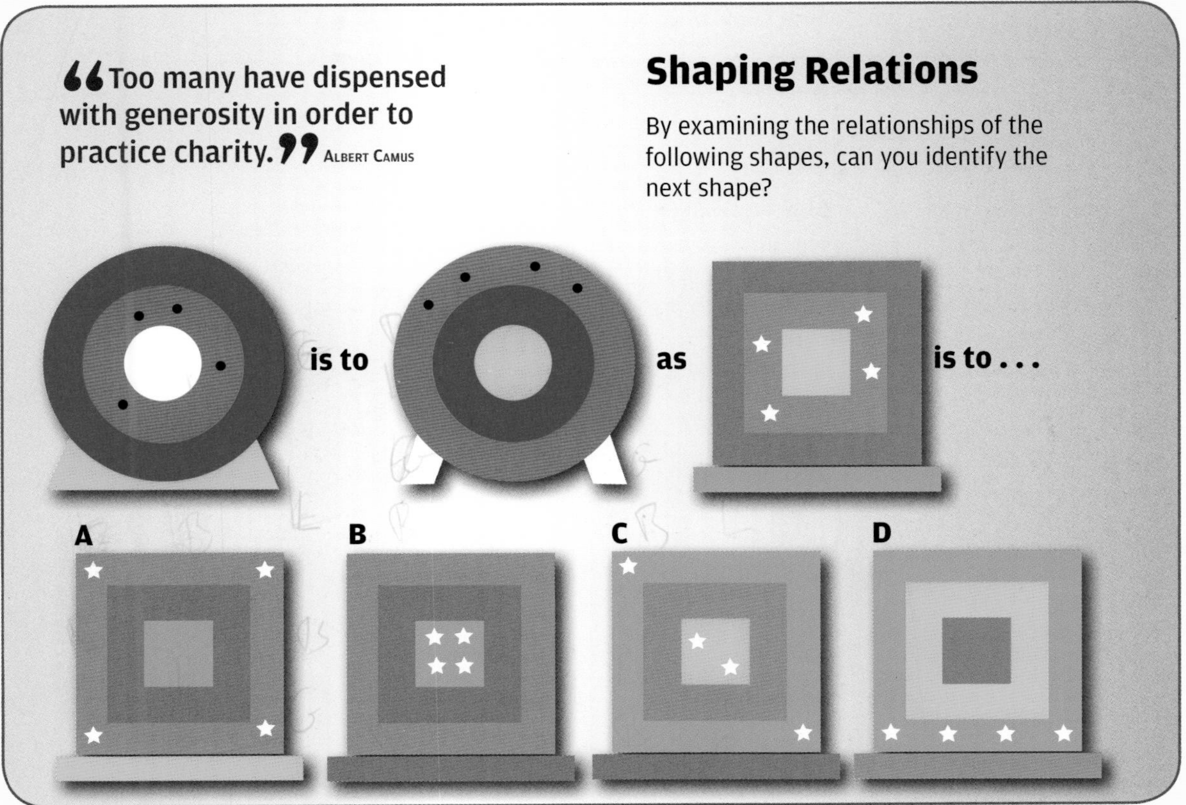

292

DIFFICULTY

Camel Capers

Can you find the approximate area the camel is occupying?

"There is no logical reason why the camel of great art should pass through the needle of mob intelligence." Rebecca West

Llamas are very closely related to camels. In fact a camel-llama crossbreed was born in Dubai in 1997. It was called Rama the cama.

293

DIFFICULTY

Star Detective

The stars shown below have been rearranged. Can you work out the new sequence from the clues given below?

- The red shapes are adjacent, the yellows are not.
- The top shape is a red circle.
- On the bottom, a square is to the right of a blue shape.

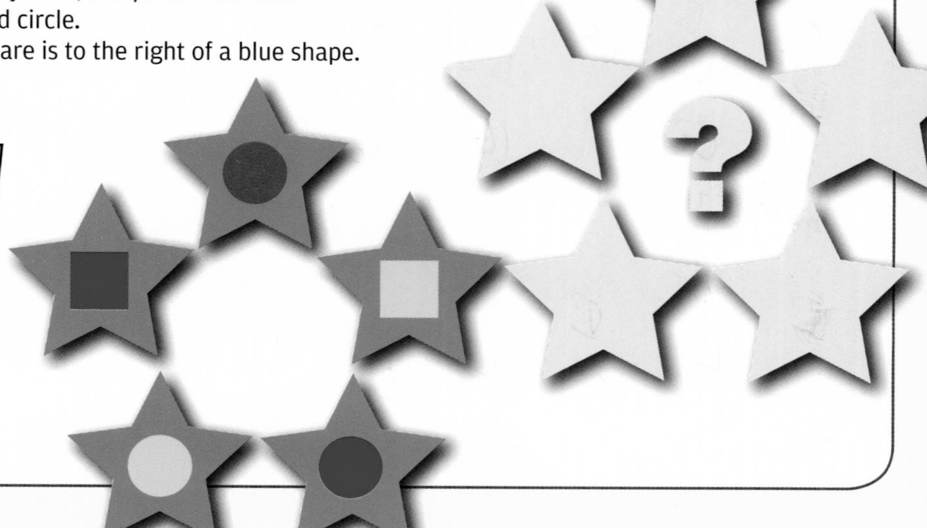

The famous National Spelling Bee was launched by the *Courier-Journal* of Louisville, Kentucky, in 1925 as an attempt to raise childrens' interest in the subject.

294 DIFFICULTY

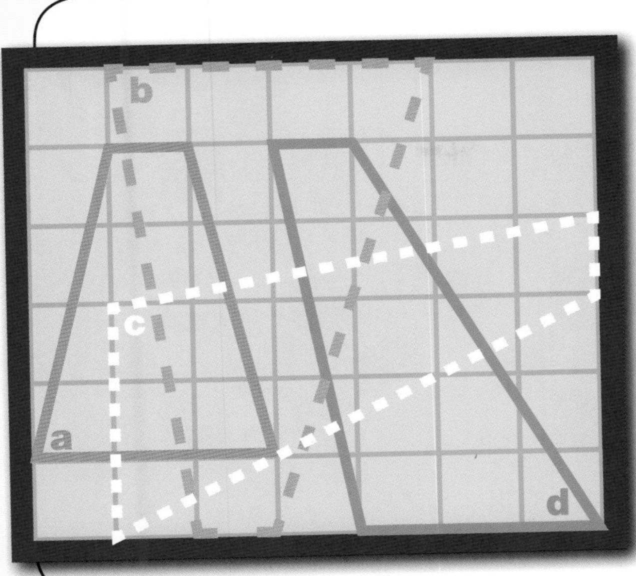

Size Matters

Can you put these shapes in order, from biggest to smallest?

"What counts is not necessarily the size of the dog in the fight; it's the size of the fight in the dog."

DWIGHT DAVID EISENHOWER

The missionary Hans Egede founded Nuuk in 1728 as the very first town in Greenland. It is now the country's capital with a permanent population of only 15,000.

295 DIFFICULTY

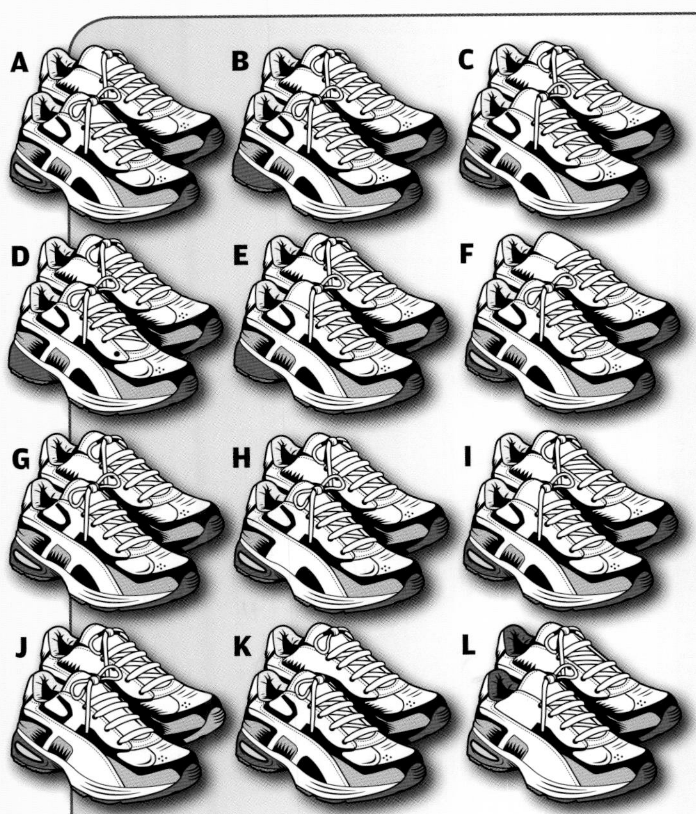

Sneaky Sneakers

Only two of these pairs are exactly the same. Can you find the matching pair?

"My verses, I cannot say poems. I was following in the exquisite footsteps of Miss Millay, unhappily in my own horrible sneakers." DOROTHY PARKER

Every year since 1985 Nike have released a new Air Jordan basketball shoe. The Air Jordan II was the first regular sneaker to have a triple-digit price tag.

296 DIFFICULTY ★★★

Building Block

Which two shapes below can be combined to create the top shape?

“The absolute yearning of one human body for another particular body and its indifference to substitutes is one of life’s major mysteries.”

Iris Murdoch

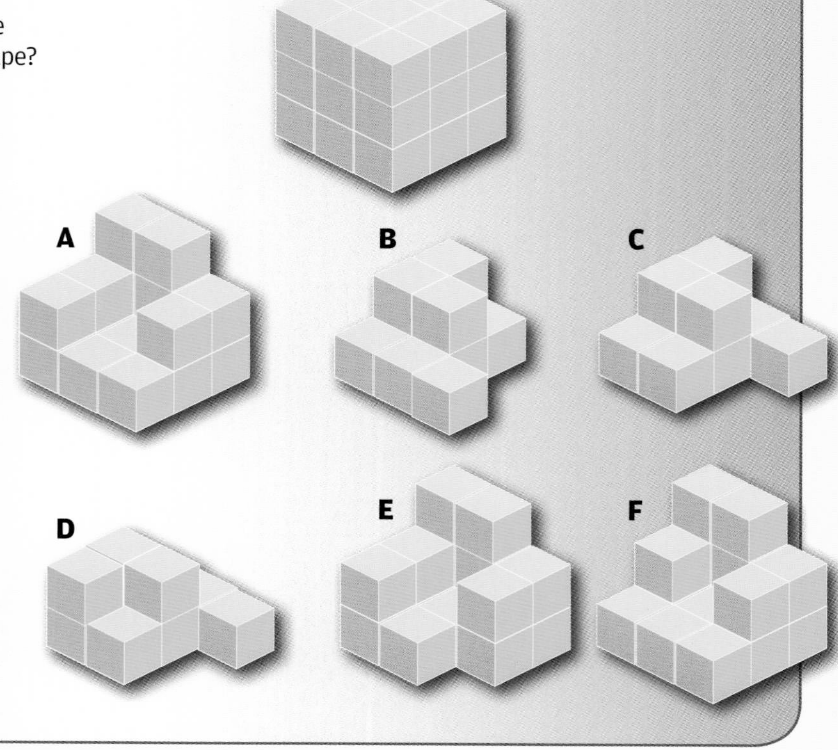

The human head contains 22 bones, consisting of the cranium and the facial bones. The cranium is formed by 8 bones and the face consists of 14 bones, including the maxilla (upper jaw) and mandible (lower jaw).

297 DIFFICULTY ☆☆★

Number Wheel

What numbers should appear in the hubs of these number wheels?

The tomato is the world’s most popular fruit. More than 60 million tons of tomatoes are produced per year—16 million tons more than the second most popular fruit, the banana. Apples are the third most popular (36 million tons), then oranges (34 million tons), and watermelons (22 million tons).

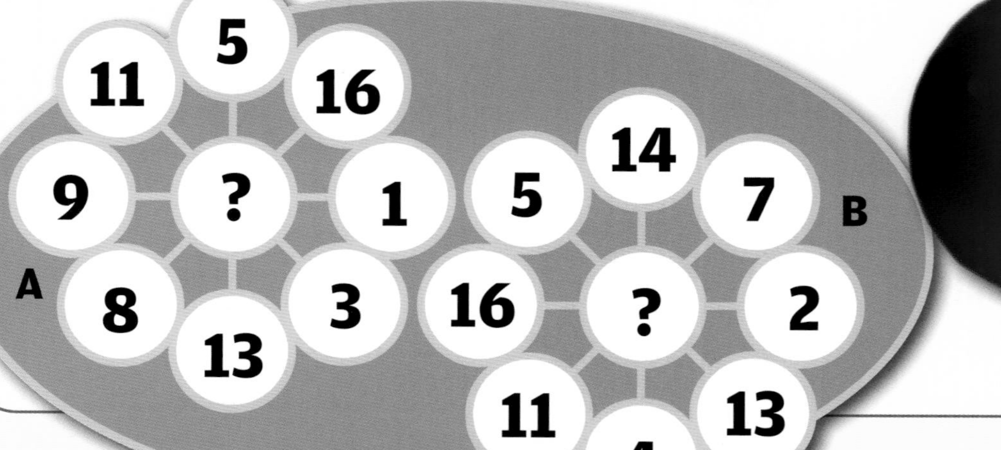

298

DIFFICULTY

Mystery Middle

The columns and rows that make up the finished grid have certain properties in common. Identify these matching qualities and you should be able to work out which of the squares below will correctly complete the grid.

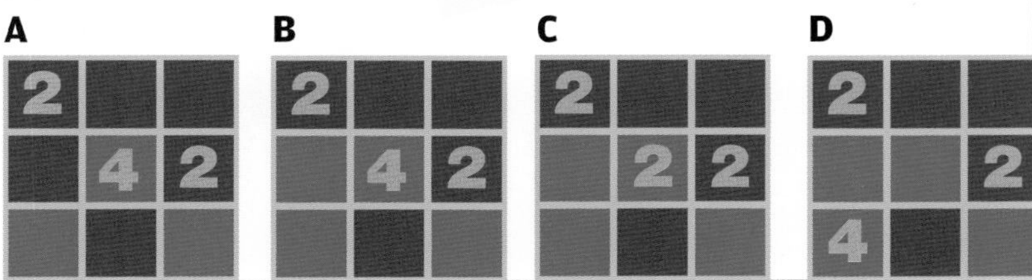

The last battle to be held on mainland British soil was the 1746 Battle of Culloden Moor, where British forces defeated the rebel Scots, who were led by the exiled "Bonnie" Prince Charlie.

299

DIFFICULTY

A Colorful Path

Find a path from one white cell to the other in the shortest way. You may only pass from a red cell to a blue one, a blue to a yellow, a yellow to a green, or a green to a red.

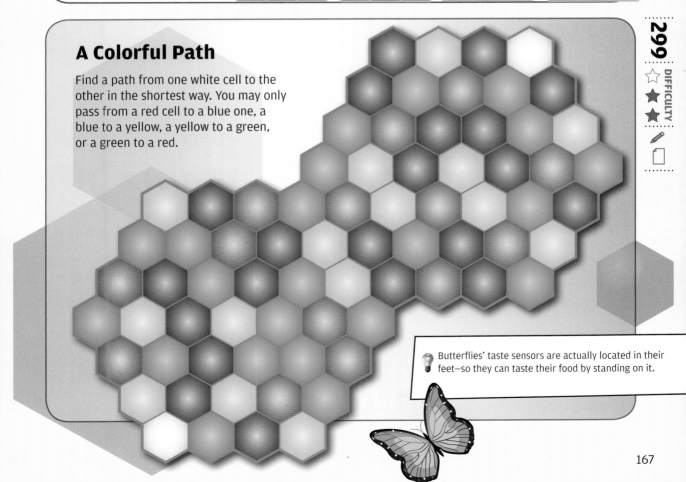

Butterflies' taste sensors are actually located in their feet—so they can taste their food by standing on it.

DIFFICULTY 300

Get the Picture

These two grids, when merged together, will make a picture. Of what?

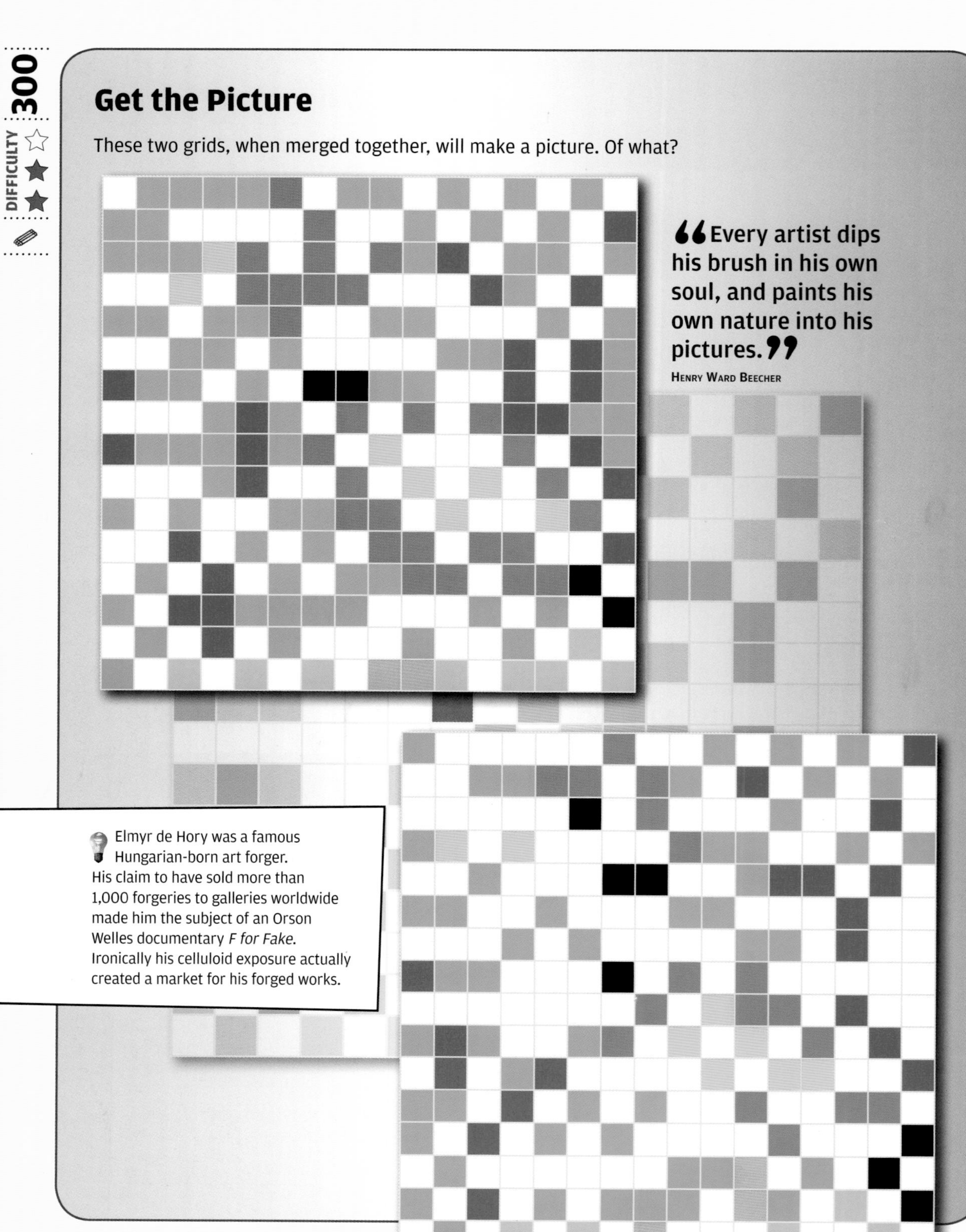

"Every artist dips his brush in his own soul, and paints his own nature into his pictures."

HENRY WARD BEECHER

Elmyr de Hory was a famous Hungarian-born art forger. His claim to have sold more than 1,000 forgeries to galleries worldwide made him the subject of an Orson Welles documentary *F for Fake*. Ironically his celluloid exposure actually created a market for his forged works.

301

DIFFICULTY

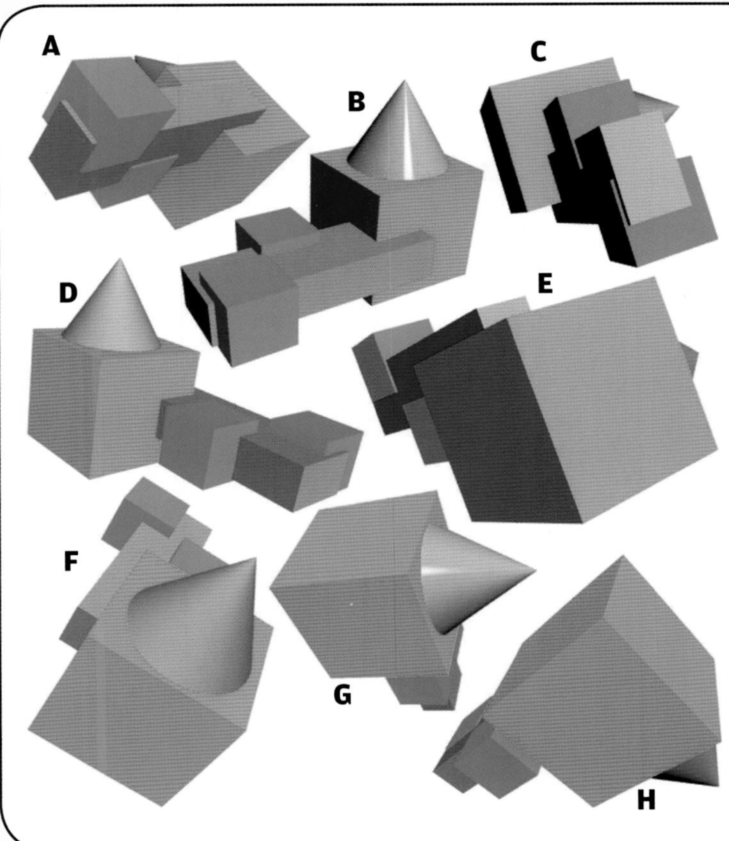

Odd One Out

Study the shapes on the left; which of the shapes is not the same as the other ones?

"Logic: The art of thinking and reasoning in strict accordance with the limitations and incapacities of the human misunderstanding."

AMBROSE BIERCE

302

DIFFICULTY

Dicey Directions

Each color represents a different direction. Starting in the middle die of the grid, follow the instructions correctly and you will visit every die in turn only once. What's the last die you visit on your trip?

Pink = Left
Red = Right
Black = Down
Yellow = Up
Purple = Up Right
Brown = Down Right
Blue = Up Left
Green = Down Left

The most famous maze in the world is situated at Hampton Court Palace near London, England. It was planted in 1702 and covers approximately 14,530 square feet.

303 DIFFICULTY

Dotty Dilemma

Complete the grid so that all rows and columns contain the numbers 1, 2, 3, 4, 5, and 6. Areas with a dotted outline contain numbers that add up to the total shown.

"Do not anticipate trouble or worry about what may never happen. Keep in the sunlight."

BENJAMIN FRANKLIN

3		11	7		12
7	**2**		10		
	10			11	3
		12	**5**		
17			6		
		10			

It is thought that plant-eating dinosaurs did not eat grass, because there wasn't any. During the Mesozoic Era, when the dinosaurs lived, conifers—cone-bearing trees and shrubs—dominated the landscape.

304 DIFFICULTY

Think Back

Study these images for a minute, cover them up, and then answer the five questions below.

Questions:

1. How many pink-flighted arrows were there in total? 2. Which color arrows scored most bull's-eyes?
3. How many blue arrows landed in the red sections? 4. How many green arrows landed in the blue sections?
5. What color was the arrow highest up on the first target?

All Will Be Revealed

The numbers by each row and column describe black squares and groups of black squares that are adjoining. Color in all the black squares and a six number combination will be revealed.

										1					
						1			3	1	5			5	
					3	5	5		5	1	5		1	1	5
1	1	1	1	1											
1	1	1	1	1											
		3	3	1											
		1	1	1											
		1	1	1											
		1	3	3											
	1	1	1	1											
	1	1	1	1											
	1	1	1	1											
		1	3	1											

More than 5 billion crayons are produced each year and it is estimated that more than 100 billion crayons have been produced so far.

305 DIFFICULTY

Scales

The arms of these scales are divided into sections—a weight two sections away from the middle will be twice as heavy as a weight one section away. Can you arrange the supplied weights in order to balance the whole scale?

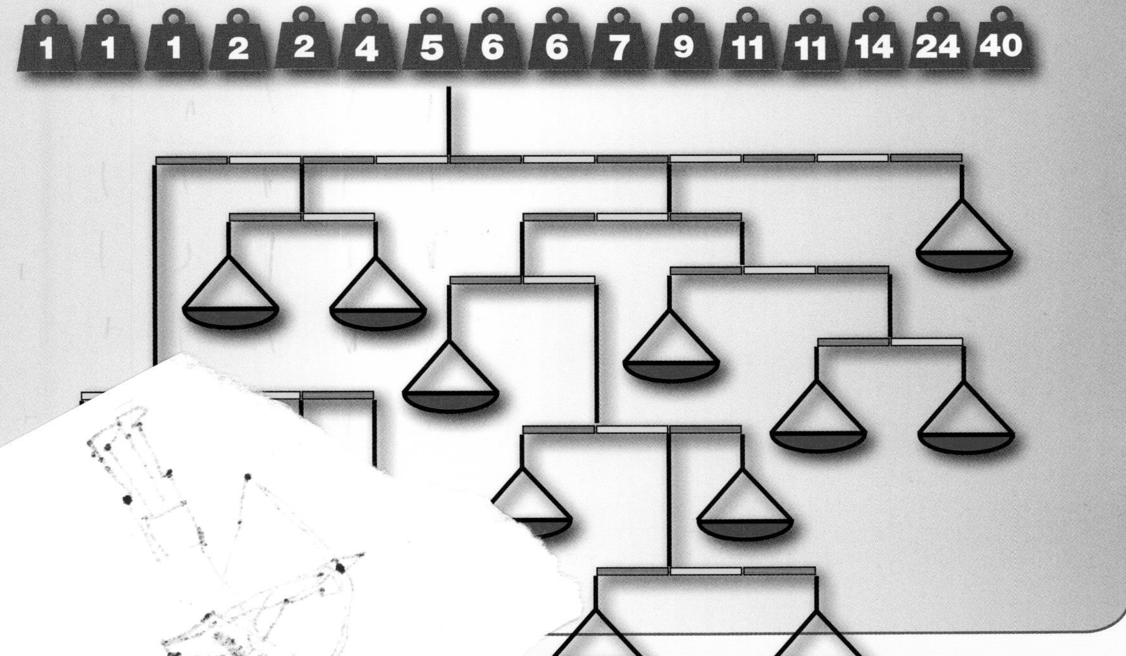

306 DIFFICULTY

307

DIFFICULTY

Bits and Pieces

These ten pieces can be arranged to spell out the name of a famous historical figure—but who?

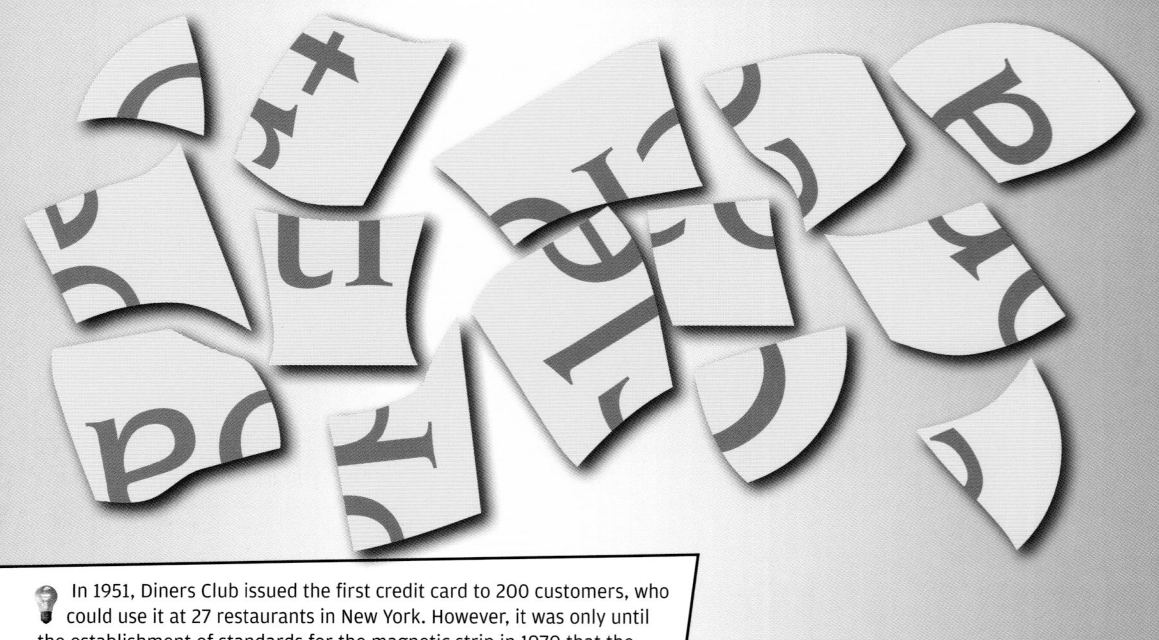

In 1951, Diners Club issued the first credit card to 200 customers, who could use it at 27 restaurants in New York. However, it was only until the establishment of standards for the magnetic strip in 1970 that the credit card became part of the information age.

308

DIFFICULTY

Next in Line

The sequence below follows a logical pattern. What number and color is next in line?

1 2 1 2 1 1 1 ?

Roy Orbison's signature sunglasses look had an innocent explanation. Early in his career, he accidentally left his regular glasses in an airplane. Unable to wear contact lenses, the only others he had were a pair of prescription sunglasses, which he wore to perform and went on to become his trademark.

309 DIFFICULTY

Shady Squares

The numbers in some squares in the grid indicate the exact number of shaded squares that should surround it. Color in the squares until all the numbers are surrounded by the correct number of shaded squares, and a number will be revealed!

	5		5		5		3		4		5		3	1
5		6		7		6		5		6		6		3
	4		6		7		6		6		5		7	
2		3		7		6		7		5		6		4
	1		6		4		5		7		6		7	
0		4		6		3		7		6		7		4
	3		8		3		5		6		5		8	
1		6		4		3		8		5		6		5
	4		6		1		3		6		6		6	
2		5		2		1		4		5		4		2

"Hide not your talents. They for use were made. What's a sundial in the shade?"

Benjamin Franklin

More than 2,700 different languages are spoken in the world, with more than 7,000 dialects. Mandarin is the most spoken language in the world, followed by English. However, as a home language, Spanish is the second most spoken in the world.

310 DIFFICULTY

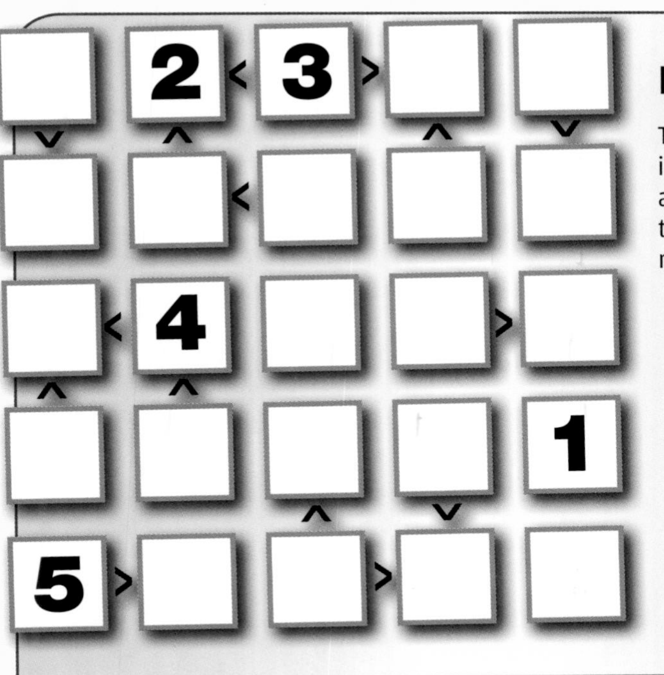

Numbers Up

The arrows indicate whether a number in a box is greater or smaller than an adjacent number. Complete the grid so that all rows and columns contain the numbers 1 to 5.

"Liberty means responsibility. That is why most men dread it."

George Bernard Shaw

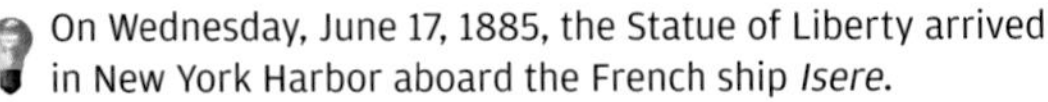

On Wednesday, June 17, 1885, the Statue of Liberty arrived in New York Harbor aboard the French ship *Isere*.

311

DIFFICULTY

Power Boats

The power boat race follows the course below. Can you work out the last buoy the boat must reach to finish?

2N, 3E, 2S, 2S, 3N, 1E, 3S, 1N, 5W, 1S, 2N, 5E, 2N, 5W, 2E, 1E, 4S, 2W, 1E, 3N, 2W, 3E, 2W, 2S, 3E, 1W, 1W, 1N, 1E.

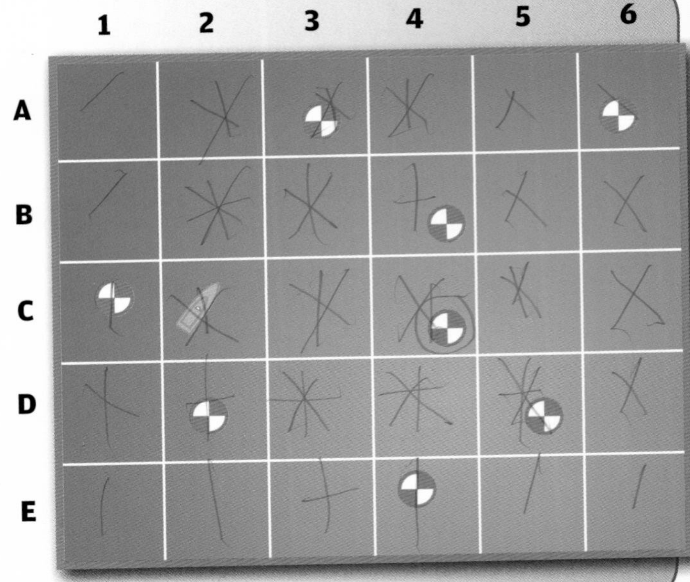

"A ship is safe in harbor, but that's not what ships are for."

WILLIAM SHEDD

312

DIFFICULTY

Strange Shapes

Only two of the shapes below are exactly the same. Can you find the matching pair?

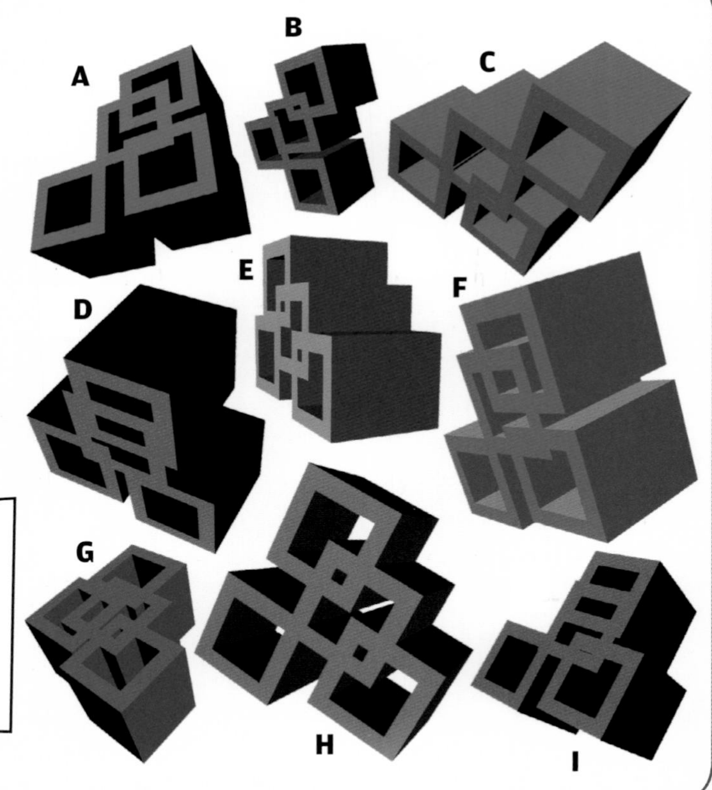

"I am not afraid of death, I just don't want to be there when it happens." WOODY ALLEN

In 1974, Australia's Northern Territory was devastated by Cyclone Tracy. The eye of the storm was only 7½ miles (12 kilometers) in diameter over Darwin—extremely small for a cyclone—yet 70 percent of the city's residential buildings suffered structural damage.

313

DIFFICULTY

Seeing Stars

Can you find three perfect five-pointed stars in this colorful collection?

"Dreams permit each and every one of us to be quietly and safely insane every night of our lives." William Dement

The first recorded use of fireworks in England was at the wedding celebrations of Henry VII in 1476. Queen Elizabeth created the post of Fireworks Master, making sure someone was in charge of displays to mark grand state occasions.

314

DIFFICULTY

Take a Tip

Three men share a taxi ride and the bill comes to $25. They each hand the taxi driver $10 and he puts it in his cash box. The taxi driver owes them $5 change, but gives them each $1 and slips the other $2 into his pocket as a tip. The men have paid $9 each, making $27. The driver has $2 in his pocket, that makes $29. Where is the other dollar?

"Never throughout history has a man who lived a life of ease left a name worth remembering."

Theodore Roosevelt

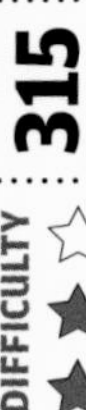

Plane Poser

Which boxes have exactly the right parts to complete the model airplane?

A

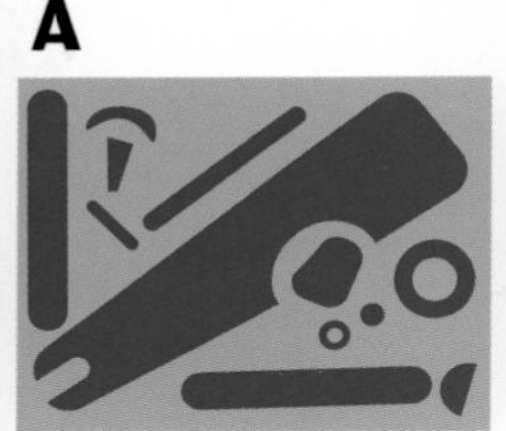

B

C

Henri Fabre's floatplane was the first aircraft to take off from water in Martigues, France, in March 1910.

"A man may die, nations may rise and fall, but an idea lives on." JOHN F. KENNEDY

316

Box Values

The value of each shape is the number of sides each shape has, multiplied by the number within it. So a square containing the number 4 has a value of 16. Find a block of four squares (two squares wide by two squares high) with a total value of exactly 60.

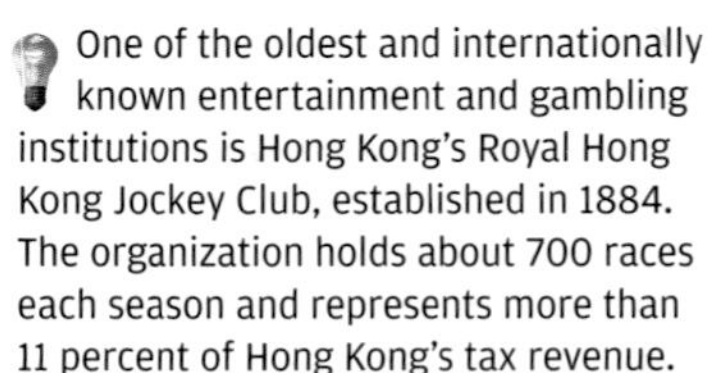

One of the oldest and internationally known entertainment and gambling institutions is Hong Kong's Royal Hong Kong Jockey Club, established in 1884. The organization holds about 700 races each season and represents more than 11 percent of Hong Kong's tax revenue.

317 DIFFICULTY ★

💡 The oldest piece of music ever discovered was for an ancient Greek play *Orestes*, written by Euripides in 408 B.C.

Spell it Out

Arrange these ten pieces to spell out the name of a famous composer.

318 DIFFICULTY ★★★

Where's the Pair?

Only two of these pictures are exactly the same. Can you find the matching pair?

"Bad times have a scientific value. These are occasions a good learner would not miss."

Ralph Waldo Emerson

💡 In 1905, Hans Wildorf, a German living in London, England, established a firm that dealt in watches with his English brother-in-law. Originally called Wildorf & Davies, it is now much better known by the brand name Rolex, which he chose in 1908.

319

DIFFICULTY ★

Get out of This!

You're playing stripes in a game of pool, and you've cleaned up all your balls. There's a solid ball between the cue and eight balls. Can you see the shot?

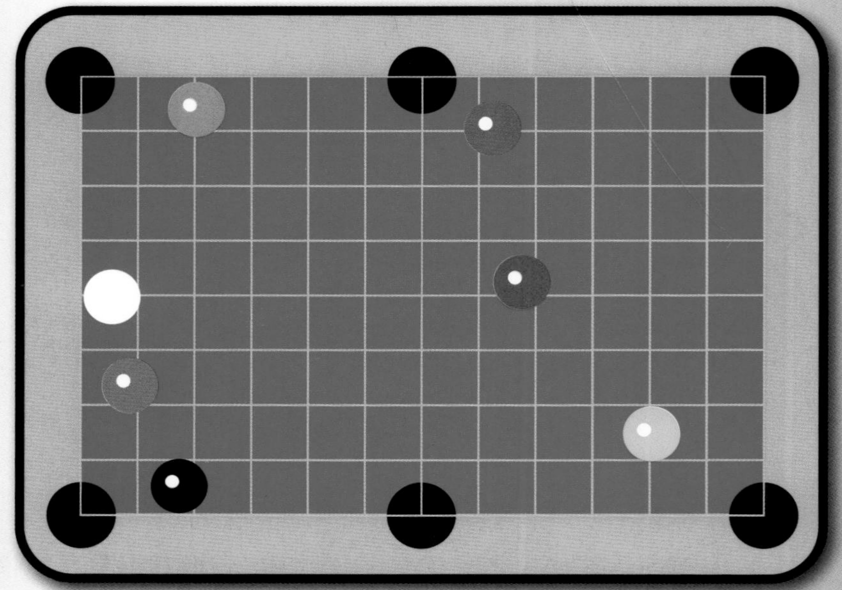

During a billiards title match held on September 1, 1865, in Detroit, Michigan, a fly landed on the ball that Louis Fox was aiming at. The distraction snapped Fox's concentration and he missed the shot; his opponent then ran the table and won the match. Two days later, Fox's body was discovered floating in a river where he'd apparently drowned himself.

320

DIFFICULTY ★

Fold and Cut

Which of the patterns below is created by this fold and cut?

"All I need is my brains, my eyes, and my personality, for better or for worse."

William Albert Allard

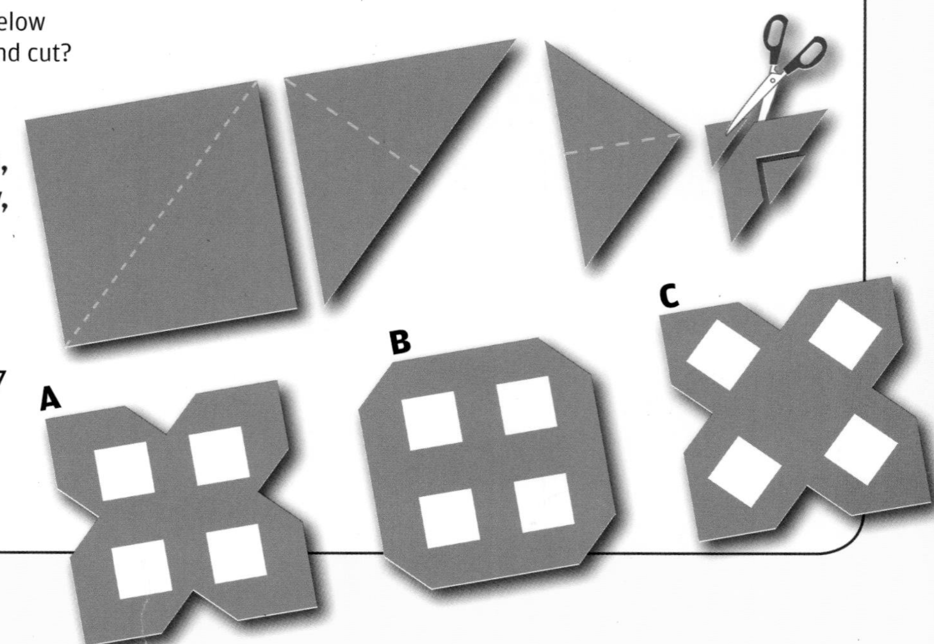

On average, women blink nearly twice as much as men.

321

DIFFICULTY

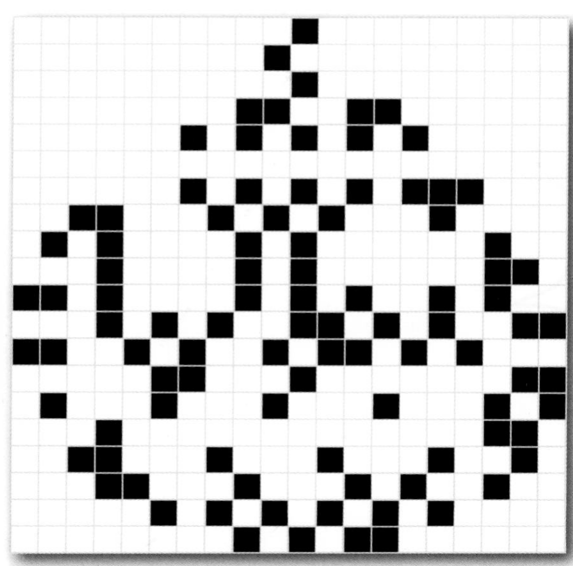

Missing Squares

This picture, when finished, is symmetrical along a vertical line up the middle. Can you color in the missing squares and see the picture?

“I believe humans get a lot done, not because we’re smart, but because we have thumbs so we can make coffee.” Flash Rosenberg

Coffee giant Starbucks takes its name from the character of the first mate in Herman Melville’s *Moby Dick*.

322

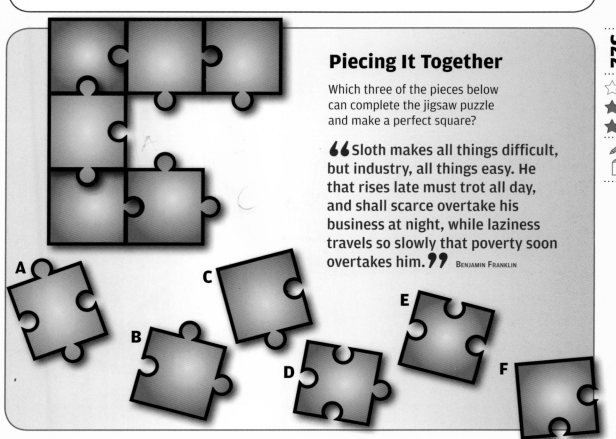

DIFFICULTY

Piecing It Together

Which three of the pieces below can complete the jigsaw puzzle and make a perfect square?

“Sloth makes all things difficult, but industry, all things easy. He that rises late must trot all day, and shall scarce overtake his business at night, while laziness travels so slowly that poverty soon overtakes him.” Benjamin Franklin

A B C D E F

323 DIFFICULTY ★

Alien Identification

Ziplock from the planet Velkro isn't green and doesn't have feelers on his head. He does have a tail though, and an odd number of eyes. Can you pick him out?

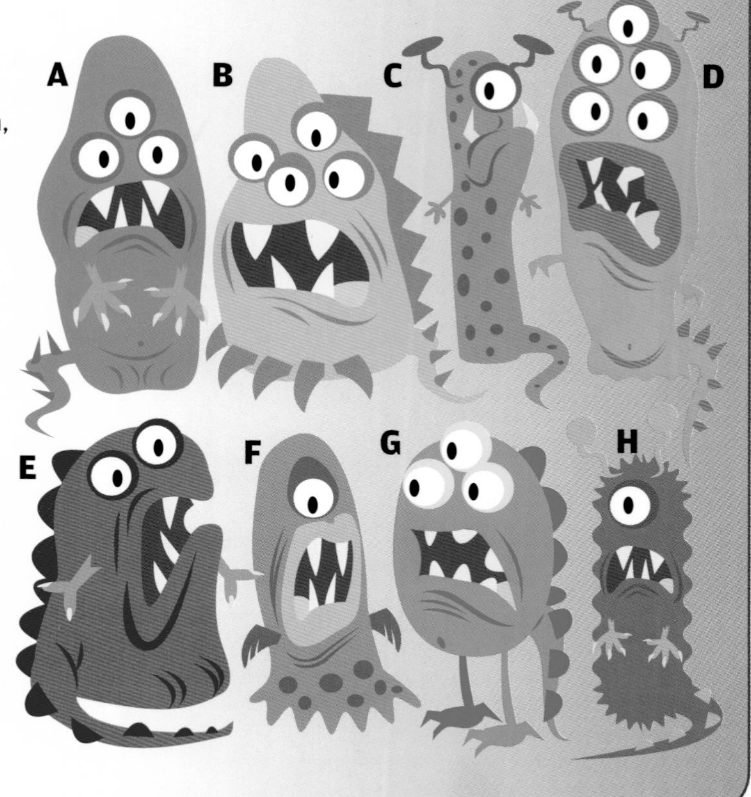

“For me every ruler is alien that defies public opinion.”

Mohandas Gandhi

The Tuatara, a rare lizardlike reptile native to New Zealand, has three eyes. The third, called a parietal eye, is well developed but is only visible in hatchlings. After time it is obscured by scales and pigmentation.

324 DIFFICULTY ★

Carrot Casino

Two rabbits were trying to sort out their complicated carrot debts and IOUs following a game of rabbit poker.

Thumper gave Cottontail as many carrots as Cottontail had. Then Cottontail gave Thumper back as much as Thumper had left. Thumper then gave Cottontail as much as Cottontail had left. At the end, Thumper had no carrots and Cottontail had 80. How many did they each start with?

The longest continuous war was the “Thirty Years War,” fought between various European countries from 1618 to 1648.

325 DIFFICULTY

View from Above

Of the plan views below, only one of them is a true overhead representation of the scene shown here. Which one is it?

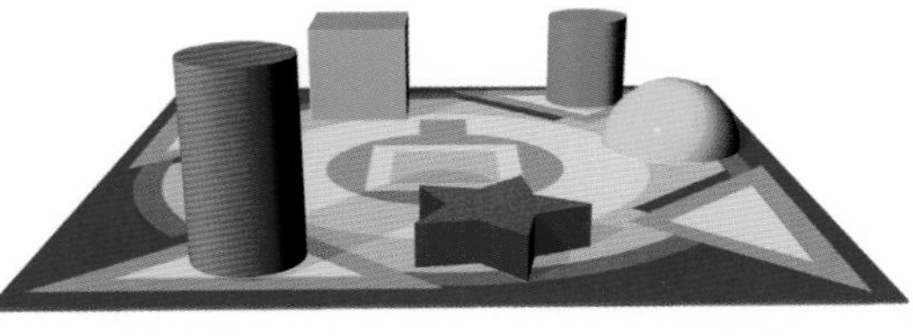

A

B

C

D

E

F

“Not everybody is perfect, and I don’t think we should be looking for perfect people.”

SIMON COWELL

It is a common mistake to say that the Great Wall of China is visible from outer space. It is, in fact, too thin to be noticed from such a great distance. The only two man-made structures visible from space are the Pyramids of Giza and the Hoover Dam.

326 DIFFICULTY

Mirror Image

Only one of these pictures is an exact mirror image of the first one. Can you find it?

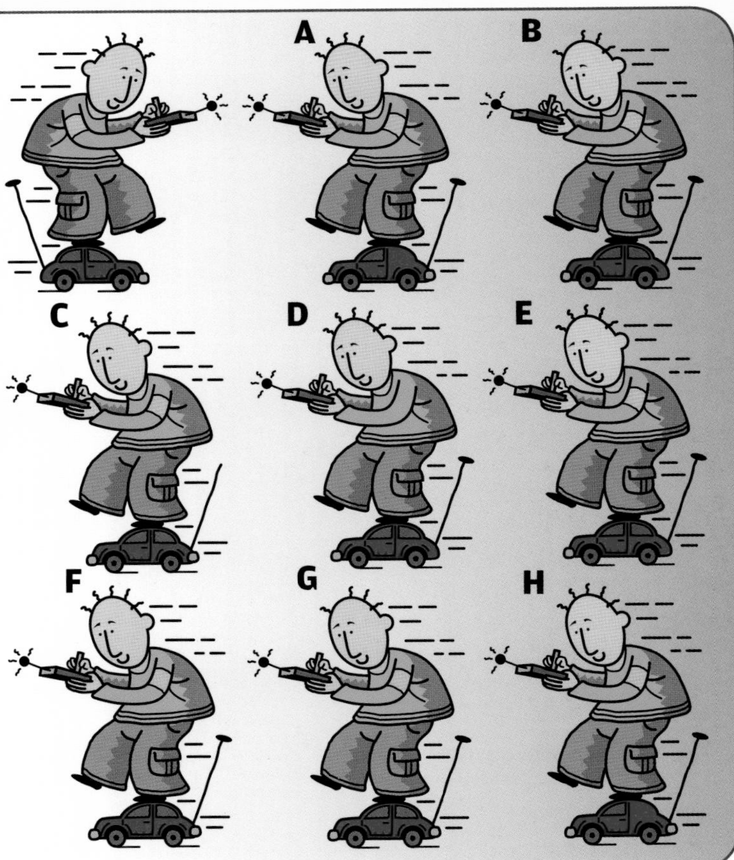

“As men get older, the toys get more expensive.”

MARVIN DAVIS

The first TV remote control was designed by the Zenith Radio Corporation in 1950. It worked using a cable that ran from the device to the TV set and was named “Lazy Bones.”

327

DIFFICULTY

Fill the Hole

The columns and rows that make up the finished grid have certain properties in common. Identify these matching qualities and you should be able to work out which of the squares below will correctly complete the grid.

Tin cans as a means of storing food were invented in 1810. Not until 1846 was the process widely adopted, and it would be another 12 years before the can opener was invented.

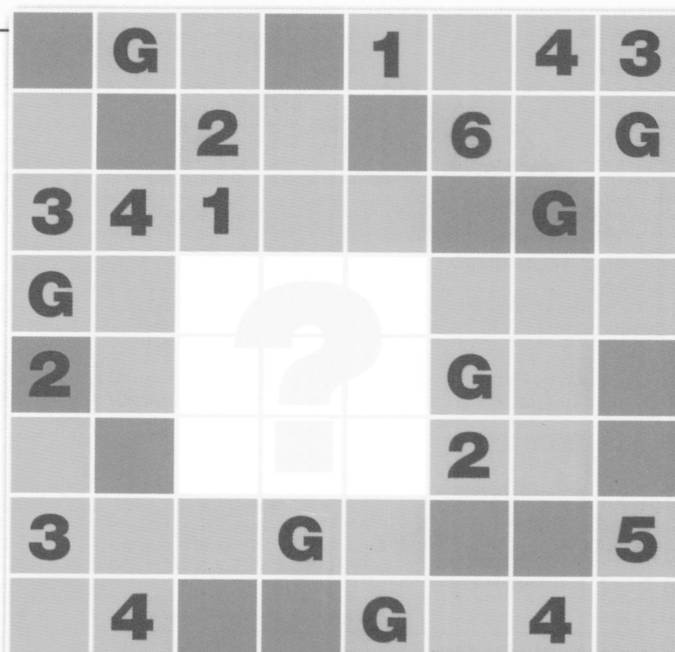

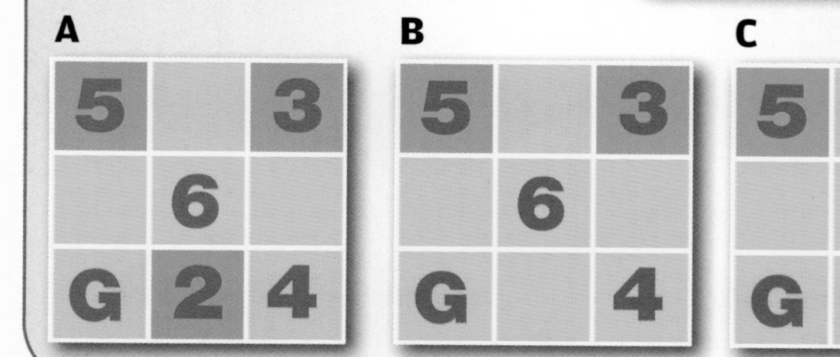

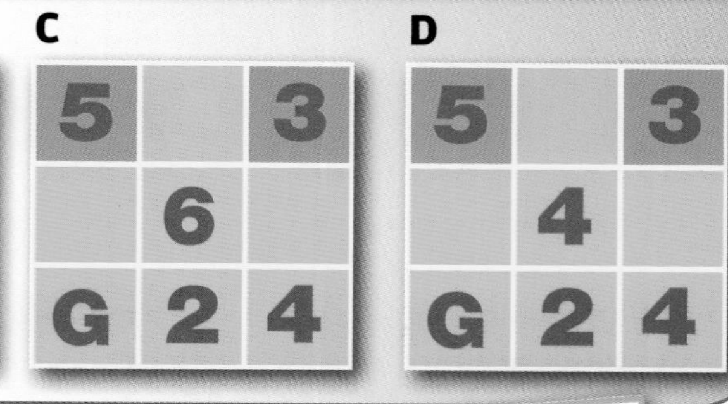

328

DIFFICULTY

Number Combination

The numbers by each row and column describe black squares and groups of black squares that are adjoining. Color in all the black squares and a six-number combination will be revealed.

The red-and-white national flags of Monaco and Indonesia are identical, except for the ratio.

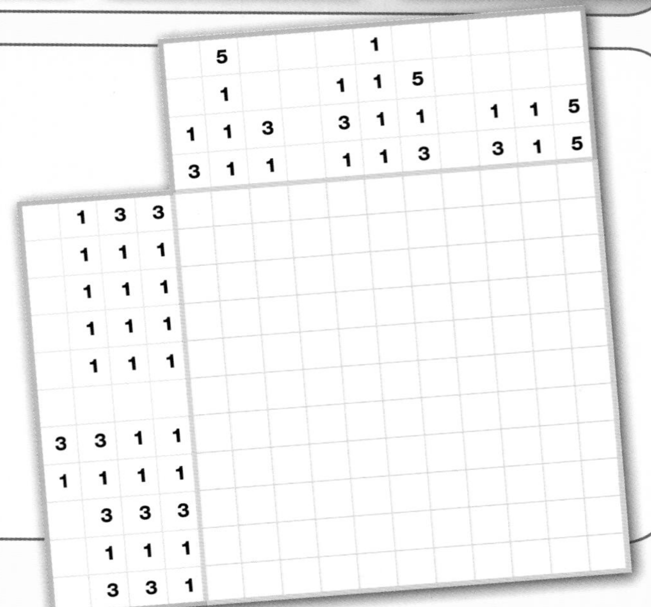

329

DIFFICULTY

"A soldier will fight long and hard for a bit of colored ribbon."
NAPOLEON BONAPARTE

Flagged Up!

In the sequence below, which of the alternatives—A, B, C, or D—should replace the question mark?

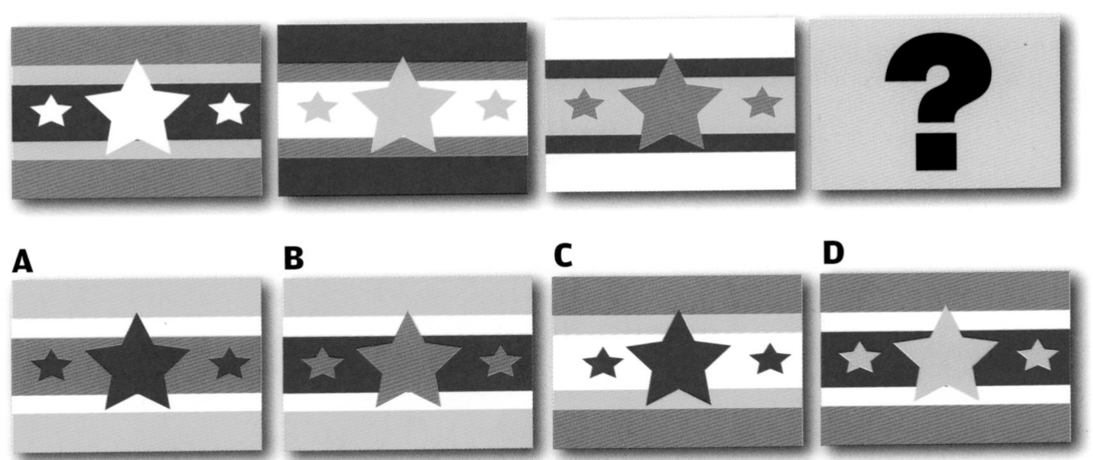

330

DIFFICULTY

All Change

The colors of each square in pattern B are directly related to the colors in pattern A. The square colors in pattern C relate to pattern B the same way. Can you apply the same rules and fill in pattern D?

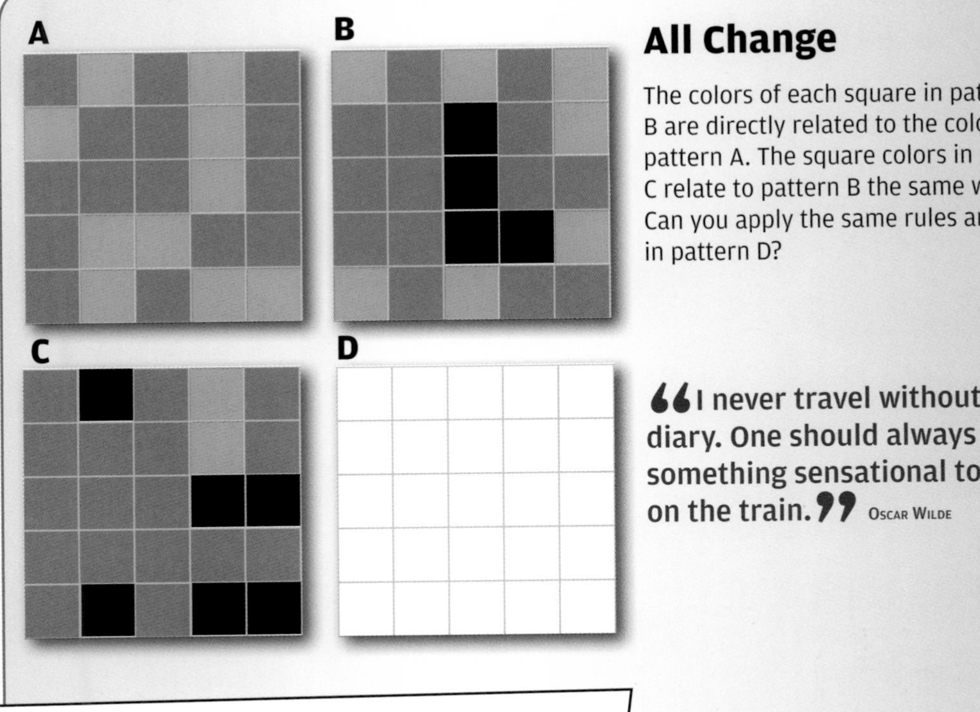

"I never travel without my diary. One should always have something sensational to read on the train." OSCAR WILDE

Ghana's Lake Volta is the largest reservoir in the world.

Boats and Buoys

Every buoy has one boat found horizontally or vertically adjacent to it. No boat can be in an adjacent square to another boat (even diagonally). The numbers by each row and column tell you how many boats are there. Can you locate all the boats?

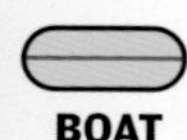

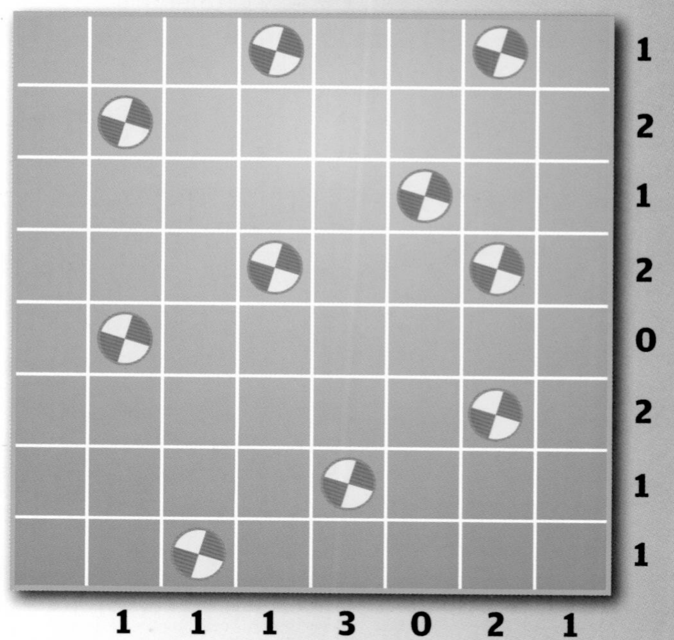

Istanbul in Turkey is the only city in the world that resides on two continents. Straddling Europe and Asia, the city is divided by the Bosphorus Strait.

Bits and Pieces

These ten pieces can be arranged to spell out a three-figure number. Can you piece it together?

333

DIFFICULTY

It's Your Turn

Playing the game of boxes, each player takes it in turns to join two adjacent dots with a line. If a player's line completes a box, the player wins the box and has another chance. It's your turn in the game below. To avoid giving your opponent a lot of boxes, what's your best move?

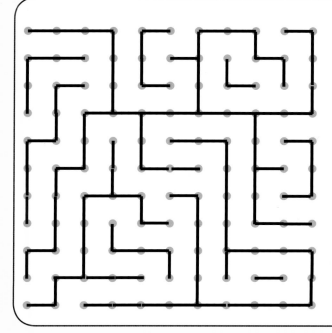

In December 1953, Marilyn Monroe appeared on the cover of *Playboy* as "Sweetheart of the Month." It was the very first issue of the magazine.

334

DIFFICULTY

Ball Recall

Study this image for a minute, cover it up with a sheet of paper, and then answer the five questions below.

Despite being extremely rare in reality, there have been several recent films that use amnesia or memory loss as a motif, including *Eternal Sunshine of the Spotless Mind, Memento, Spirited Away, The Bourne Trilogy,* and *Finding Nemo.*

Questions:
1. What is the total of the even numbered balls?
2. What is the total of the red, yellow, and blue balls?
3 Which two balls can you see most of?
4 Which ball can you see least of?
5 Subtract the far left ball from the green ball.

335 DIFFICULTY

Number Sweep

Color in the squares until all the numbers are surrounded by the correct number of shaded squares. When the puzzles is correctly solved the shaded squares will reveal a number!

1	3		5		4		2		4		5		4	
3		6		6		4		4		5		7		4
	7		5		4		5		6		5		8	
5		6		4		4		3		3		6		5
	8		4		4		4		3		5		7	
5		6		5		7		3		5		7		3
	8		3		5		6		5		7		3	
4		6		5		7		6		8		6		2
	5		6		6		6		8		7		5	
1		4		5		3		3		5		5		3

Octopuses collect crustacean shells and other objects from the ocean in order to build fortresses, or "gardens," around their lairs.

336 DIFFICULTY

Price Puzzle

Shopping for a present for your grandmother, you find yourself in a shop devoted to tea, which she loves. You buy a teapot and six cups, together with some teabags and spoons. You spent exactly 50 dollars. How many boxes of teabags and spoons have you bought?

Iced tea is said to have made its first appearance at the 1904 St. Louis World Fair.

"All well-regulated families set apart an hour every morning for tea and bread and butter." JOHN ADDISON

337

DIFFICULTY

Macaw Mathematics

These symbols represent the numbers 1 to 4. If the purple parrot represents the number 2, what do the other color parrots represent? Finish the equation.

“Teach a parrot the terms ‘supply and demand’ and you’ve got an economist.”

THOMAS CARLYLE

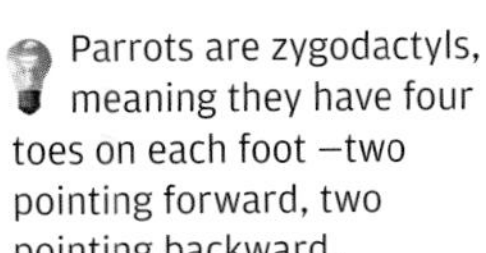

Parrots are zygodactyls, meaning they have four toes on each foot—two pointing forward, two pointing backward.

338

DIFFICULTY

Magic Squares

Complete the square using nine consecutive numbers, so that all rows, columns, and large diagonals add up to the same total.

		14
	11	
8		

“There are three kinds of lies: lies, damned lies, and statistics.”

BENJAMIN DISRAELI

The top-selling fiction writer of all time is Agatha Christie, the creator of the detectives Hercule Poirot and Miss Marple. Her 78 crime novels have sold an estimated two billion copies.

339 DIFFICULTY ★★★

Loopy Numbers

Connect adjacent dots with either horizontal or vertical lines to create a continuous unbroken loop that never crosses over itself. Some but not all of the boxes are numbered. The numbers in these boxes tell you how many sides of that box are used by your unbroken line.

3		2		3
	2		3	
2		2		2
	1		3	2
3	2		2	

The International Criminal Police Organization, known as Interpol, has its headquarters in the French city of Lyons.

340 DIFFICULTY ☆★★

A Game of Two Halves

Which two shapes below will pair up to create the top shape?

“Lies are essential to humanity. They are perhaps as important as the pursuit of pleasure and moreover are dictated by that pursuit.” MARCEL PROUST

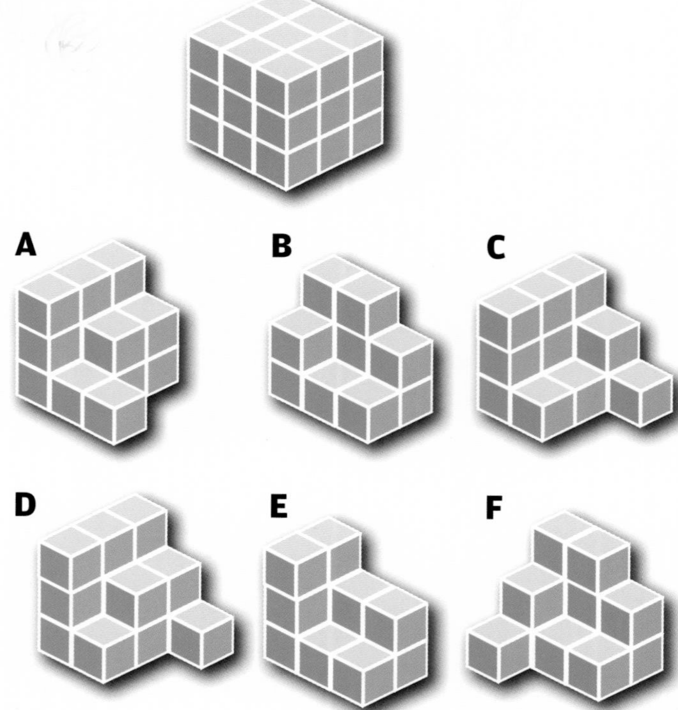

The first Superbowl half-time show in 1967 featured two marching bands from the universities of Michigan and Arizona—a far cry from today's showbiz spectacle.

341

DIFFICULTY

In the Hole

Which of the squares below correctly completes the grid?

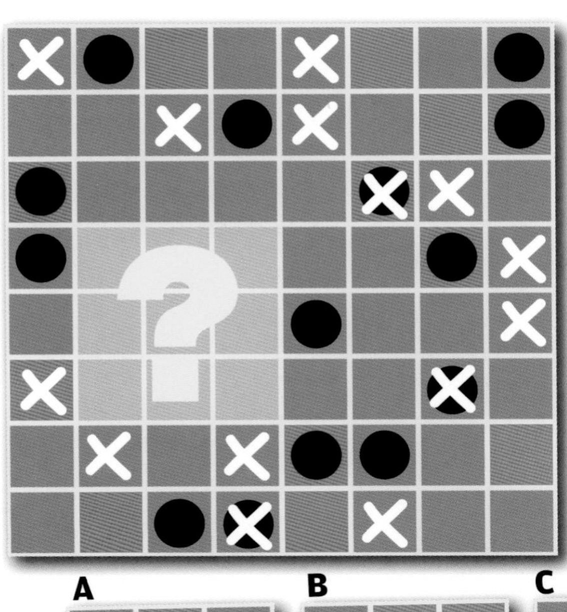

“Only in men’s imagination does every truth find an effective and undeniable existence. Imagination, not invention, is the supreme master of art as of life.” JOSEPH CONRAD

342

DIFFICULTY

Troublesome Tiles

Below is a plan of a living room, showing fitted units that can’t be moved. Can you tile the whole floor using only the tile shown? The tiles are not reversible!

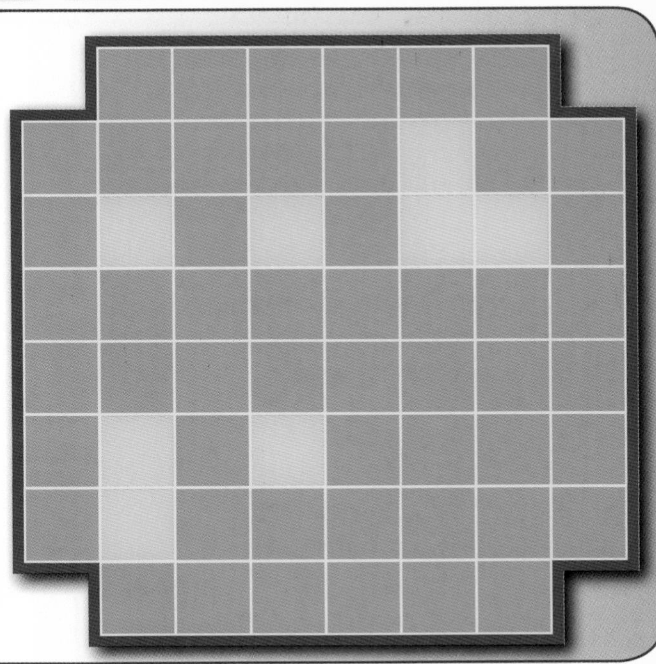

The term for the currency in Botswana is *Pula*, meaning literally “rainwater.” Rain and water are both scarce in the landlocked southern African nation.

343

DIFFICULTY ★

Beautiful Balloon

This balloon is made up of pink, green, and cream panels, with no adjacent panels in the same color. What color should the marked panel be?

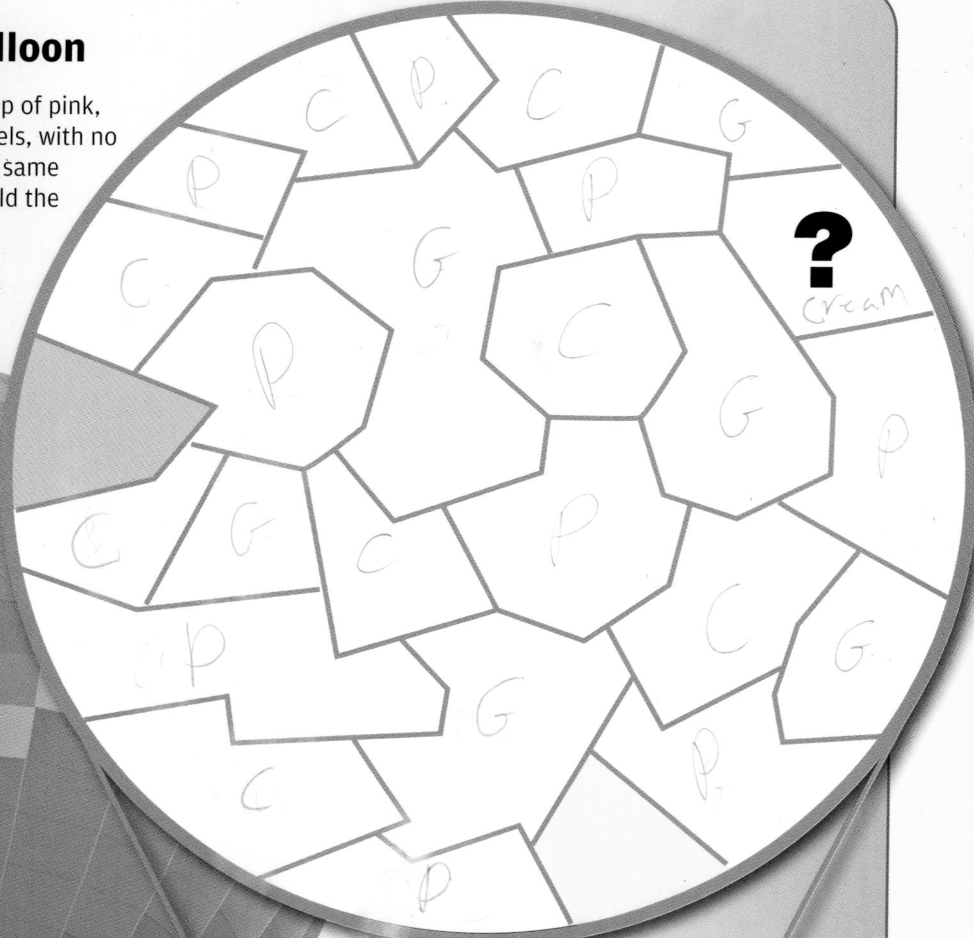

?

"My definition [of a philosopher] is of a man up in a balloon, with his family and friends holding the ropes which confine him to earth and trying to haul him down." Louisa May Alcott

Hydrogen balloons were used by both sides during the U.S. Civil War for aerial reconnaissance missions.

Box of Parts

344 DIFFICULTY

Which box has exactly the right pieces to make the image of the weight lifter?

“Only actions give life strength; only moderation gives it charm.”

JEAN PAUL RICHTER

Arrows

345 DIFFICULTY

Complete the grid by drawing an arrow in each box that points in any one of the eight compass directions (N, E, S, W, NE, NW, SE, and SW). The numbers in the outside boxes in the finished puzzle will reflect the number of arrows pointing in their direction.

1	0	0	2	1	1
0					0
0					0
2					1
2					1
1	2	0	0	1	1

“Billabong” is an Australian-English word for an oxbow lake, a curved stagnant pool of water attached to a waterway.

Find Your Way

Each color represents a different direction. Starting in the middle die of the grid, follow the instructions correctly and you will visit every die in turn. What's the last die you visit on your trip?

Orange = Left
Black = Right
Green = Down
Purple = Up
Pink = Up Right
Red = Down Right
Yellow = Up Left
Blue = Down Left

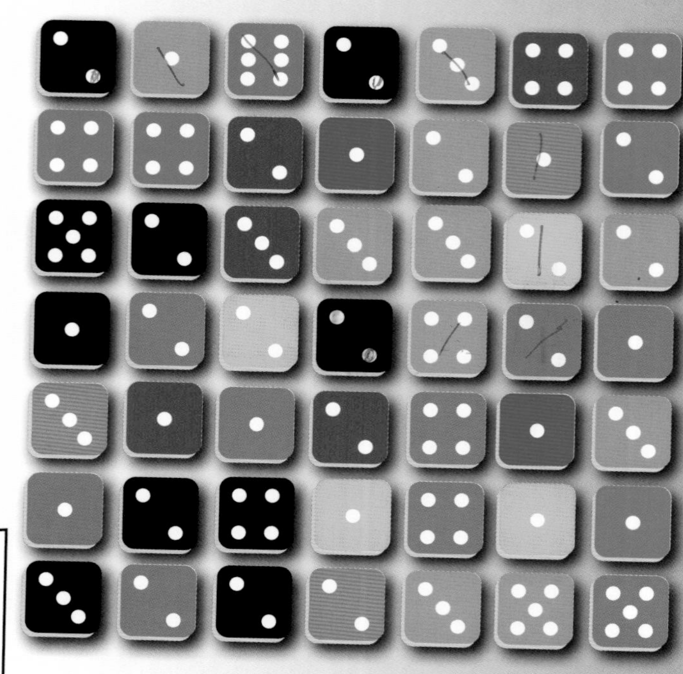

In 1985, Blondie's Debbie Harry was immortalized in a set of rock 'n' roll stamps issued in Gambia, Liberia, Mali, and Tanzania. The "Women of Rock" stamps also featured Connie Francis, Janis Joplin, Cyndi Lauper, and Carly Simon.

A Question of Art

Can you crack the logical secret behind the numbers on the back of these paintings, and find the number that should replace the question mark on the work by Matisse?

"Art is not a handicraft, it is the transmission of feeling the artist has experienced." Leo Nikolayevich Tolstoy

In 1961, Henri Matisse's *Le Bateau* was hung upside down for 47 days in New York's Museum of Modern Art (MOMA) until a visitor pointed out the error.

348

DIFFICULTY

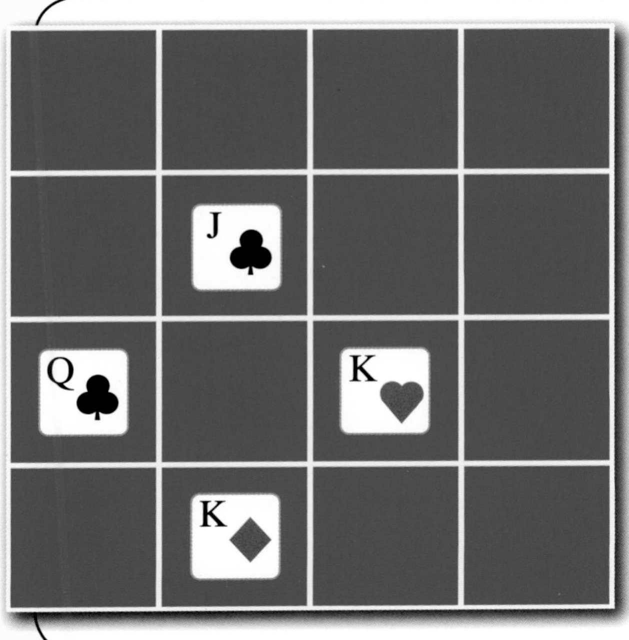

Shuffle Box

Fill up the shuffle box so that each row, column, and long diagonal contains a jack, queen, king, and ace of each suit.

The phrase "mad as a hatter" pre-dates Lewis Carroll's memorable creation. His Mad Hatter reflected a real-life affliction as hat-makers had long been affected by mercury vapors—a chemical used during the process of curing felt. Prolonged exposure left many with nervous disorders and the symptoms of "madness".

349

According to a 2007 survey, the Honda Civic GX is the most environmentally friendly car on the market—just beating the Toyota Prius.

Matching Pair

Only one of the tiles below is unique; the other 14 all have an exact matching pair. Can you find it?

350

DIFFICULTY ☆★★

Think of a Number

At the Sea View guest house in Bournemouth, England, over the course of one week 459 breakfasts were served: 153 guests had a poached egg, 51 had a scrambled egg, 136 had cereal, and 119 had fruit. What fraction of guests had an egg, and what fraction didn't?

In 1906, the Battle Creek Toasted Corn Flakes Company, founded by W. K. Kellogg, began production of Kellogg's Corn Flakes—and a cereal dynasty was born.

351

DIFFICULTY ☆☆★

Shape Shifting

Fill in the empty squares so that each row, column, and long diagonal contains five different colored stars.

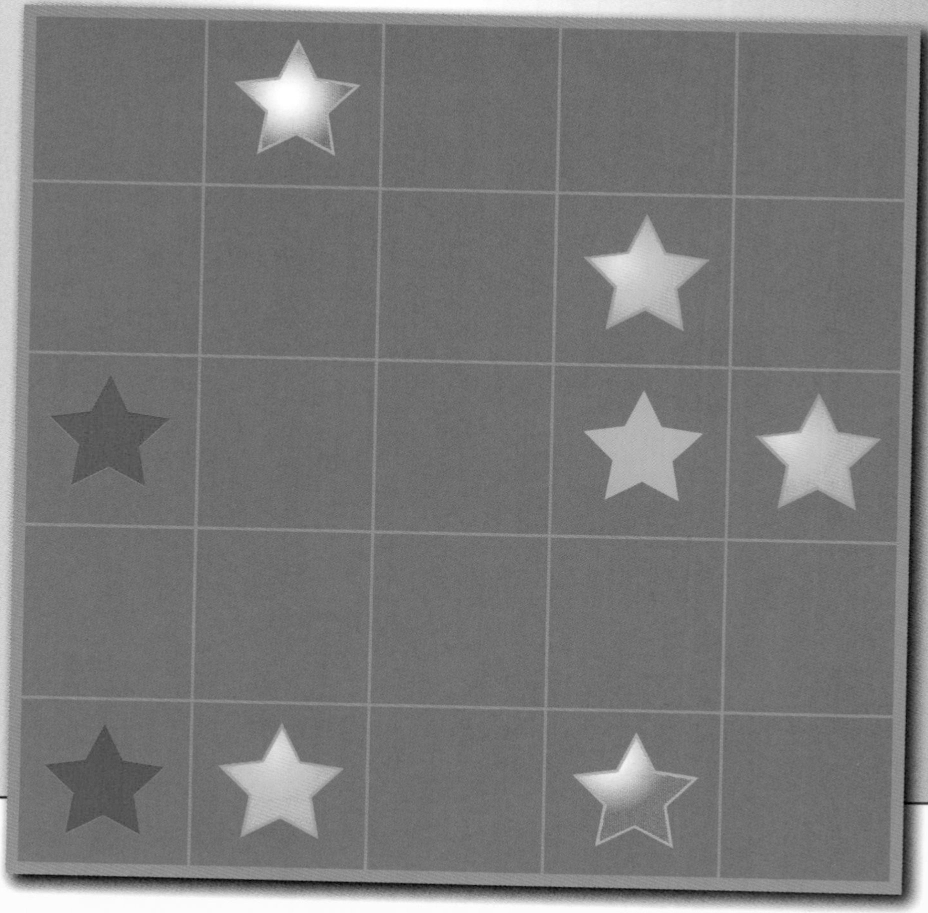

352

DIFFICULTY

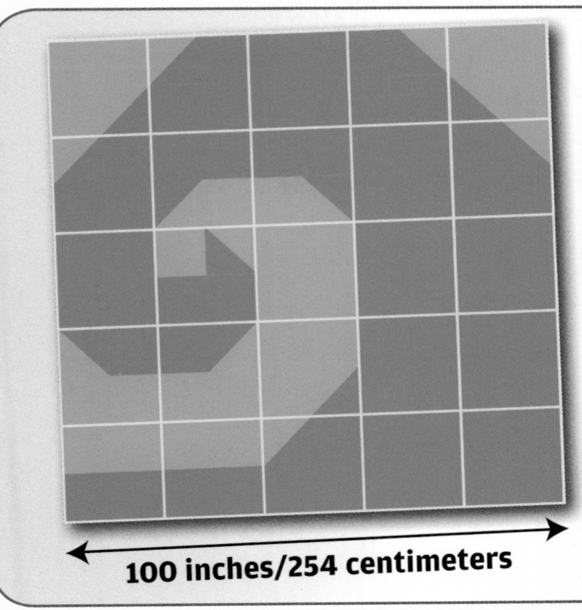

Size of the Wave

What is the approximate area that this wave is occupying?

“The wind and the waves are always on the side of the ablest navigator.” Edward Gibbon

When a surfer is seen to be in the white foam of a wave after it has broken, he is said to be “in the soup.”

100 inches/254 centimeters

353

DIFFICULTY

Swan Scene

The four squares below can all be found in the picture grid; can you track them down? Beware: They may not be the right way up!

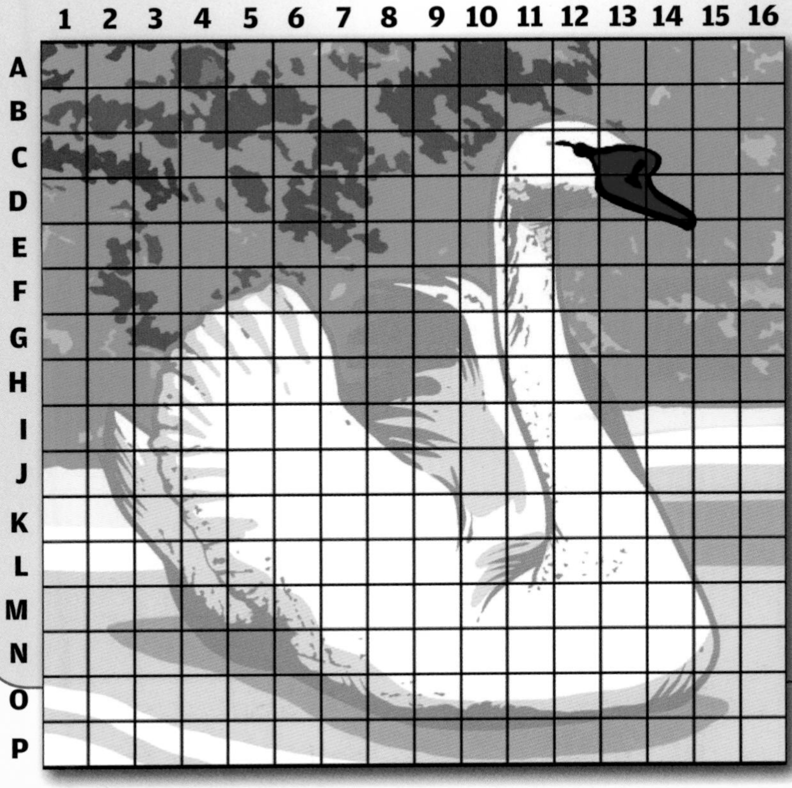

1 2 3 4 5 6 7 8 9 10 11 12 13 14 15 16
A B C D E F G H I J K L M N O P

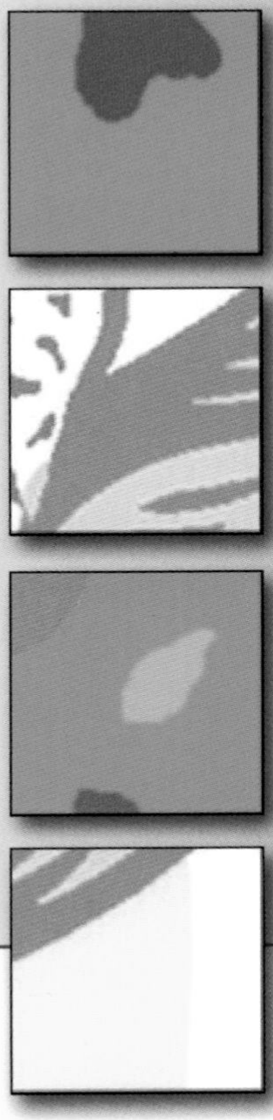

354

DIFFICULTY ★★★

Building Blocks

Assuming all blocks that are not visible from this angle are present, how many blocks have been removed from this 6 x 6 x 6 cube?

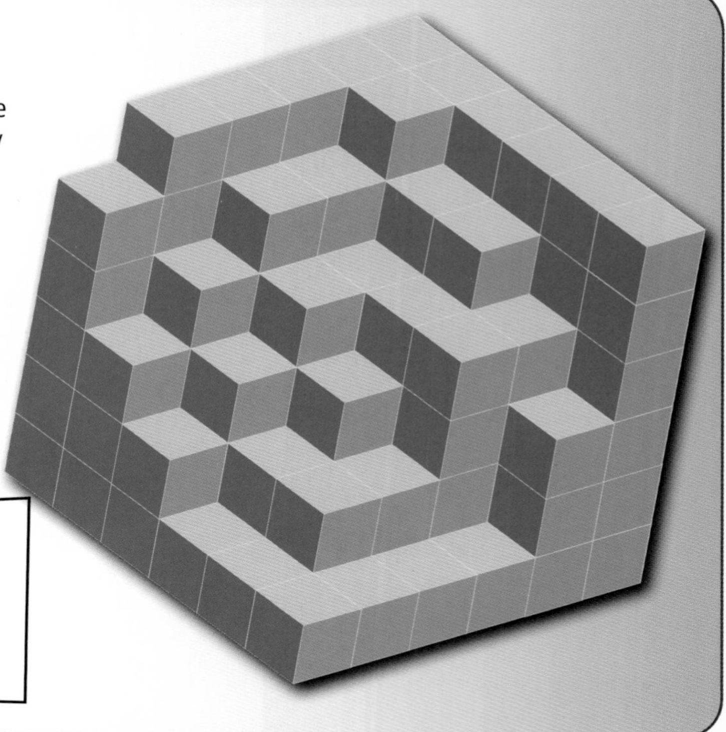

> **“We used to build civilizations. Now we build shopping malls.”**
>
> Bill Bryson

Russian Alexey Pajitnov originally designed and programmed the video game Tetris in June 1985, while he was working for the Dorodnicyn Computing Center of the Academy of Science in Moscow, USSR.

355

DIFFICULTY ☆★★

Codoko Six

Complete the first grid so that every row and column contain all the letters M, A, G, L, K, and I. Do the same with grid 2 and the numbers 1, 2, 3, 4, 5, and 6. To decode the finished grid, add the numbers in the shaded squares to the letters in the matching squares in the second (A + 3 = D, Y + 4 = C) to get six new letters, which can be arranged to spell the name of a world city.

	M			A	
M				I	
A		K			
			A		G
G		L		M	
	K		M		I

	3		6		
5				3	4
3		6			
	1			5	2
		5	1		3
	2			4	

356

DIFFICULTY ★★★

Colored Cap Capers

Five caps—three blue and two red—are in a box. Three clever kids, Janet, Jules, and Jim, know exactly how many caps of each color are in there. Someone turns the light off in the room so it is completely dark. Then they each select a cap, put it on, and close the box. When the light is turned back on, each can see the others two caps, but not their own. Janet says she can't work out what color her cap is, and Jules says she can't either, at which point, Jim says "I know!" What color is Jim's hat? And by the way—Jim is blindfolded.

"If anybody says he can think about quantum physics without getting giddy, that only shows he has not understood the first thing about them." NIELS BOHR

357

DIFFICULTY ☆☆★

Color Amaze

Find a path from one white square to the other. You may only pass from a green square to a red one, a red to a yellow, a yellow to a blue, or a blue to a green, and you may not travel diagonally.

"The charm of history and its enigmatic lesson consist in the fact that, from age to age, nothing changes and yet everything is completely different." ALDOUS HUXLEY

 Denmark is the most taxed nation in the world. Its highest rate of income tax is 68 percent, with the basic rate starting at 42 percent.

358

DIFFICULTY

Shape Stacker

Can you work out the logic behind the numbers in these shapes, and the total of A + B?

> **“Physical bravery is an animal instinct; moral bravery is much higher and truer courage.”**
>
> WENDELL PHILLIPS

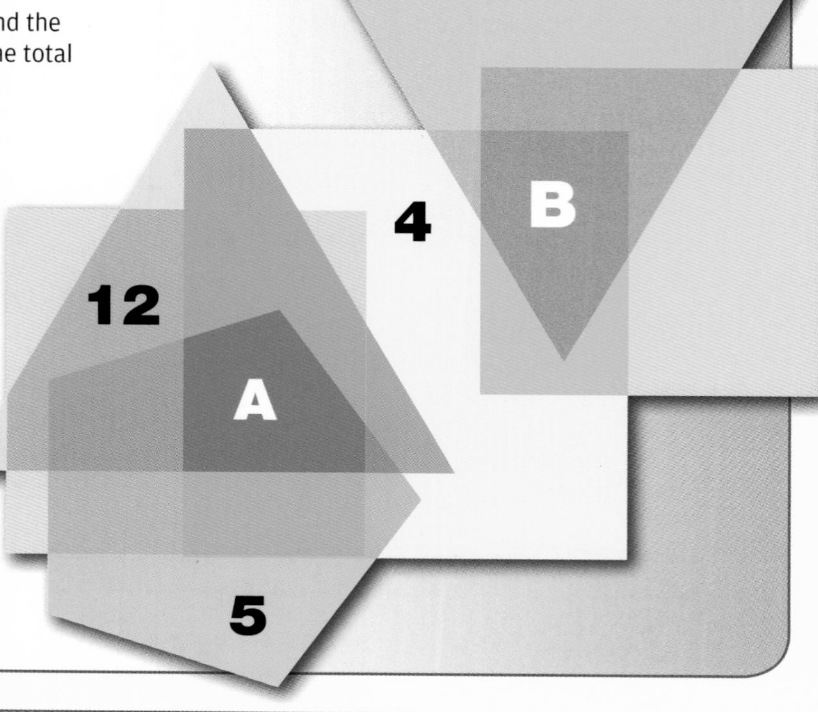

It takes 1,851 gallons of water to refine one barrel (42 gallons) of crude oil.

359

DIFFICULTY

Pool Poser

You’re playing stripes in a game of pool, and you’ve cleaned up all your balls. A solid ball is between the cue ball and eight ball. Can you see the shot?

George Henry Sutton, of Toledo, Ohio, had no hands, yet won a national billiard championship, and he once made a consecutive run of 3,000 balls.

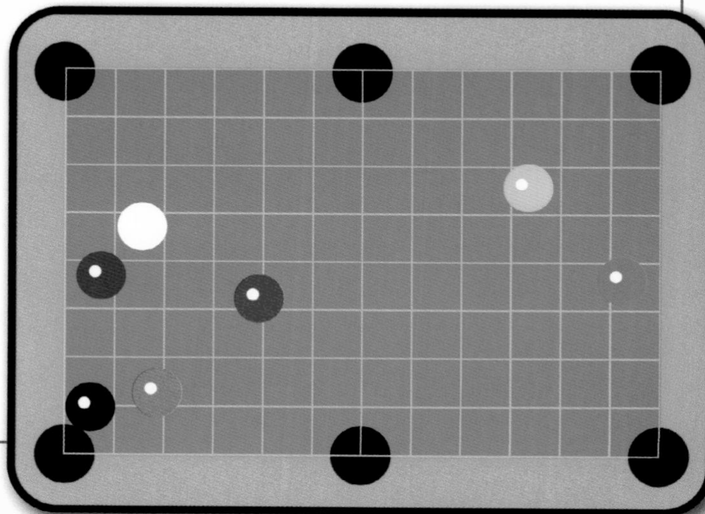

360

DIFFICULTY ☆☆★

Rounders

Which of the wheels—A, B, C, or D—is missing from the set above?

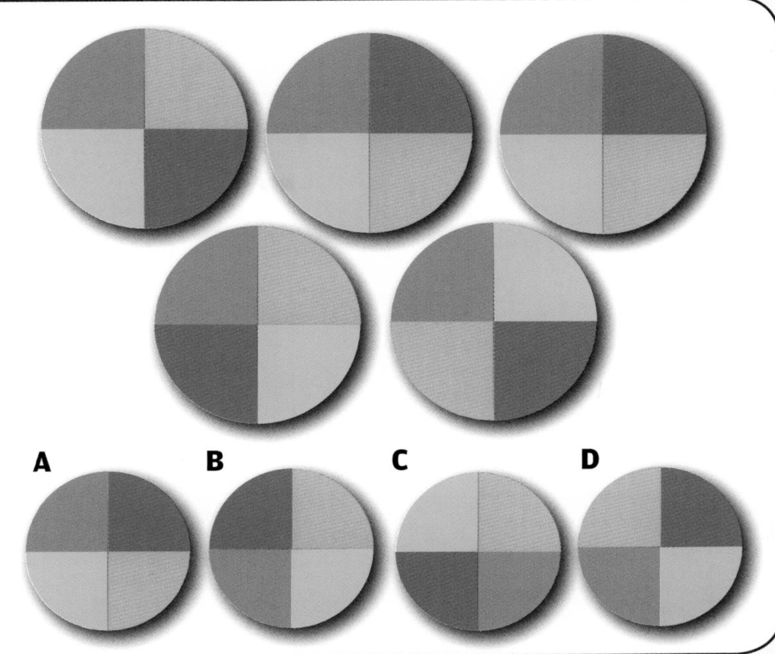

“The key to change . . . is to let go of fear.”

ROSANNE CASH

The six-day war between El Salvador and Honduras in July 1969 is popularly known as “La guerra del fútbol” or “Soccer War,” although soccer was not at the root of the conflict.

361

DIFFICULTY ★★★

Jeep Jumble

Only two of these pictures are exactly the same. Can you spot the matching pair?

A B C D E F G H

362 DIFFICULTY ★★★

Latin Square

Complete the grid so that every row and column, and every outlined area, contains the letters A, B, C, D, E, and F.

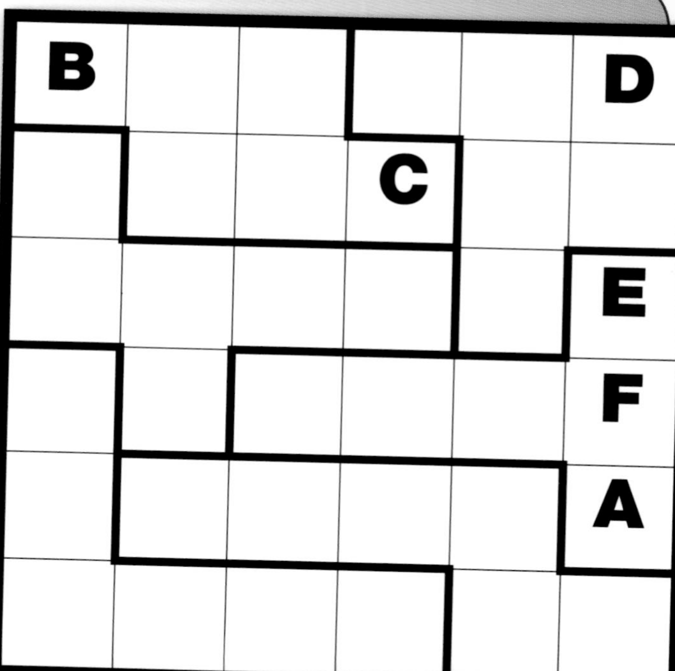

The ancient Mayan ball game was a solemn and ritualized sport where two teams competed to get a ball through a hoop without using their hands. In keeping with the Mayan beliefs, the winning team received great acclaim, while the captain of the losing team was offered as a human sacrifice. In some Mayan areas, this was reversed and the winning captain was killed.

363 DIFFICULTY ★☆☆

The Complete Kitty

Which boxes have exactly the right parts to complete the picture on the left?

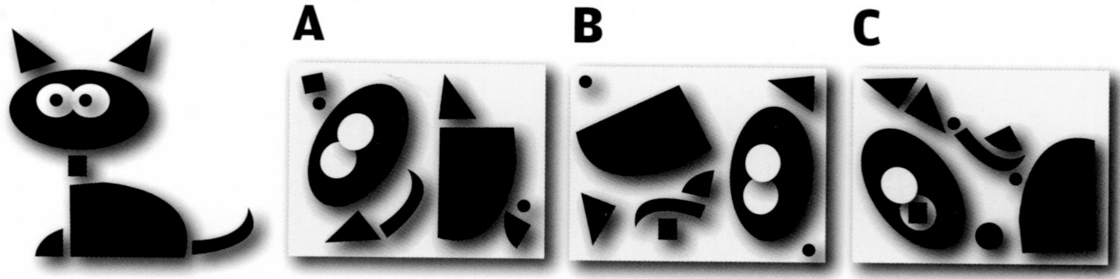

Irish playwright George Bernard Shaw famously won both an Oscar (for *Pygmalion*, 1938) and a Nobel Prize (for Literature, 1925).

364 DIFFICULTY

Dice Mystery

What is the total of the unseen sides of these dice?

> “I shall never believe that God plays dice with the world.”
>
> ALBERT EINSTEIN

365 DIFFICULTY

All Change

The colors of each triangle in pattern B are directly related to the colors in pattern A. Can you apply the same rules and fill in pattern C?

> “Nobody can go back and start a new beginning, but anyone can start today and make a new ending.”
>
> MARIA ROBINSON

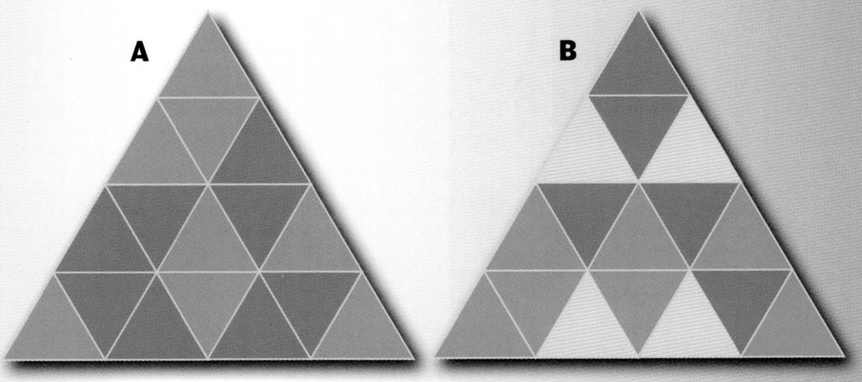

A Boston, Massachusetts, beer company currently holds the record for the world's strongest beer. At almost 25 percent proof, Samuel Adams' Utopias is twice as strong as a bottle of wine and retails at over $100 per bottle. It is a limited edition, with only 8,000 bottles brewed.

SOLUTIONS

1: Flintlock Freddy is pirate E.

2:

3: B. Each row and line in the grid contains four black and four green squares.

4:

4	9	2
3	5	7
8	1	6

5: The rug is made up of 50 squares: 6 blue, 10 green, and 34 yellow. Double these numbers to reveal a percentage breakdown of: blue 12%, green 20%, and yellow 68%.

6:

7:

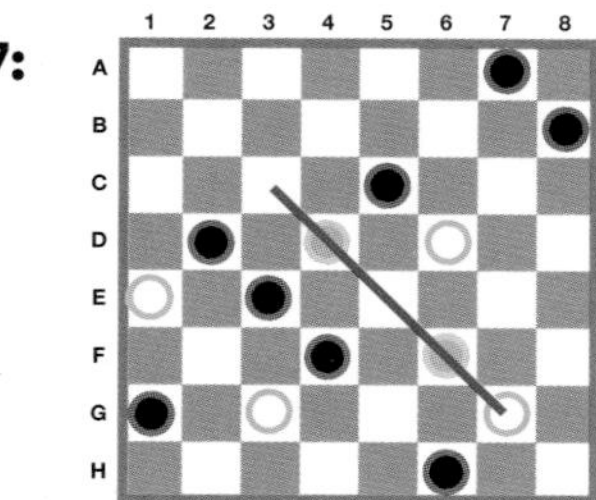

8: F.

9:

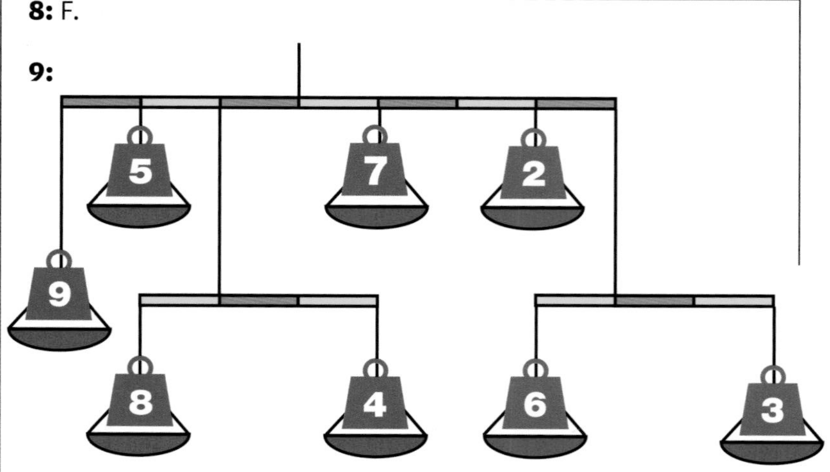

10: Each vertical and horizontal line contains one central square that is red, one that is green, and one that is white. Each line also contains one top center square that is black. Finally, each line has two images with brown squares top left and bottom right and the opposite squares in green, and one image where these positions have been reversed. The missing image should have a green central square, a black top center square, and the top left and bottom right squares in green.

11:

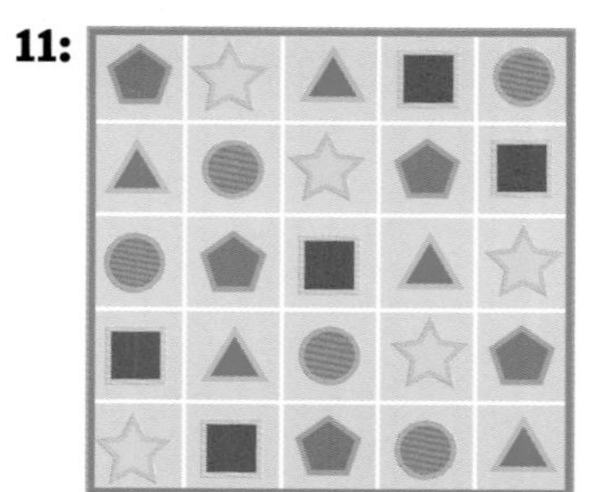

12:

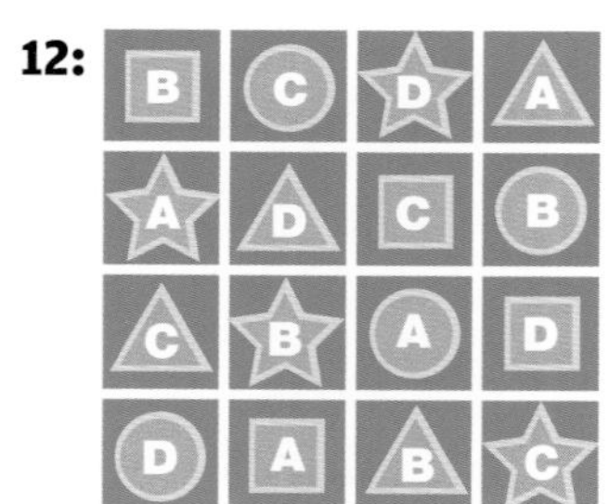

13:

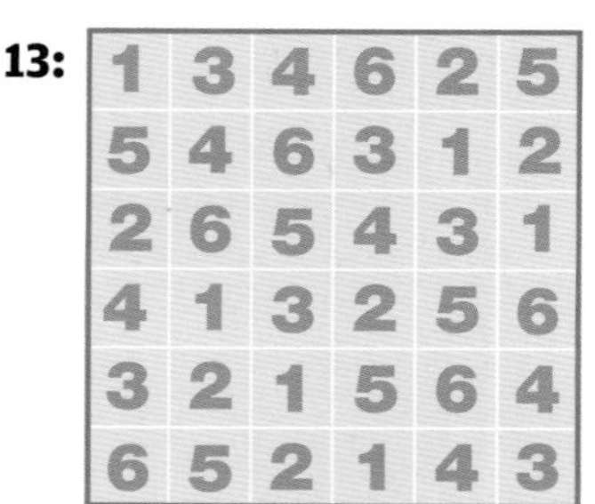

1	3	4	6	2	5
5	4	6	3	1	2
2	6	5	4	3	1
4	1	3	2	5	6
3	2	1	5	6	4
6	5	2	1	4	3

14:

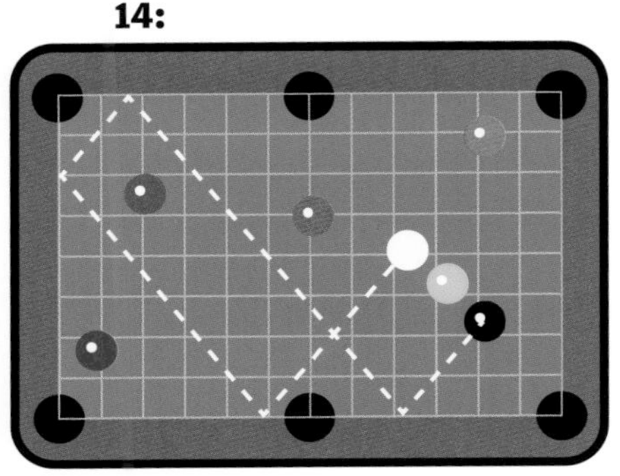

15: F is the odd one out.

16:

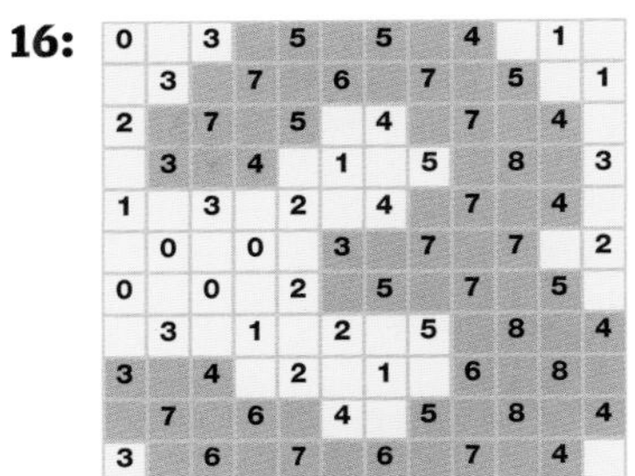

17:

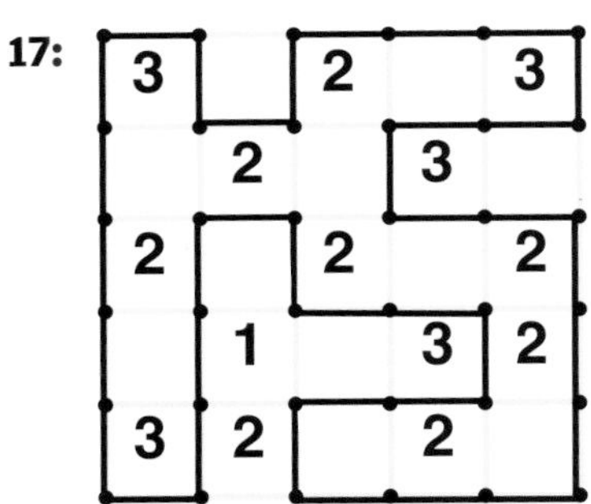

18: 25. Multiply the bottom two red corners and subtract the top two from your total. 8 x 5 = 40. 40 - 9 - 6 = 25.

19:

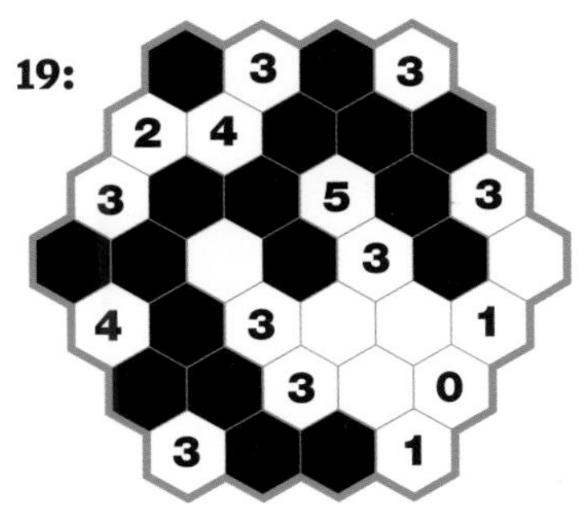

20:

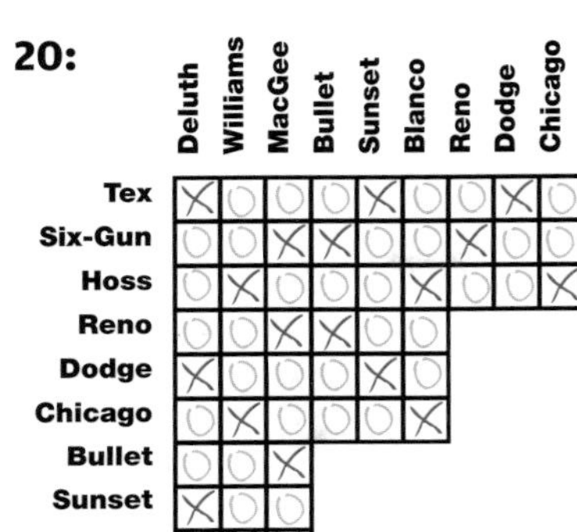

21:

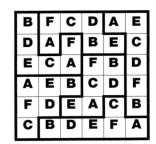

B	F	C	D	A	E
D	A	F	B	E	C
E	C	A	F	B	D
A	E	B	C	D	F
F	D	E	A	C	B
C	B	D	E	F	A

22: ?=18.

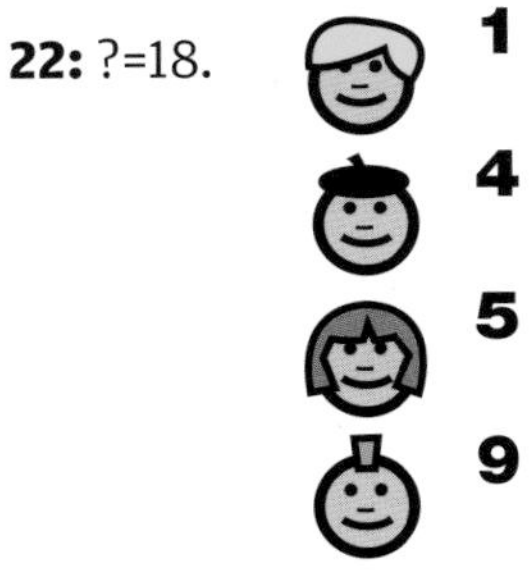

23: Second tile on the bottom row.

24:

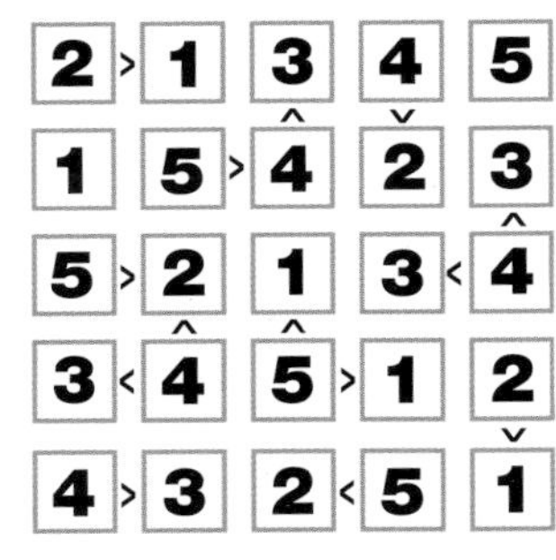

25:

26:

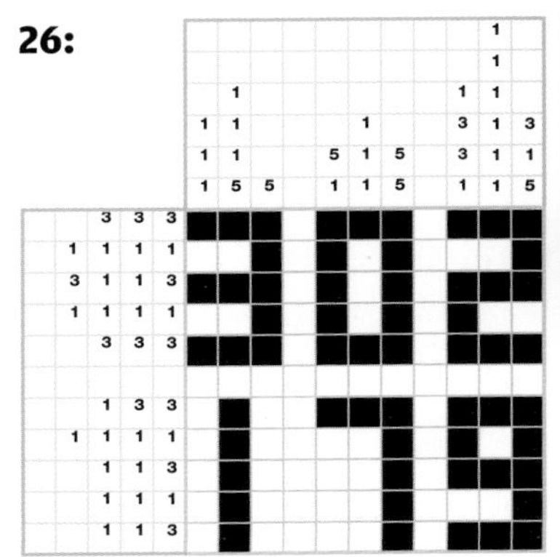

27:

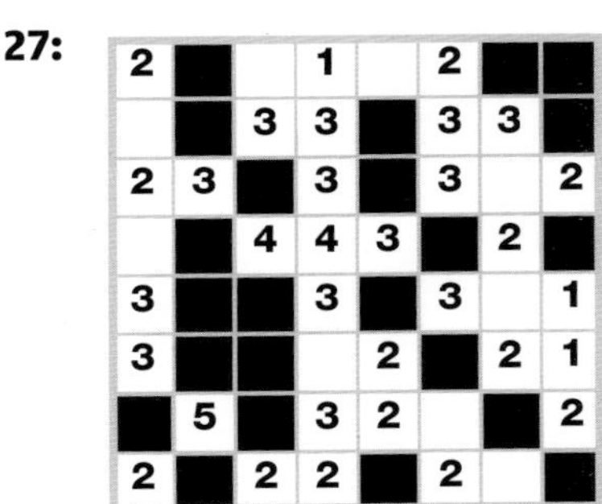

28: 4.

29: A) 6. Add opposite numbers and multiply the integers of the total.
B) 12. Multiply the opposite numbers, then multiply the integers of the total.

30:

1	2	6	9	7	8	5	3	4
8	4	7	1	3	5	2	9	6
3	5	9	6	4	2	1	7	8
9	6	1	8	5	3	7	4	2
7	3	4	2	1	6	9	8	5
2	8	5	7	9	4	6	1	3
4	1	2	3	6	7	8	5	9
6	7	3	5	8	9	4	2	1
5	9	8	4	2	1	3	6	7

31: F and H are the pair.

32: If its bordering squares (not diagonals) are predominantly black, a square becomes black. If they are predominantly white, it becomes white. If the bordering cell colors are equal in number, the square becomes yellow, and if the bordering squares have now become predominantly yellow, a square also becomes yellow.

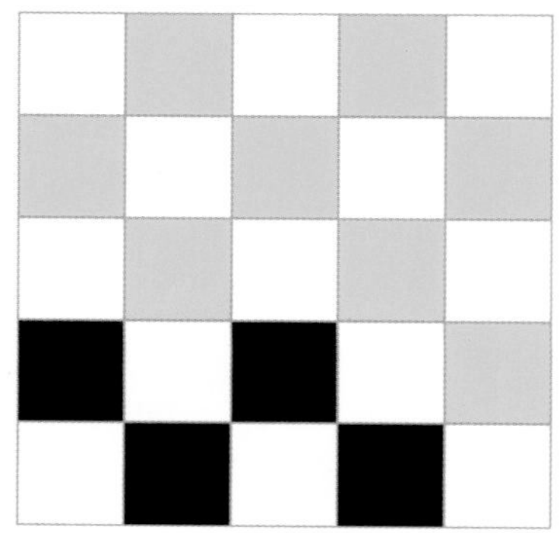

33:

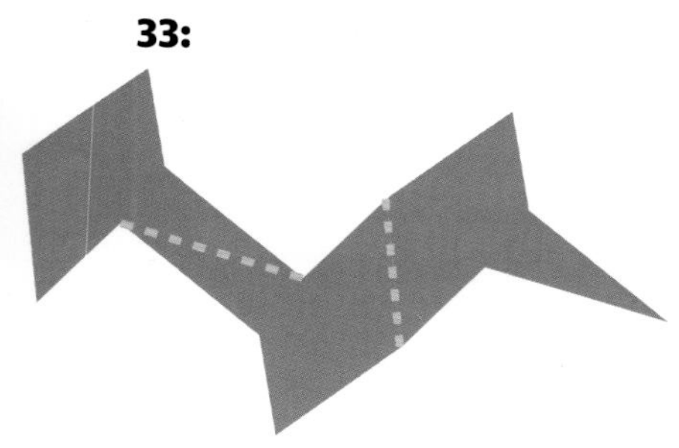

34: B. The blue dot and the blue square move one square counterclockwise around the pattern with each new picture.

35: C.

36:

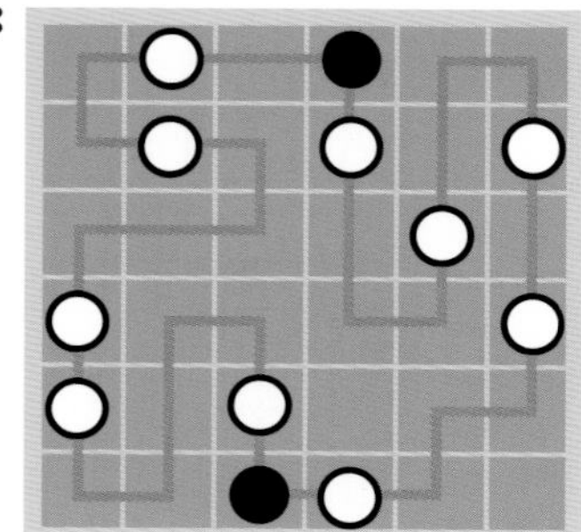

37: A, C, D, and G.

38: A, C, D, and G. B, E, F, and H.

39: 60.

40:

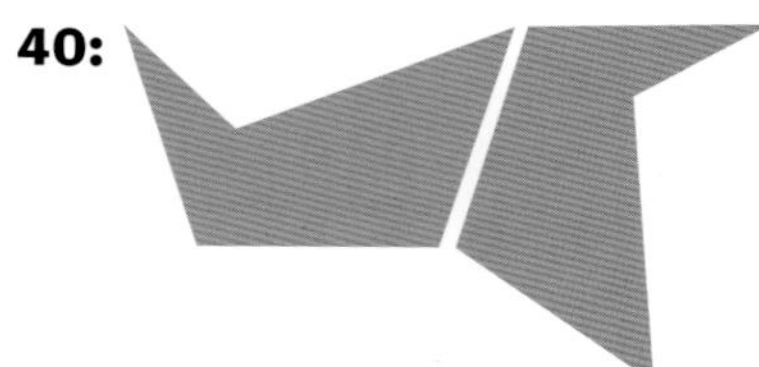

41:

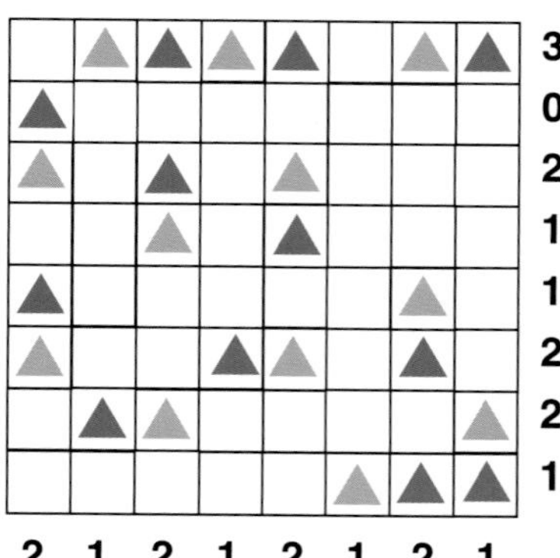

42:

43: 4. Subtract the right face from the front face and multiply by the top one.

44: A and F.

45: Add the top two corners, then add the bottom two. Then multiply the two totals. 3 + 1 = 4. 8 + 2 = 10. 4 x 10 = 40.

46:

47: A yellow square. Two different shapes are followed by a yellow shape. Two different colored shapes are followed by a square.

48:

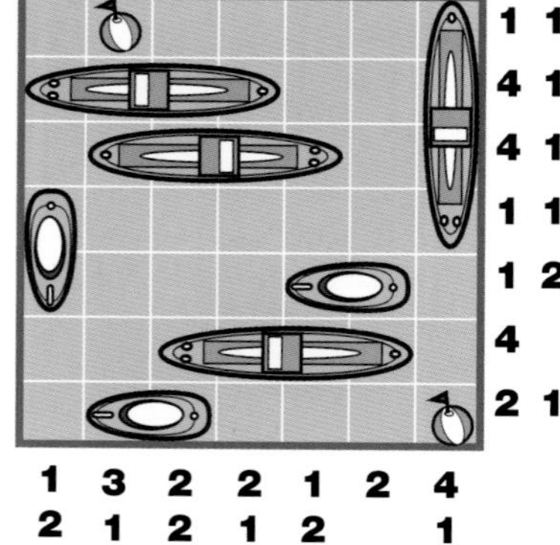

49: A yellow square. Every row and column in the grid contains three yellow and three red shapes, and the sides on the shapes in each row and column should add up to 24.

50: Each pentagon contains numbers that add up to 25. The sides nearest adjoining pentagons also contain the same number.

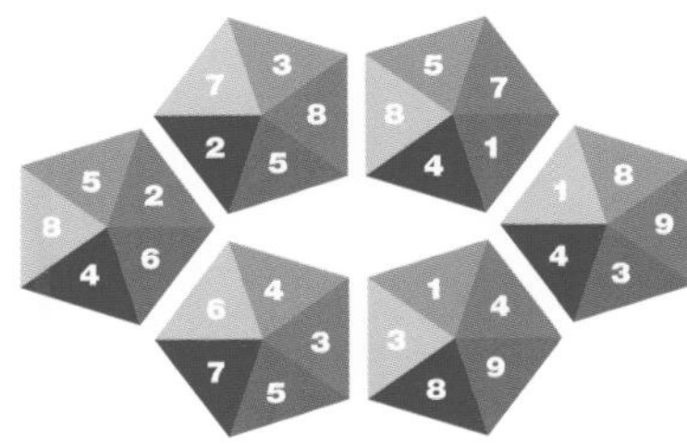

51: A. Each row and line in the grid contains three green, three red, and one yellow square.

52: B, C, D, and H.

53:

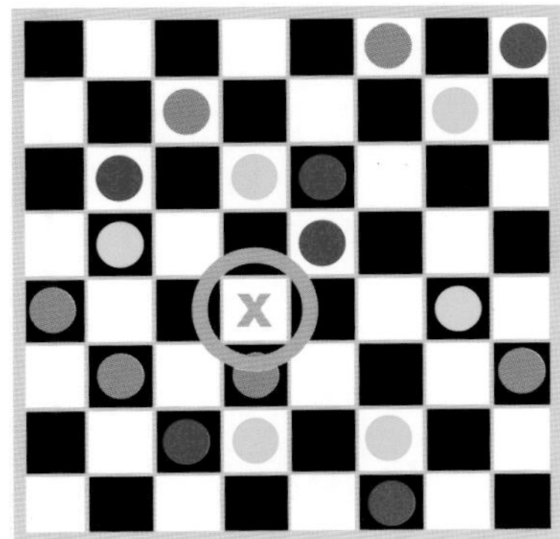

54: A) 15. Multiply opposite numbers, then subtract the yellow one.
B) 18. Halve the yellow numbers and multiply by their opposite number.

55:

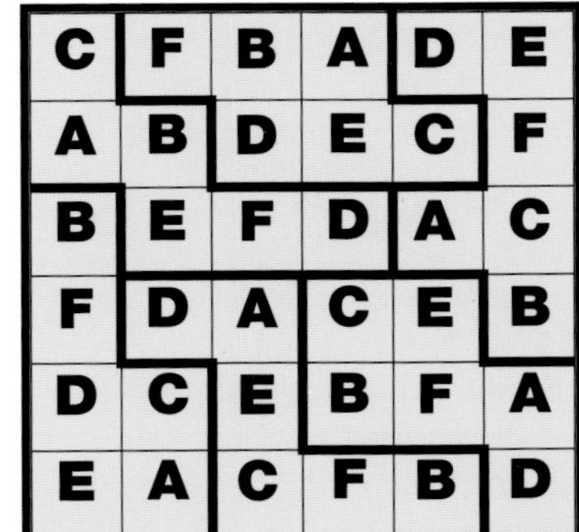

C	F	B	A	D	E
A	B	D	E	C	F
B	E	F	D	A	C
F	D	A	C	E	B
D	C	E	B	F	A
E	A	C	F	B	D

56:

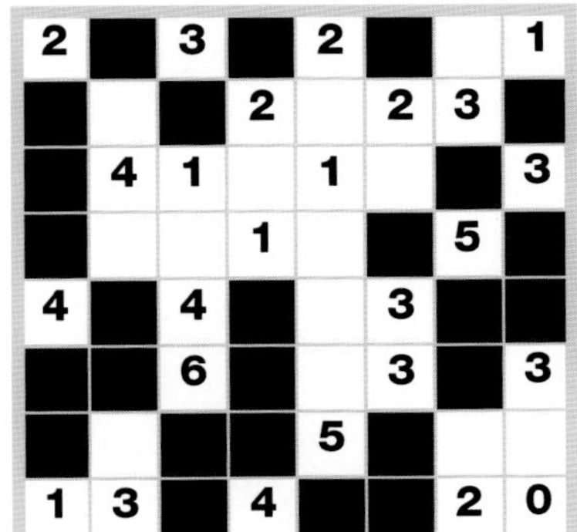

57:

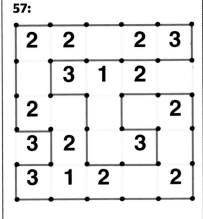

2	2		2	3
	3	1	2	
2				2
3	2		3	
3	1	2		2

58: Each vertical and horizontal line contains one shape with all green triangles, one with all pink triangles, and one with half-pink and half-green triangles. Each line also contains two shapes with a white dot in the center and one with no white dot. The missing shape must have all green triangles and a white dot.

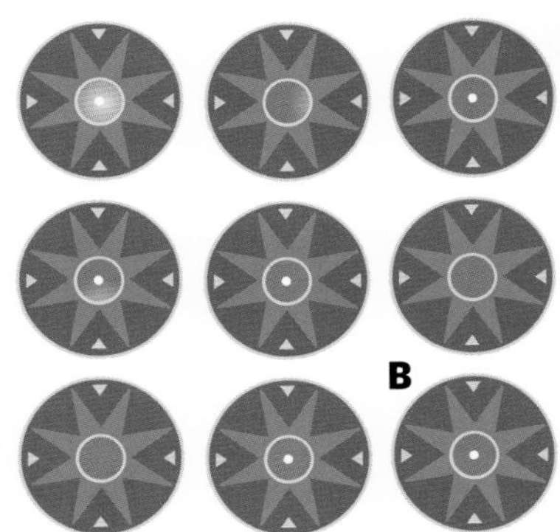

59:

18	13	14
11	15	19
16	17	12

60:

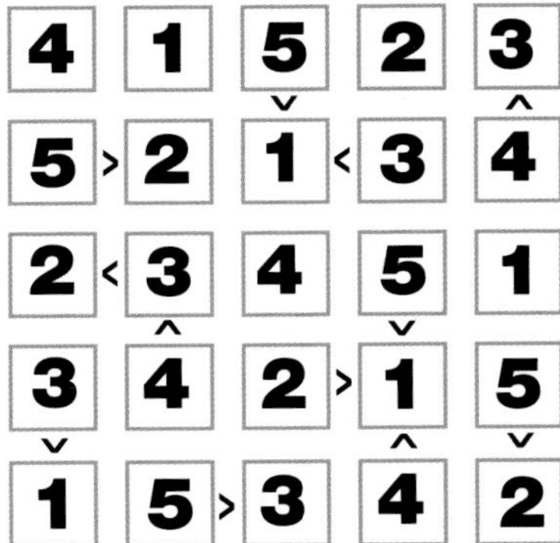

61:

1	7	9	2	8	6	5	4	3
2	5	6	9	3	4	8	7	1
4	8	3	1	5	7	2	9	6
7	2	5	3	6	9	4	1	8
9	6	8	4	2	1	3	5	7
3	4	1	5	7	8	9	6	2
6	9	7	8	4	2	1	3	5
5	1	2	7	9	3	6	8	4
8	3	4	6	1	5	7	2	9

62:

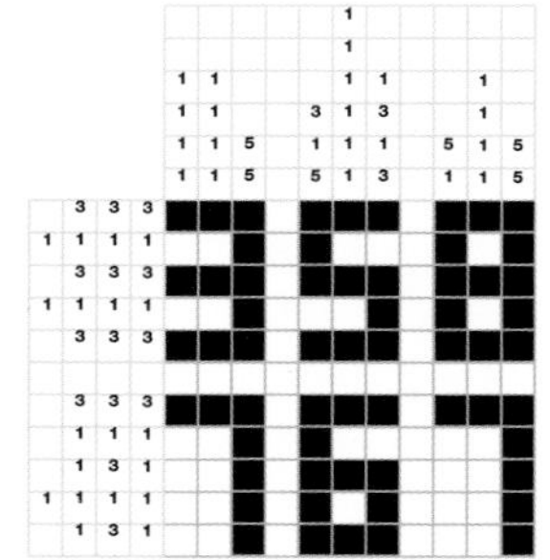

63: Yellow.

64:

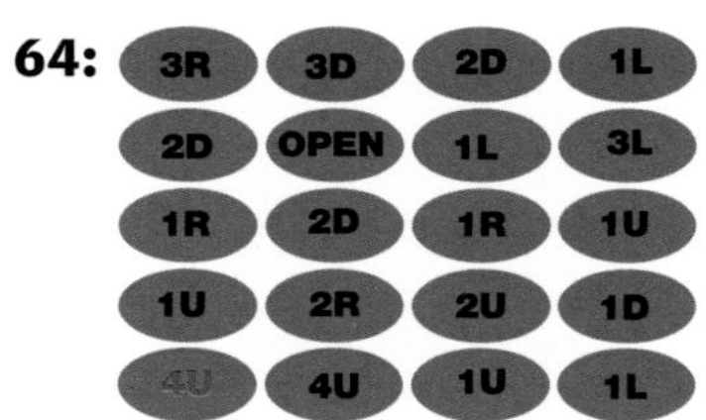

65:

	Hellmuth	Chan	Brunson	100 Dollars	250 Dollars	375 Dollars	Full House	Four Kings	Ace Flush
Mac	O	O	X	O	X	O	O	O	X
Jack	X	O	O	X	O	O	X	O	O
Zac	O	X	O	O	O	X	O	X	O
Full House	X	O	O	X	O	O			
Four Kings	O	X	O	O	O	X			
Ace Flush	O	O	X	O	X	O			
100 Dollars	X	O	O						
250 Dollars	O	O	X						
375 Dollars	O	X	O						

66: A.

67: A black letter "A." Each row and column contains 1, 2, and 3 of each letter and each color.

68:

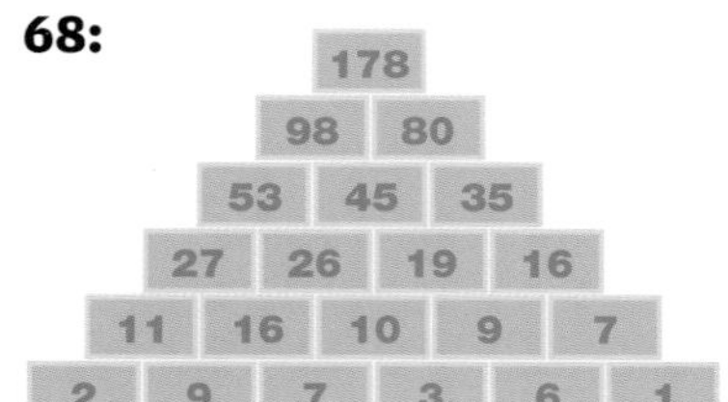

69: D. The two outer shapes exchange colors, and the inner shape's color and outline color are also exchanged.

70: Blue = 1, Green = 2, Yellow = 3, Red = 4, Purple = 5. Three red balls are required.

71: ?=16.

2

3

4

5

72: The car is made up of 50 squares: 2 gray, 4 blue, 16 black, and 28 red. Double these numbers to reveal a percentage breakdown of: gray 4 percent, blue 8 percent, black 32 percent, and red 56 percent.

73: F11, L6, P14, and I6.

74: B.

75:
1. 2.
2. None.
3. 2.
4. Blue.
5. Green.

76: A. Each block of nine squares has been turned 90 degrees and the bottom left and top right symbols have been swapped over.

77: 5,500 square inches (13,770 square millimeters). Each 20 x 20 square represents 400 square inches (1,016 square centimeters). 8 squares, 3 half-sized triangles, 4 half squares, 3 quarter squares and 11 eighth triangles are used.

78: A yellow number 4 on a pink background.

79: Up.

80:

	Indian	Pacific	Caribbean	Germany	USA	Australia	Coconuts	Mangoes	Pineapples
Zanga	X	O	O	X	O	O	O	X	O
Binoo	O	X	O	O	X	O	O	O	X
Biro Biro	O	O	X	O	O	X	X	O	O
Coconuts	O	O	X	O	O	X			
Mangoes	X	O	O	X	O	O			
Pineapples	O	X	O	O	X	O			
Germany	X	O	O						
USA	O	X	O						
Australia	O	O	X						

81: An orange star on a black circle. Two different colored circles are followed by an orange circle. Two stars the same color are followed by a black circle.

82:

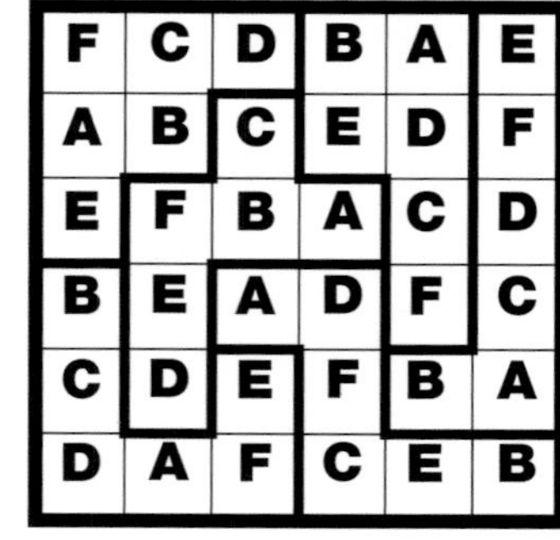

F	C	D	B	A	E
A	B	C	E	D	F
E	F	B	A	C	D
B	E	A	D	F	C
C	D	E	F	B	A
D	A	F	C	E	B

83: 66.

84:

85:

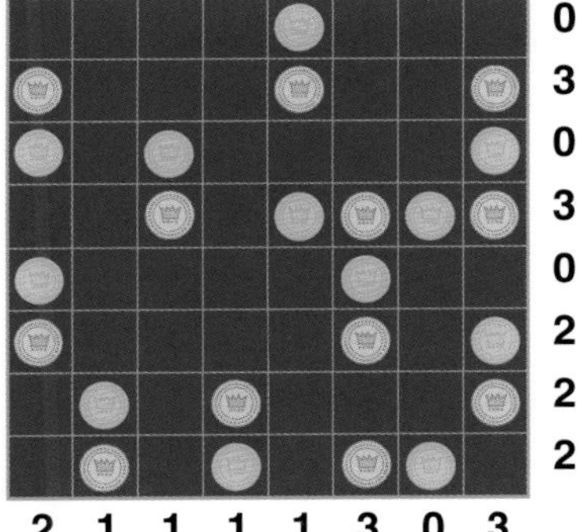

86: A, C, F, and H.

87:

88:

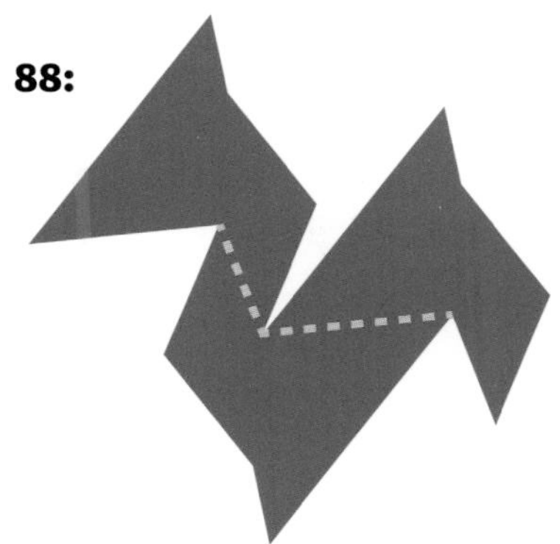

89: Each vertical and horizontal line contains one shape the right way up, one rotated 90 degrees, and one rotated 180 degrees. Each line also contains one green shape with a blue outline and two yellow shapes with a red outline. The missing shape should be the right way up, and yellow with a red outline.

90:

1	7	3	2	8	5	6	4	9
5	9	8	1	4	6	2	7	3
2	4	6	3	7	9	1	5	8
4	1	5	9	6	8	3	2	7
6	2	7	4	1	3	8	9	5
3	8	9	5	2	7	4	1	6
7	6	1	8	5	4	9	3	2
8	3	2	7	9	1	5	6	4
9	5	4	6	3	2	7	8	1

91: 32 percent. The total number of items is 350, which, divided by 3.5 makes 100. The hat production of 112 when divided by 3.5 gives us 32, or 32 percent.

92: Purple.

93:

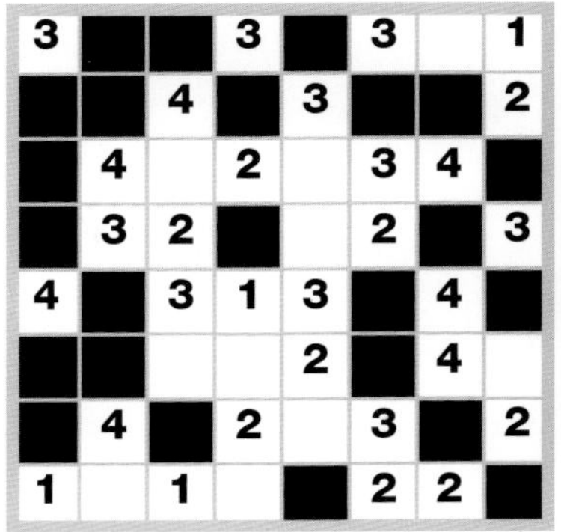

94: Hoss McGrew is cowboy A.

95: A green question mark.

96: Brown = 1, Black = 2, Green = 3, Blue = 4, Yellow = 5. Five black sacks are required.

97: ?=22.

98:

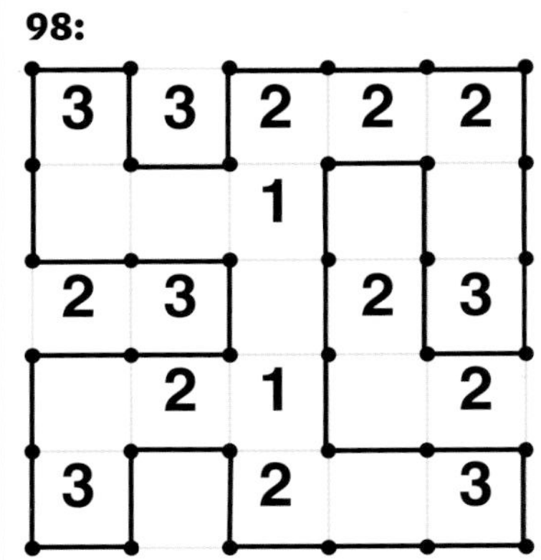

99:

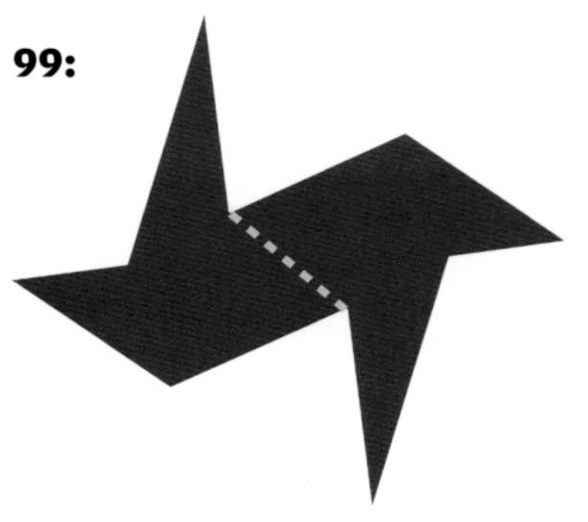

100:

101: 32. Using opposite corner stars, subtract the smaller number from the larger. Then multiply the two totals together:
9 - 1 = 8, 7 - 3 = 4, 4 x 8 = 32.

102:

103:

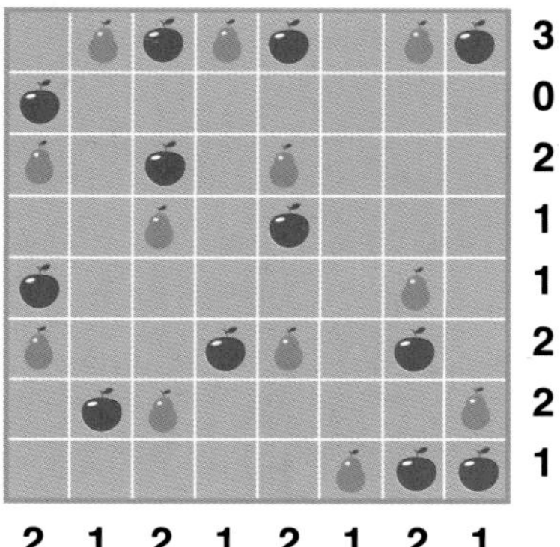

104: A blue circle. Two shapes the same are followed by a blue shape. Two different colored shapes are followed by a circle.

105: C.

106:

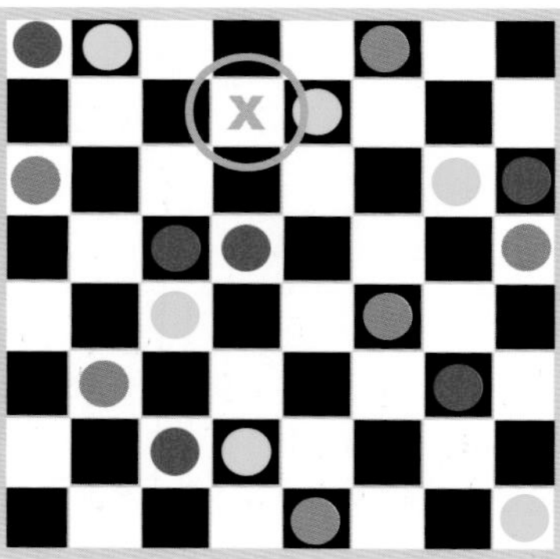

107: C and E.

108: Tokyo.

109:

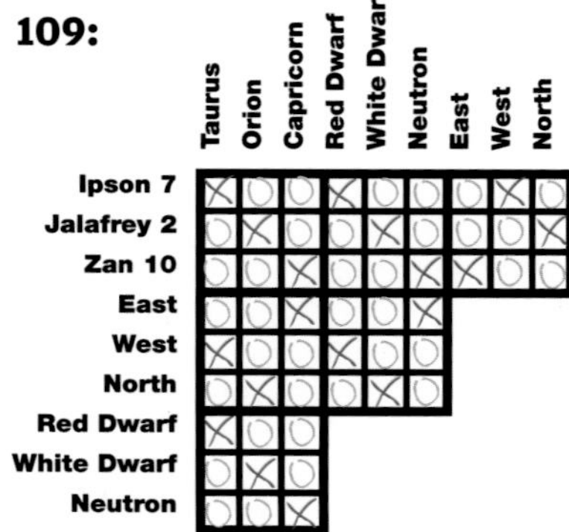

110: Both. Pythagoras tells us that the square of the hypotenuse is equal to the sum of the squares of the other two sides on a right angled triangle. The diagonal of the box floor is then 5 yards (5 meters) long (4 x 4 = 16, 3 x 3 = 9. 9 + 16 = 25, the square root of which is 5). This diagonal forms the base of a new right angled triangle with a hypotenuse 6 yards (5.8 meters) long, leaving enough room for both pieces of mast.

111:

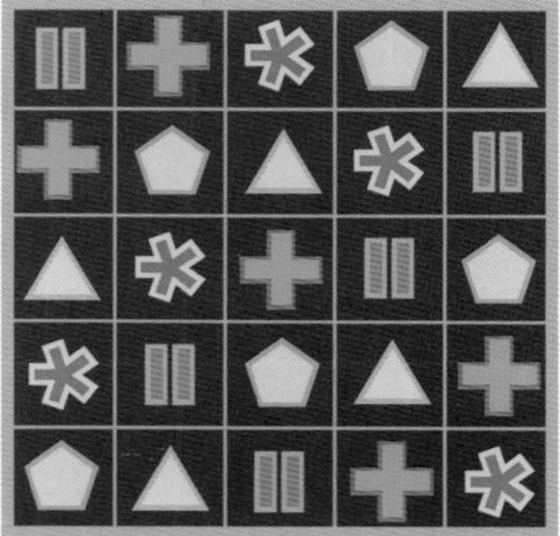

112: E is the odd one out.

113: A line on the left or bottom of this square will give up just one box to your opponent.

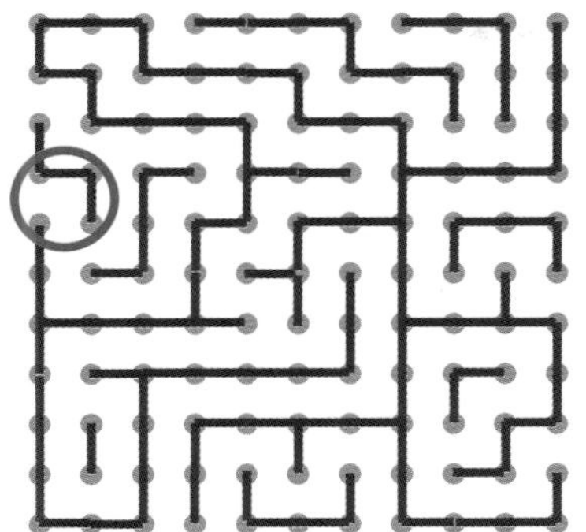

114: Two-and-a-half revolutions of cog A, which will make exactly 4 revolutions of cog B and 5 revolutions of cog C.

115: D. With each new image, the colors of the parts of the car change as follows: Wheels—old cap. Cap—old top. Top—old bottom. Bottom—old door. Door—old wheels.

116:

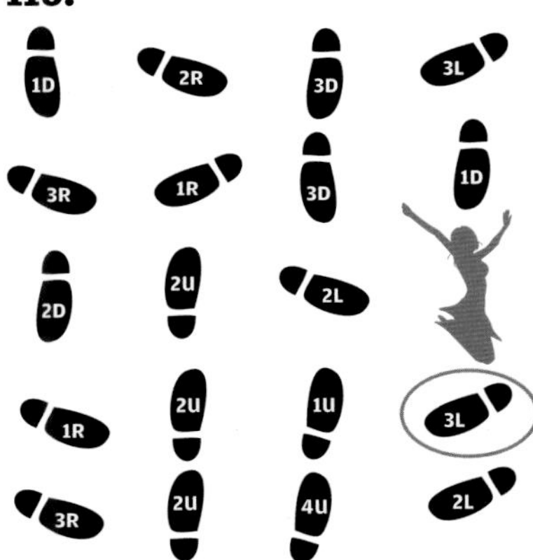

117: Red = 1, Purple = 2, Green = 3, Blue = 4, Yellow = 5. Two blue balls are required.

118: A, C, D, and G. B, E, F, and H.

119:

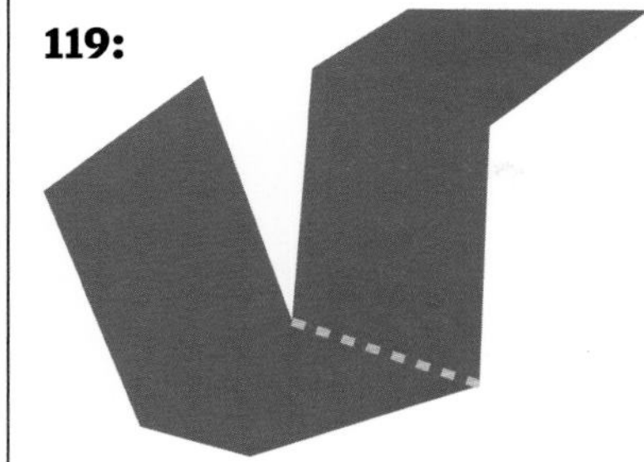

120:

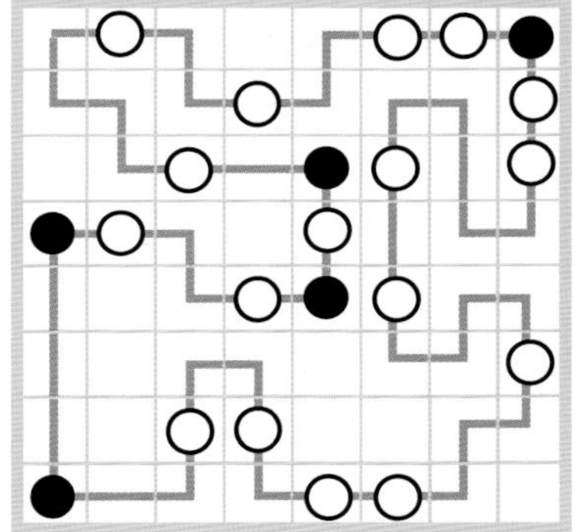

121:

8	7	9	6	1	4	2	5	3
1	2	4	3	5	9	6	7	8
5	6	3	7	8	2	1	4	9
2	1	6	9	3	7	4	8	5
4	3	8	5	2	1	9	6	7
7	9	5	8	4	6	3	1	2
9	4	1	2	7	5	8	3	6
6	8	7	1	9	3	5	2	4
3	5	2	4	6	8	7	9	1

122: A black letter "A." Each row and column contains 1, 2, and 3 of each letter and each color.

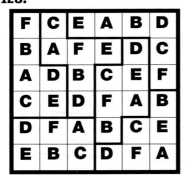

123: 35 - 7 ÷ 4 - 4 = 3.

124:

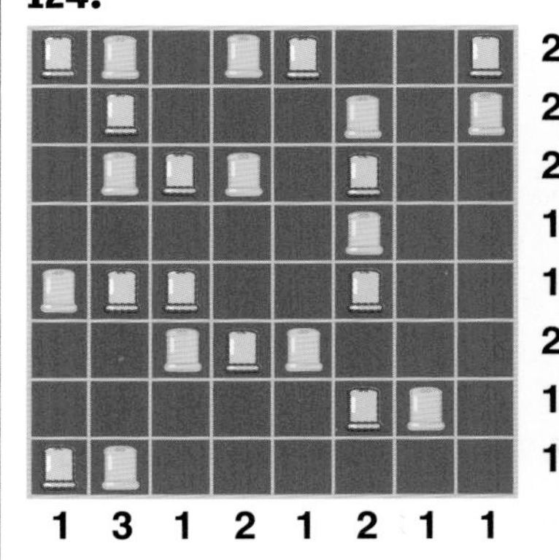

125: A and F.

126:

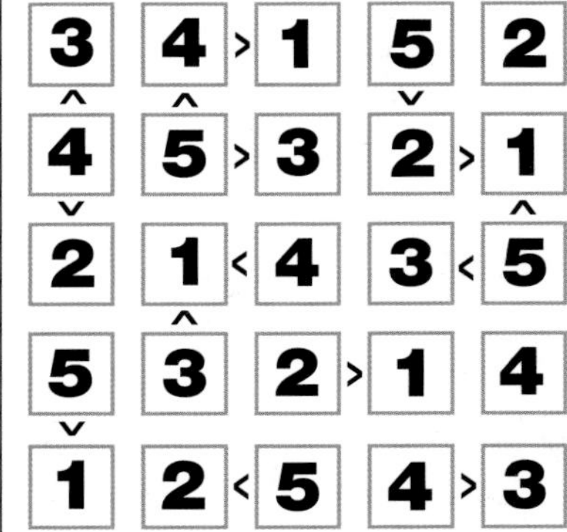

127: C, D, E, and H.

128:

F	C	E	A	B	D
B	A	F	E	D	C
A	D	B	C	E	F
C	E	D	F	A	B
D	F	A	B	C	E
E	B	C	D	F	A

129: Down.

130:

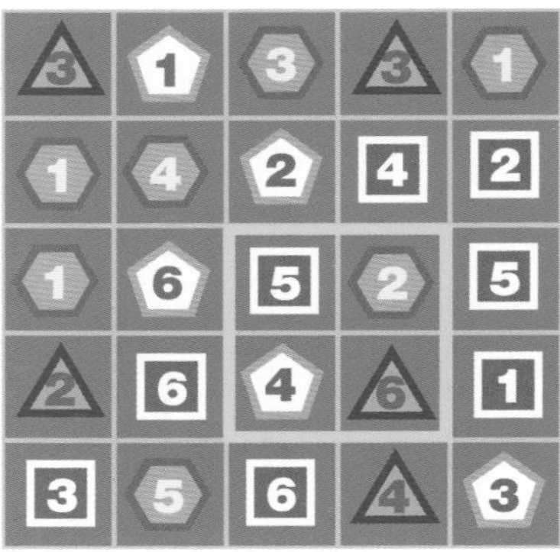

131:

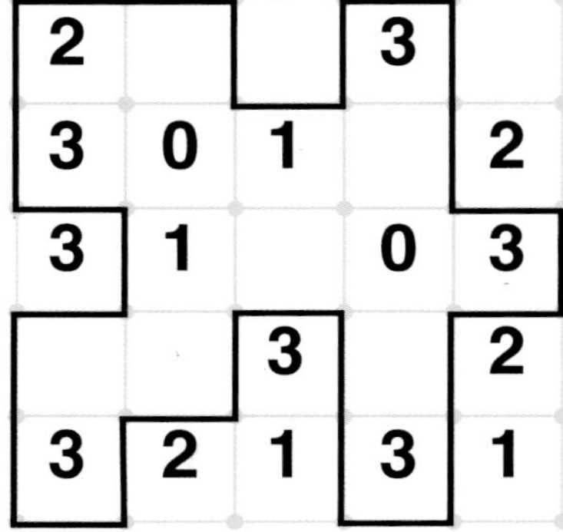

132: B is the odd shape out.

133: A pink triangle. Two shapes the same are followed by a pink shape. Two different colored shapes are followed by a triangle.

134:

3	4	3	4	5	4	4
5	X	O	O	X	X	6
4	O	X	O	O	X	3
2	O	O	X	X	O	6
5	O	X	X	O	X	3
3	X	O	O	X	O	4
4	5	3	5	4	5	3

135:

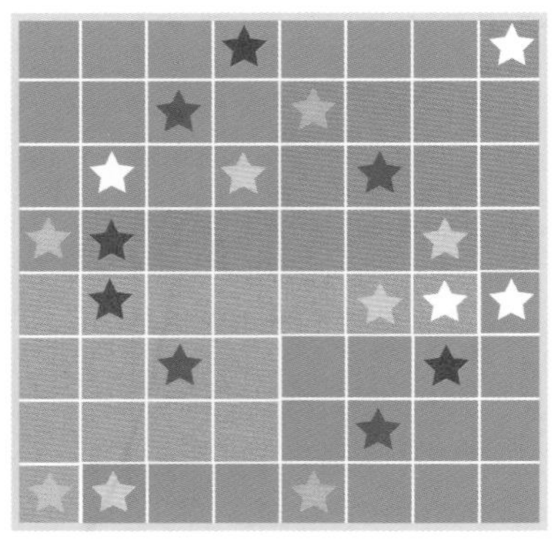

136: D. Each row and line in the grid contains four dark blue, three light blue, and one pink square.

137: B. The inner shape takes the color of the previous outer shape. The outer shape takes the color of the previous 'through' shape, and the 'through' shape takes the color of the previous inner shape.

138: 75.

139: In the 7 space. The ball travels at a speed of 20 feet (6 meters) per second (relative to the wheel) for 15 seconds, making a distance of 3,500 inches (9,000 centimeters) in a clockwise direction. The circumference of the wheel is 125 inches (320 centimeters) (2 x pi (3.2) x radius/20 inches). The ball must then travel exactly 28 laps of the wheel (3,500 divided by 320 = 28) or (9,000 divided by 320 = 28.125) placing it one eighth of the way around the wheel in a clockwise direction, in the 7 space.

140: G.

141: 16.

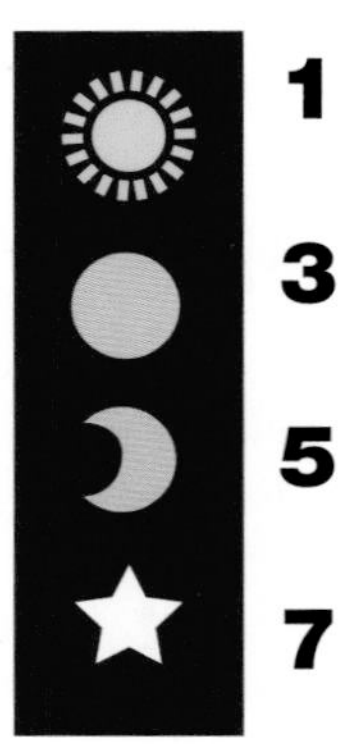

142: The inner numbers are made up of the two outer numbers of the opposite segment, the smaller of which is subtracted from the larger. 4 - 3 = 1.

143: 4.

144: Take the alphabetical position of the first letter of the city, and multiply by the number of letters in the word. 13 (M) x 8 = 117.

145: 260. The numbers represent the number of sides in the shape they occupy. When shapes overlap, the numbers are multiplied. 40 + 160 + 60 = 260.

146: K and B.

147:

3	3	4	2	3	1
4	X	O	O	O	2
5	X	X	O	O	3
3	X	X	O	O	3
5	O	X	X	X	3
1	4	4	4	4	3

148:

149:

243
146 97
83 63 34
43 40 23 11
19 24 16 7 4
6 13 11 5 2 2

150:

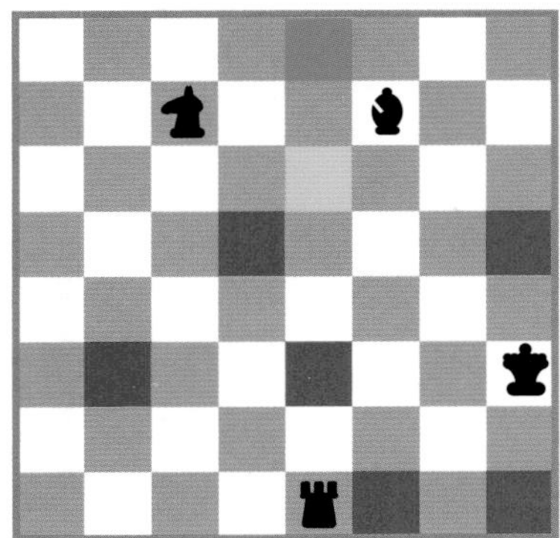

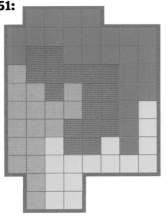

151:

152:

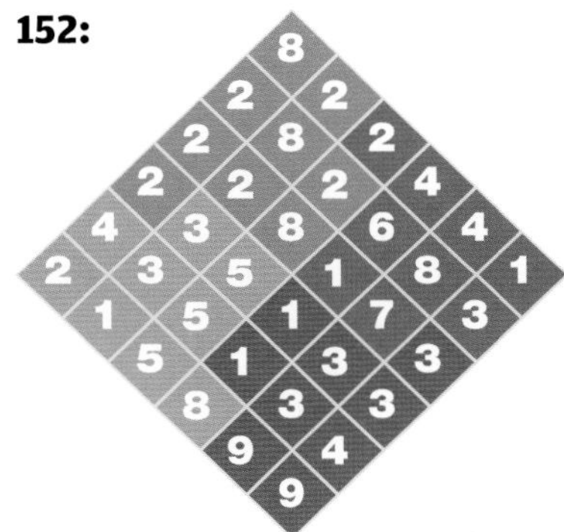

153: d) 16.5 a) 16 b) 15 c) 14.

154: 5 helmets, 5 shields, 6 axes, and 2 swords.
5,155 + 11,715 + 7,650 + 5,480 = 30,000.

155: Red and yellow.

156:

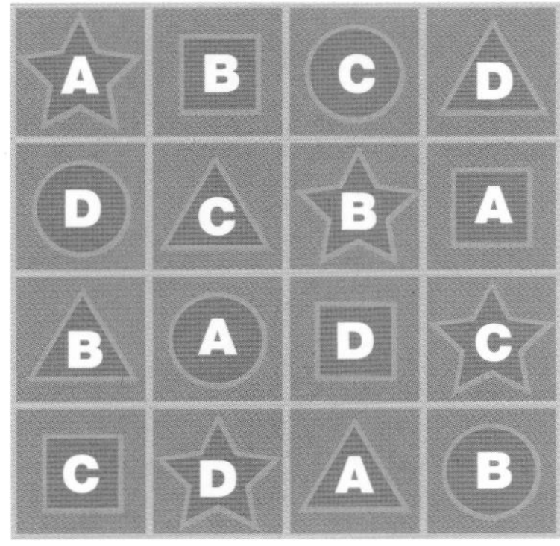

157: A.

158: 24. The overall pattern is symmetrical.

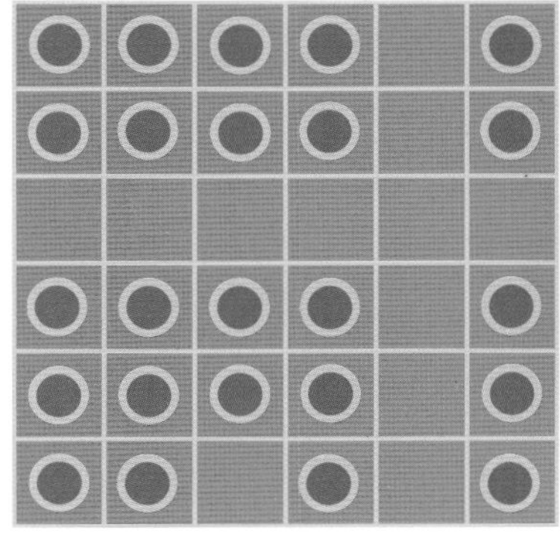

159: B.

160:

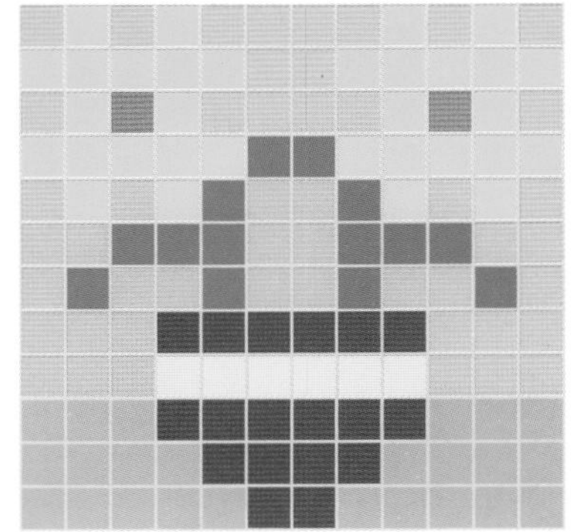

161: H.

162:

163: 3 and 7
The inner numbers in the blue segments are made by adding the other two numbers in the segment. The inner numbers in the orange segments are made by subtracting the smaller from the larger of the other two numbers in the segment.

164: Yellow = 1, Red = 2, Green = 3, Blue = 4.

165:
A) 6. Multiply opposite numbers, then subtract the white one.
B) 24. Multiply opposite numbers, then add the white one.

166:

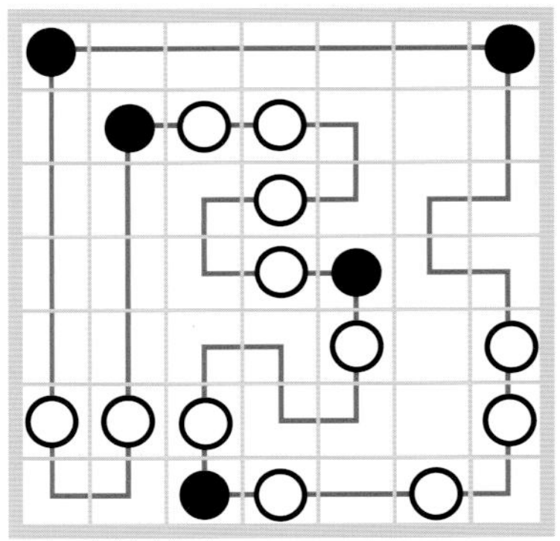

167:

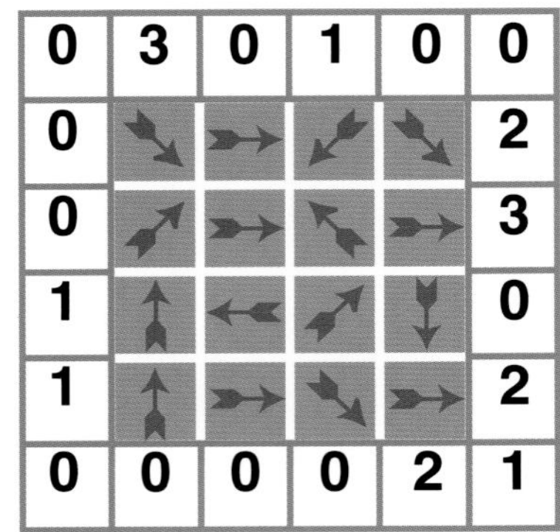

168:

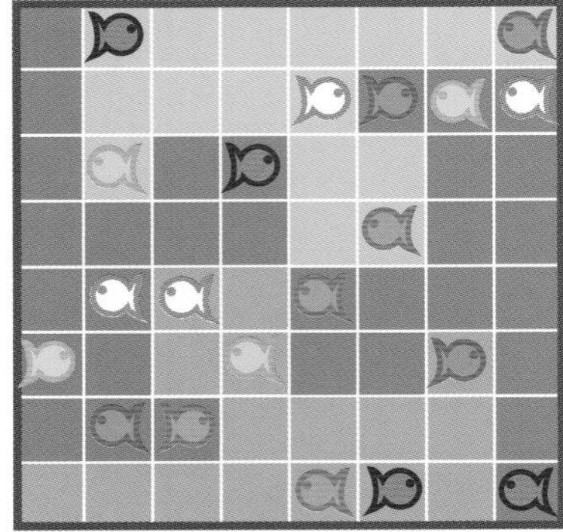

169: A is the odd shape out.

170: 5,100 square inches (12,954 square centimeters). Each 20 x 20 square represents 400 square inches (1,016 square centimeters). 8 squares, 4 half-sized triangles, 3 half squares, 4 quarter squares and 2 eighth triangles are used.

171:

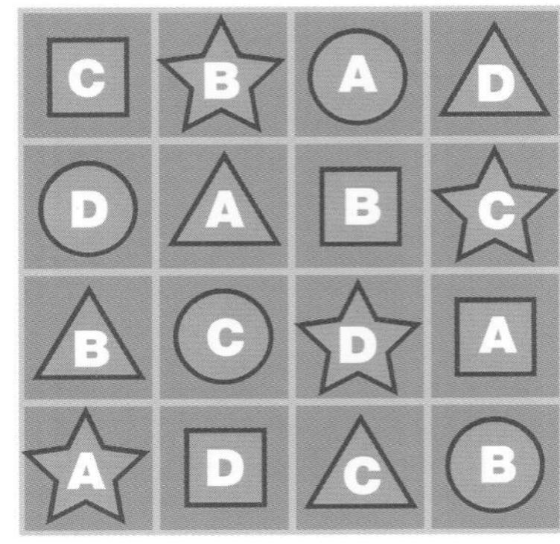

172: A. Each row and column in the grid contains two yellow squares, and every other row and column contains a red square.

173:

174: The color of each circle is dependent on how many other circles it touches.

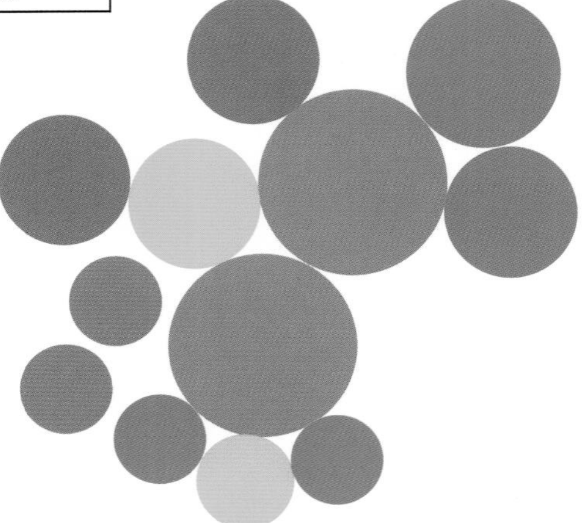

175:
The final dice in your trip is the yellow 2, four dice down in the center column.

176:

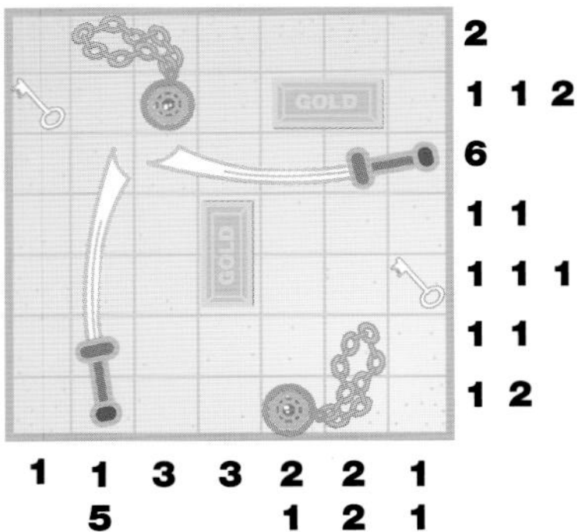

177: A line on the bottom or left of this square will only give up one box to your opponent.

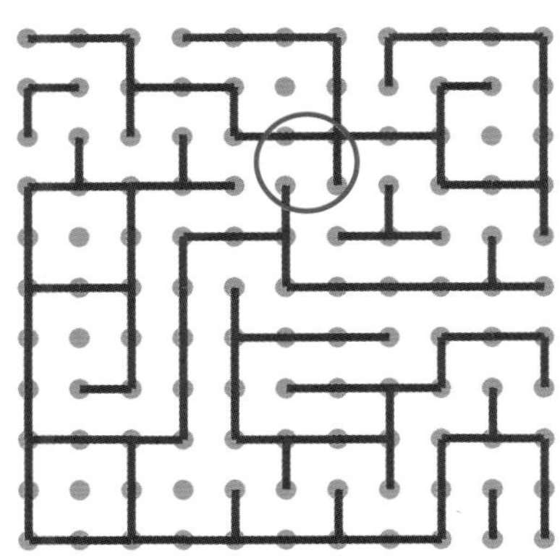

178: The top shape replaces the inner shape. The large shape replaces the top shape. The inside shape replaces the large shape. The top shape's color becomes that of the old inner shape. The inner shape color becomes that of the old large shape, and the large shape takes the old top shape's color.

179:
1. 4.
2. None.
3. 56.
4. 5.
5. 8.

180: F and C.

181: D.

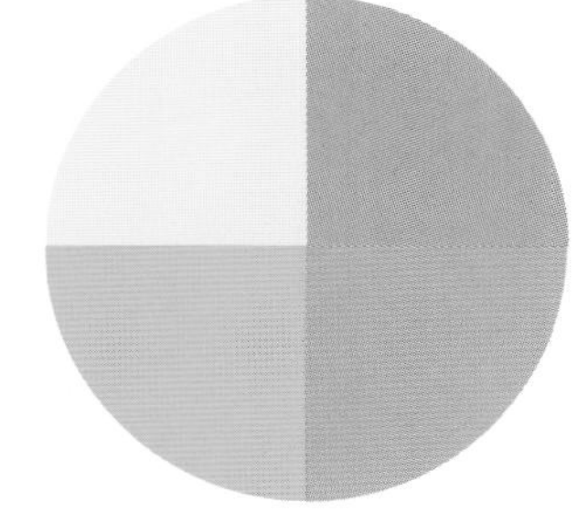

182: Each vertical and horizontal line contains one white pentagon and two yellow ones. Each line also contains one white inner star and two blue ones. And each line also contains one small yellow star and two small white ones. The missing shape should have a yellow pentagon, a white inner star, and a small yellow star.

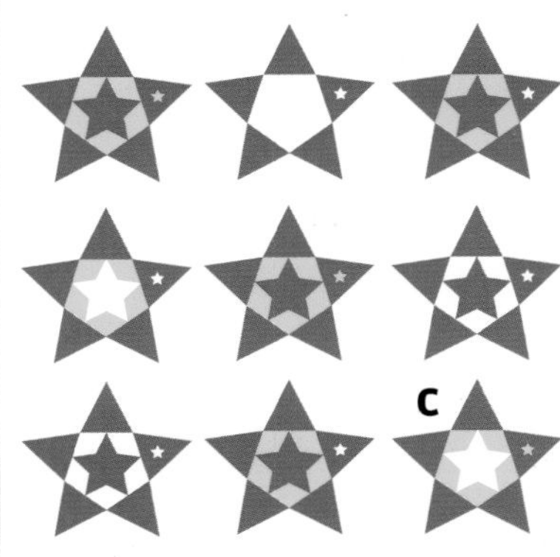

183:

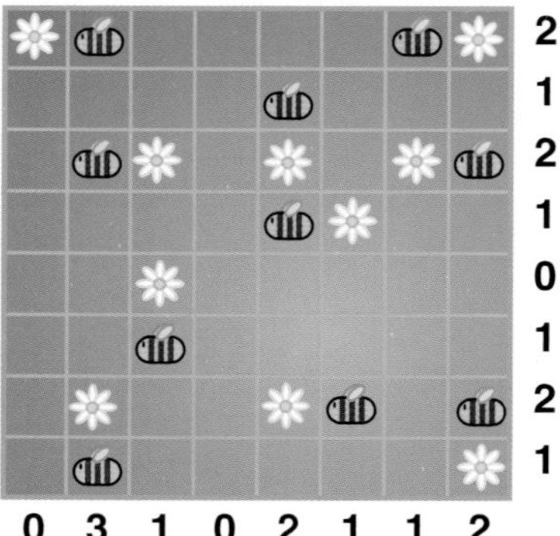

184: Each vertical and horizontal line contains one purple, one yellow, and one white outer box. Each line also contains one purple inner diamond and two yellow ones. Finally each line contains one purple star and two yellow ones. The missing image should be a yellow outer box with a purple inner diamond and a yellow star.

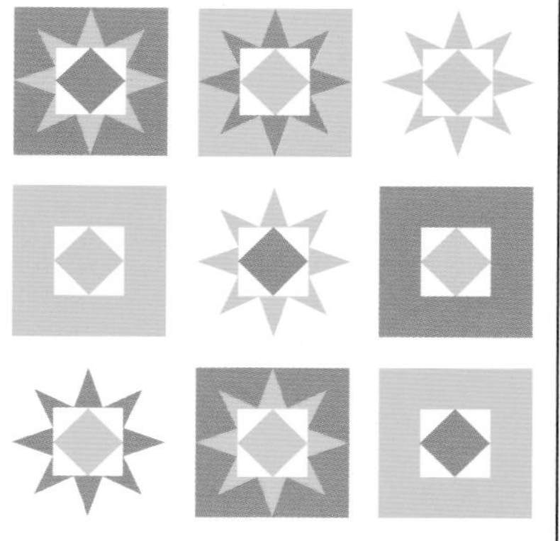

185: 5,000 square inches (12,700 square centimeters). Each 20 x 20 square represents 400 square inches (1,016 square centimeters). 12 and a half squares are used.

186:

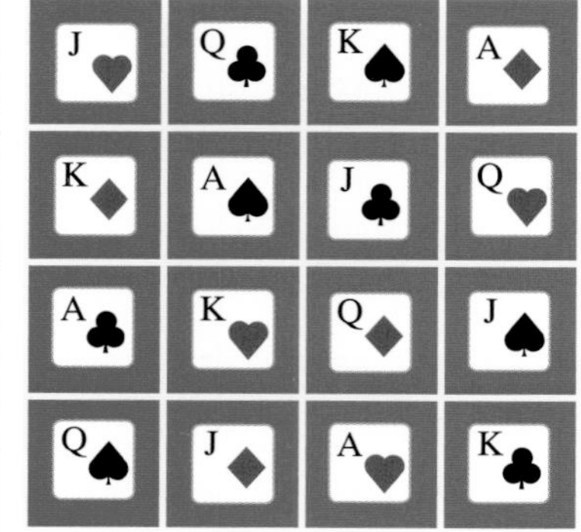

187:

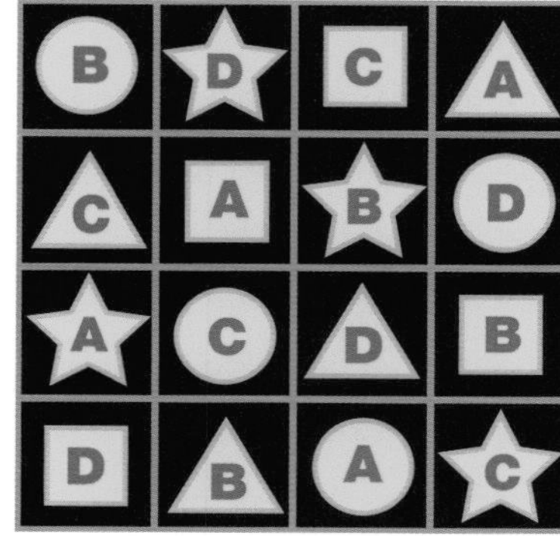

188: A is the odd shape out.

189: $9,075. 1st bet wins $140, + your bet back = $150. Second bet is $75 and wins $1,050 + your bet = $1,125 Third bet is $562.50 and wins $7,875 + your bet = $8,437.50 Add the $75 you kept from your first bet, and the $562.50 you kept from your second and your winnings are $9,075.00.

190:

191:

192: He took the test. On reaching into the bag, he drew out a piece of paper and ate it before anyone could see what was on it. The other piece of paper carried a cross, of course, so the one he had eaten must have had a checkmark on, right? Well, that's what the crowd believed, and that's what mattered.

193: 360. The numbers represent the number of sides in the shape they occupy. When shapes overlap, the numbers are multiplied. 3 x 4 x 5 x 6 = 360.

194: Last tile on the middle row.

195:

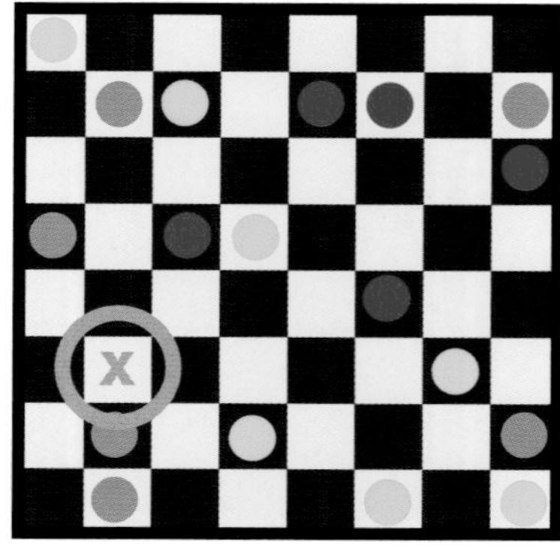

196: D. The bottom half and outline of the new design adopts the colors from the dots and background of the first design. The dots and background of the new design adopts the colors from the bottom half and outline of the first design.

197: 4,950 square inches. Each 20 x 20 square represents 400 square inches. 6 squares, 3 half-square triangles, 2 half-squares, 9 quarter squares, and 13 eighth-square triangles are used.

198: A red house with the light on. Two houses the same color are followed by one with the light on, two houses with different lighting (off and on) are followed by a red house.

199:
1. 3.
2. 2.
3. Japan. Red circle, white background.
4. 4: white, red, blue, and yellow.
5. Orange and black.

200:

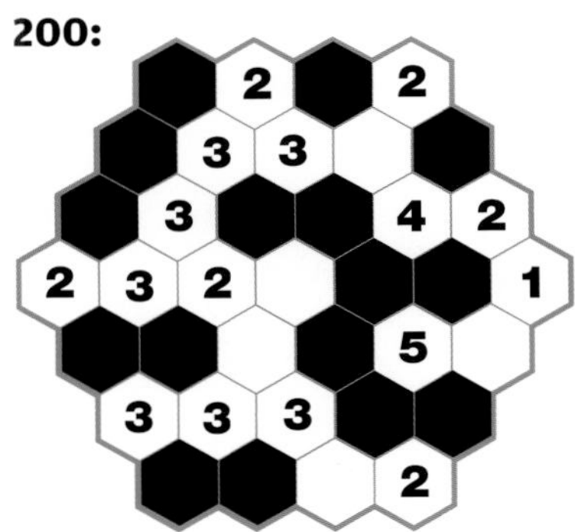

201: They ended their walk on the bench at square 1C. The only square they didn't visit was 5C, which is in the middle of the pond.

202:

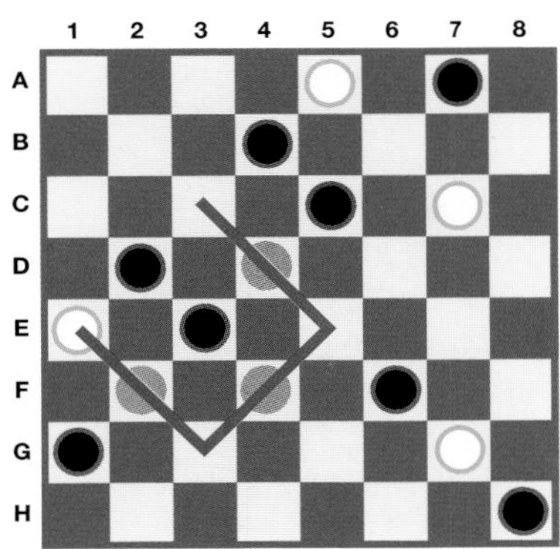

203:
Green 1.
Orange 2.
Black 3.
Blue 4.

204:

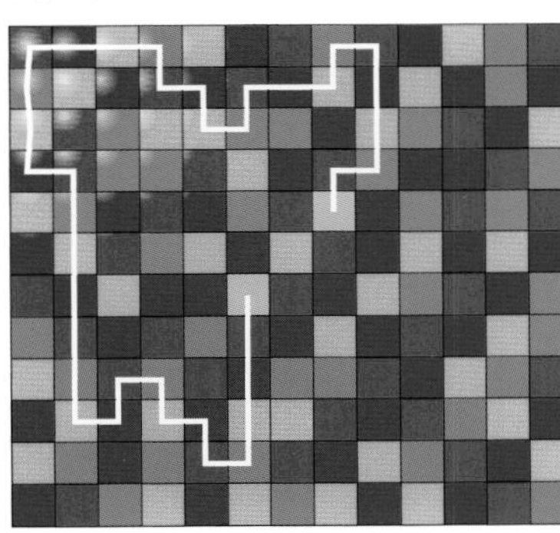

205:

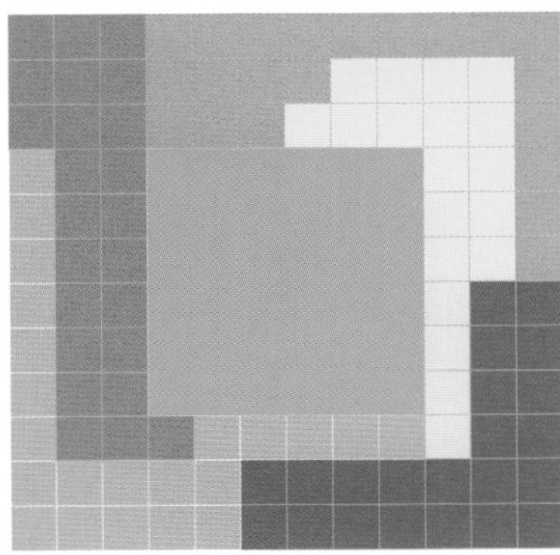

206:

		5	1	5	5		
		2	9	2	2		
5	4	3	9	8	8	2	1
2	2	4	7	8	4	2	1
1	8	3	3	9	6	4	3
2	4	5	4	1	4	9	4
		7	8	1	3		
		4	2	2	2		

207:

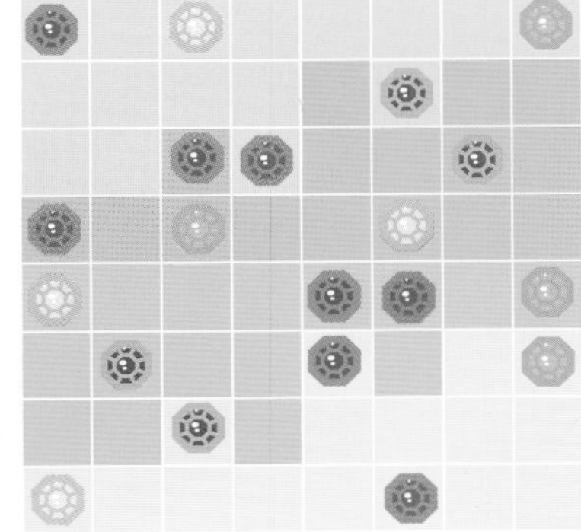

208: Van Gogh.

209: B and F.

210: Green.

211: A.

212:

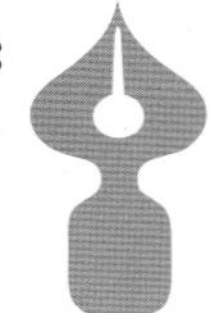

213: D and E are the pair.

214: b) 18 a) 16 c) 15 d) 14.

215: Each vertical and horizontal line contains one shape with a red outline and two shapes with a black outline. Each line also contains one shape where the inner quartered circle has been removed and one shape that has been rotated through 90 degrees. The missing shape should not be rotated; it should have a red outline and the inner circle should be missing.

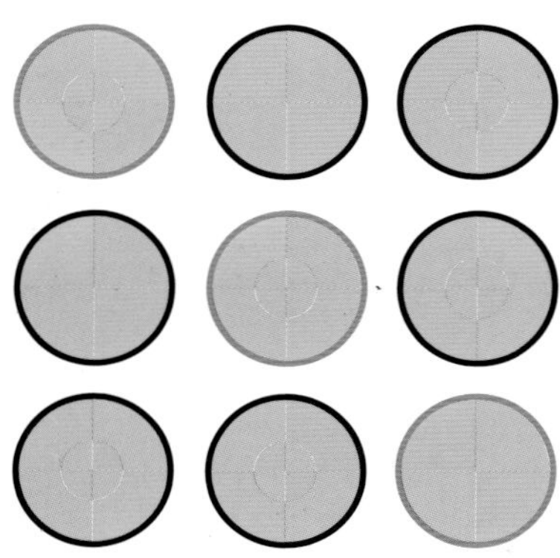

216: L5, D11, F1, F10.

217:

L	G	Y	W	R	M
Y	M	G	L	W	R
M	W	R	G	L	Y
W	R	M	Y	G	L
R	L	W	M	Y	G
G	Y	L	R	M	W

4	6	2	1	3	5
3	1	6	2	5	4
5	4	3	6	2	1
6	2	1	5	4	3
2	5	4	3	1	6
1	3	5	4	6	2

G + 6 = M L + 3 = O Y + 1 = Z W + 4 = A M + 5 = R R + 2 = T
Solution: Mozart

218: Each pentagon contains numbers that add up to 30. The sides nearest adjoining pentagons all add up to 10.

219: 2. Add all the pink numbers and divide the total by the highest pink number. Do the same with the yellow numbers.
HUB 1: Pink: 4 + 3 + 3 + 5 = 15, ÷ 5 = 3. Yellow: 2 + 3 + 3 + 4 = 12, ÷ 4 = 3
HUB 2: Pink: 4 + 3 + 2 + 9 = 18, ÷ 2 = 2. Yellow: 1 + 2 + 4 + 7 = 14, ÷ 2 = 2.

220: Pig = 1, Piglet = 5, Chicken = 4, Chick = 2, Egg = 1. Seven chicks are required.

221: F and H.

222: A.

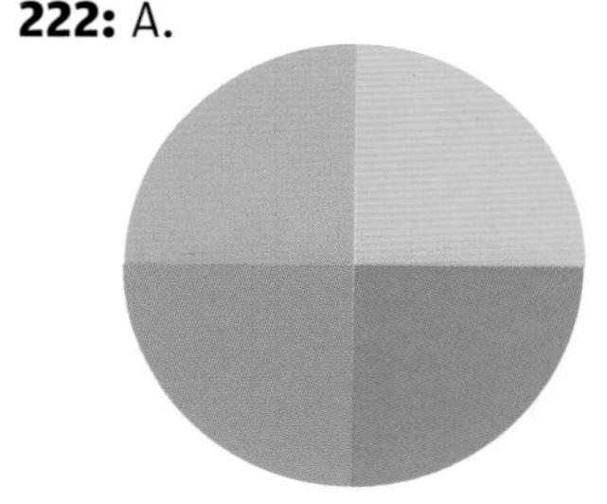

223: A. With each new image, the bottom row of dots moves to the top before the corner colors are swapped with their diagonal opposites.

224:
1. 3.
2. Top left.
3. X.
4. 4.
5. 13.

225: 23.

226: H.

227:

228:

4	2	3	3	2	0
3	X	O	O	O	3
4	X	X	O	O	3
2	O	O	X	O	2
4	O	X	X	X	3
0	4	3	4	3	4

229:

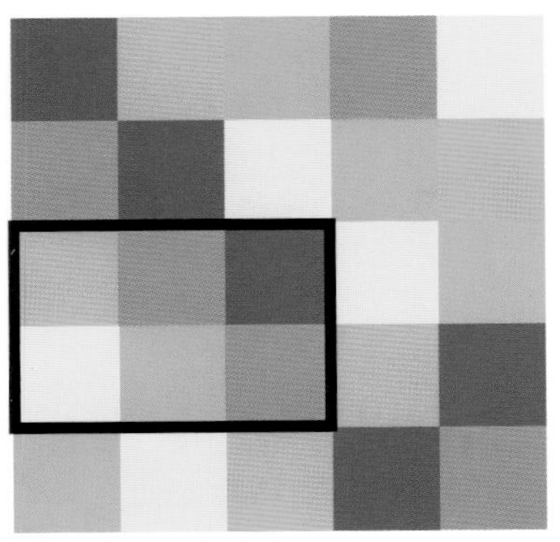

230: 1 watermelon (4.85), 3 pineapples (6.84), 4 bananas (1.80), and 3 oranges (1.26)
4.85 + 6.84 + 1.80 + 1.26 = 14.75.

231:

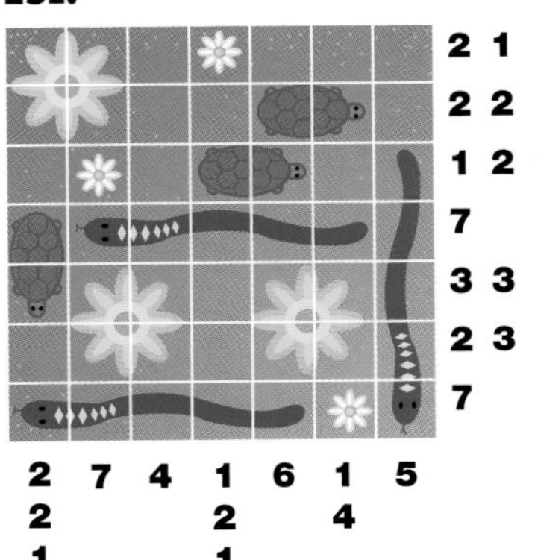

232: A.

233: Red.

234:

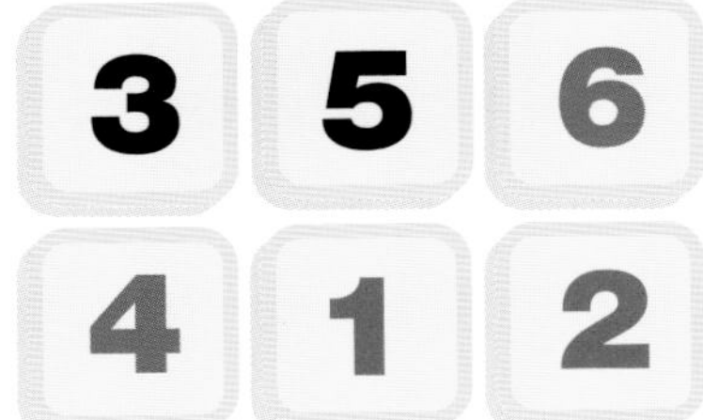

235:

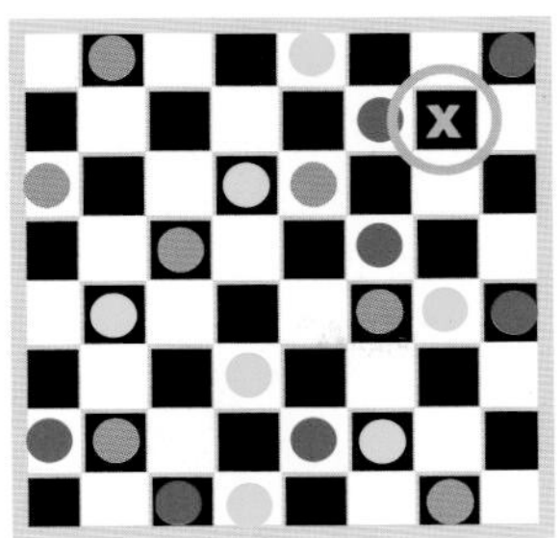

236: Samantha, Jennifer, Jessica, Elizabeth, Hannah, Michelle, Julia, Grace, Angela, and Monica.

237: 25. Kaplutski has solved 12 cases and Wojowitz has solved 13. Multiply both numbers by four to get a percentage.

238: 48 percent is blue, 52 percent is orange. 12 out of 25 triangles that make up the shape are blue, 13 are orange. Multiply both numbers by 4 and you get a percentage.

239:

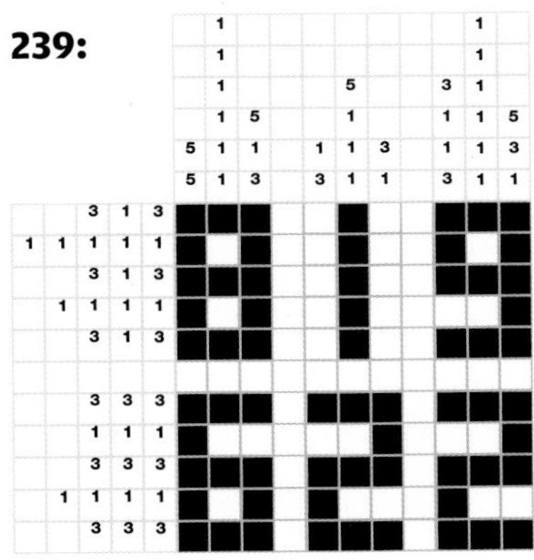

240: 1,008. The numbers represent the number of sides in the shape they occupy. When shapes overlap, the numbers are multiplied.
A: 3 x 4 x 4 x 6 = 288
B: 3 x 3 x 4 x 4 x 5 = 720
288 + 720 = 1,008.

241: 80. Multiply the alphabetical position of the first letter of each name by the number of vowels it contains. T = 20 and Tom Cruise contains 4 vowels. 20 x 4 = 80.

242:

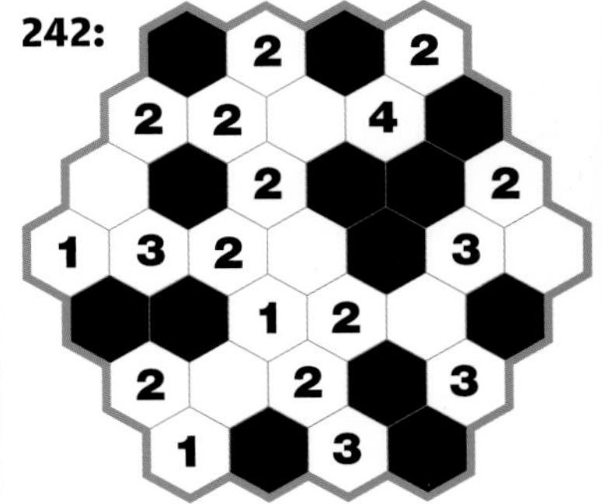

243: C.

244: 30 percent is gray, 70 percent is green. 12 out of 40 triangles in the shape are gray, 28 are green. Multiply both numbers by 2.5 and you get a percentage.

245: 10. Add the top and front faces and divide by 2. Then multiply by the front face.

246:

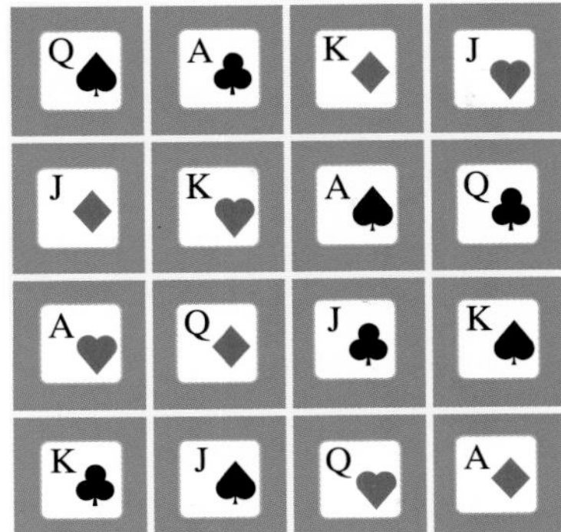

247:

248:

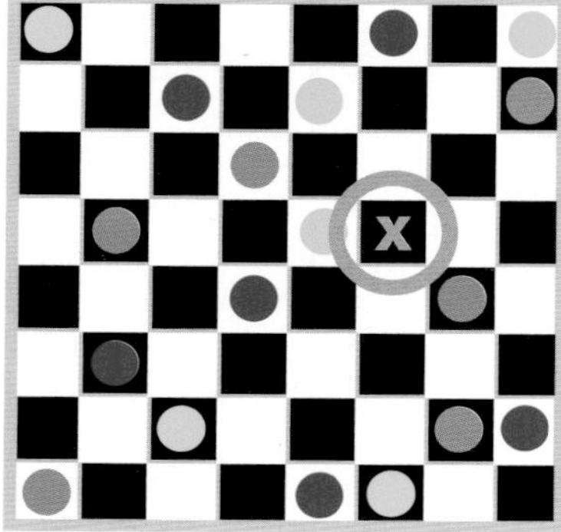

249:

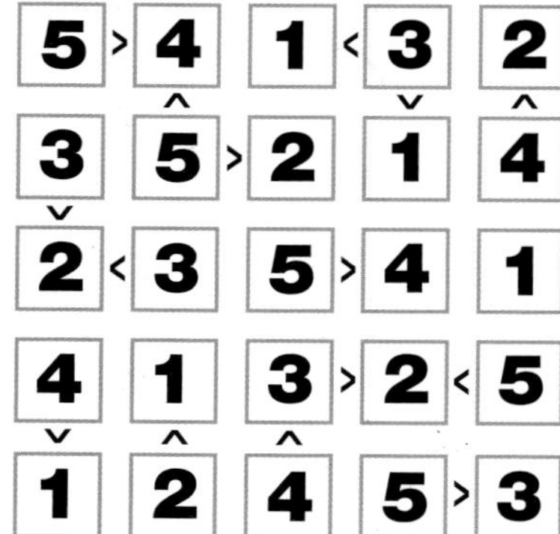

250: From the lower square to the higher one, the direction of movement each color indicates is: Green-Up, Orange-Left, Blue-Right, Purple-Down.

251: Blue.

252:

253:

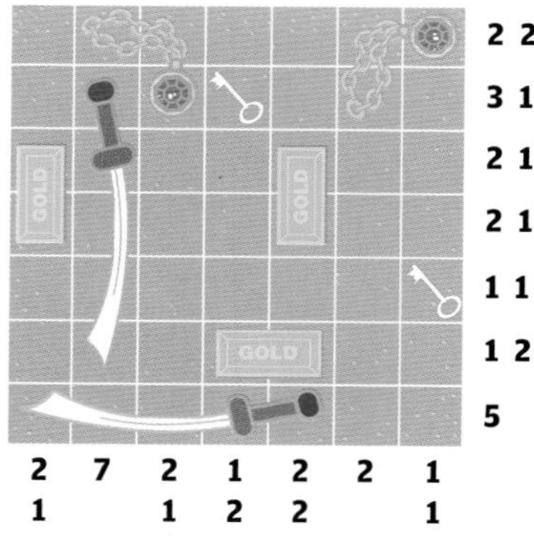

254: D.

255: 54. Add the three largest white numbers together and multiply by the smallest.
7 + 6 + 5 = 18 x 3 = 54.

256:
A) 6. Multiply opposite numbers and add up the integers of the total.
B) 14. Add the integers in opposite numbers.

257:

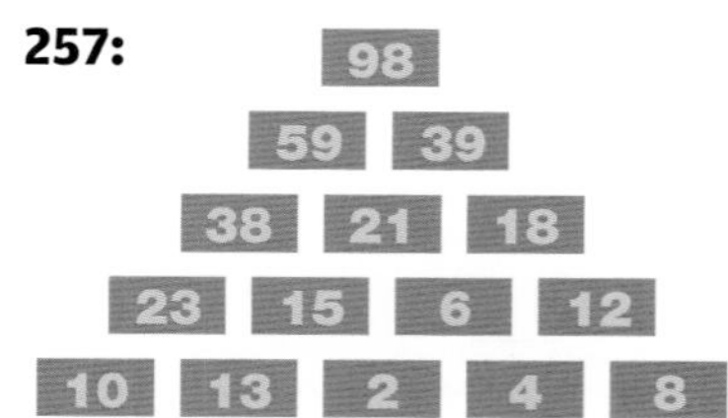

258:

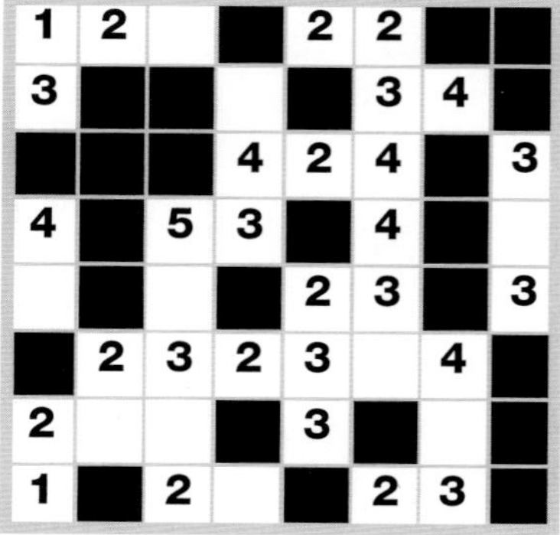

259: C and I are the pair.

260: 4,750 square inches (12,065 square centimeters). Each 20 x 20 square represents 400 square inches (1,016 square centimeters). 10 squares, 4 half squares, 1 quarter square, and 5 eighth triangles are used, and subtract four quarter square windows.

261:

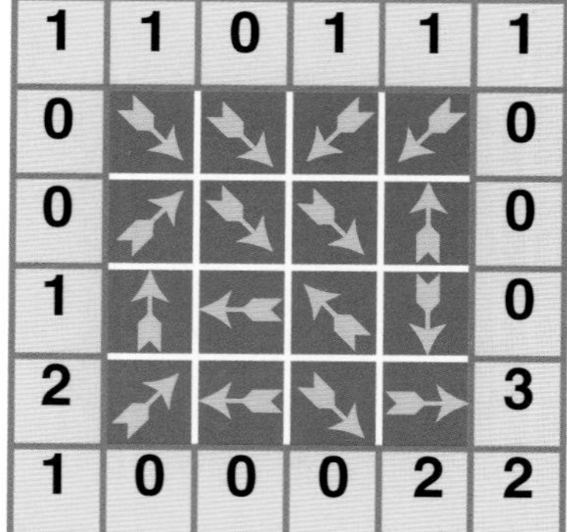

262: Tom Cruise.

263:

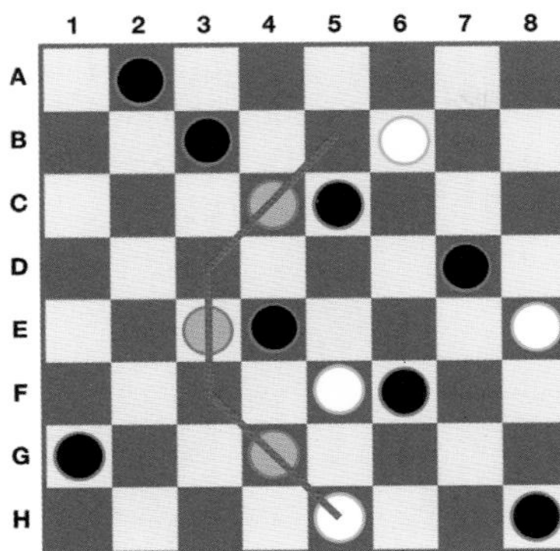

264:

265:

		1	1	1	1		
	4	2	2	2	2	6	
1	2	3	3	3	3	2	2
2	3	4	7	4	4	3	1
3	4	0	3	9	5	4	2
2	1	0	4	1	3	1	2
	1	7	6	1	4	1	
		1	8	2	0		

266: C.

267: The jewels are in the cab in square 5d.

268: 6. Multiply the right face and the front face and subtract the top one.

269: C and D.

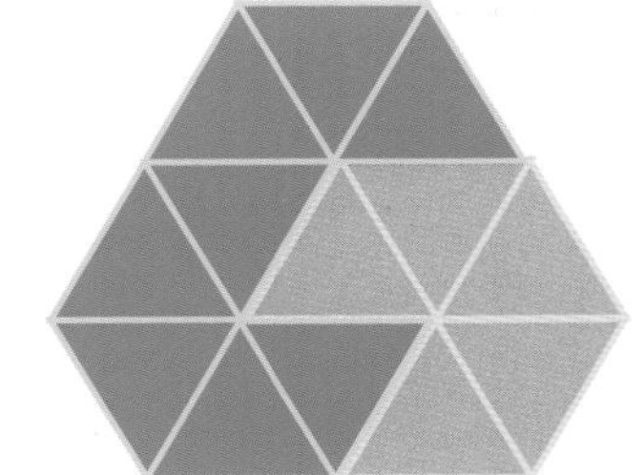

270:

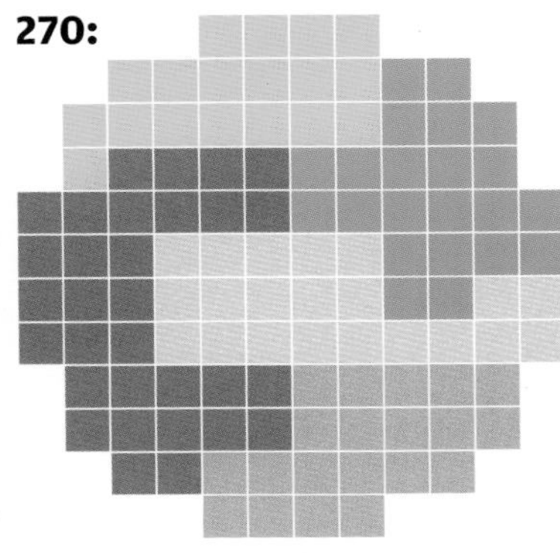

271: From the lower square to the higher one, the direction of movement each color indicates is: Green-Up, Pink-Left, Orange-Right, Blue-Down.

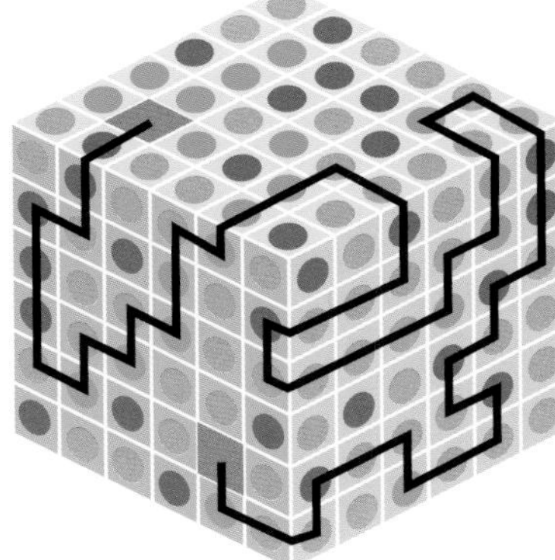

272: E.

273:

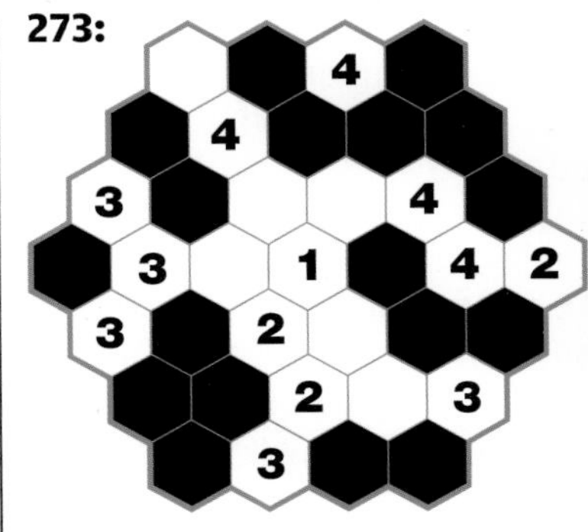

274: J and D.

275: C and F.

276:

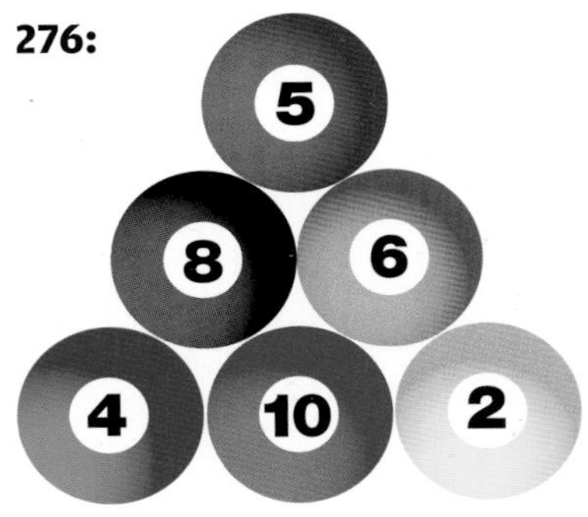

277:

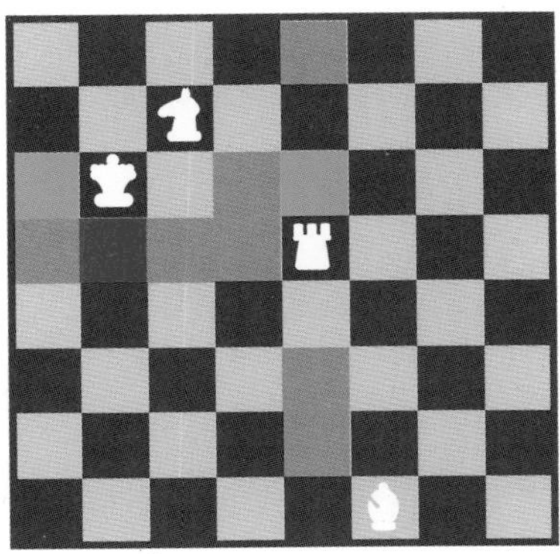

278:

279: He lent them a boat. With 18 boats, Manuela can have 9, Maria can have 6, and Monica can have 2, fulfilling their father's will. 9 + 6 + 2 = 17, so following the division of the fleet, they are able to return the fisherman's boat.

280: A2, G2, L1, O5.

281:

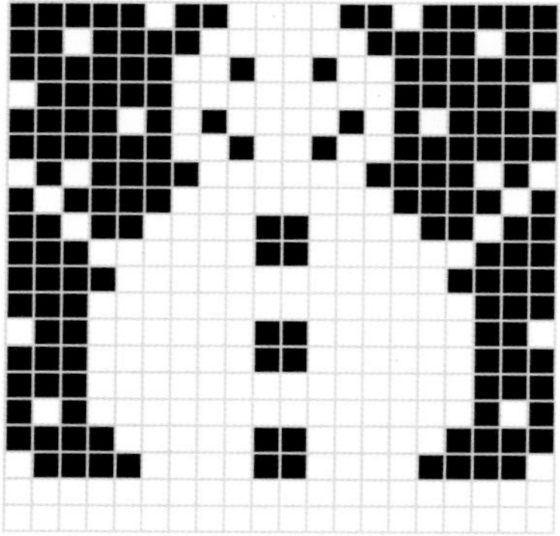

282:

3	4	3	2	3	1
3	X	O	O	O	3
4	X	O	O	O	2
5	X	X	X	X	5
3	O	X	O	X	3
1	5	3	4	4	3

283: A and E are the pair.

284: D.

285:

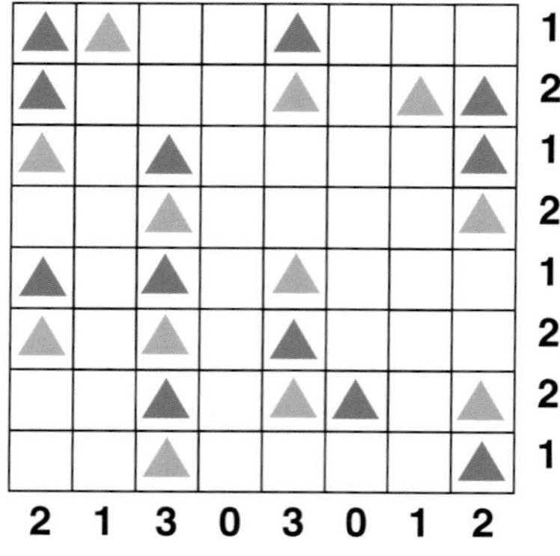

286: H.

287: Lilac.

288: 11 and 10. The total of the numbers in each section is the reverse of the total of the opposite section—23 and 32. 38, and 83 etc.

289: Each pentagon contains numbers that add up to 30. The sides nearest adjoining pentagons are the numbers 1 to 12 in order.

290: 24. Score one for a consonant and two for a vowel, then multiply the totals together.
4 x 6 = 24.

291: A. The main outer shape swaps color with the shape just inside it. The inner shape swaps color with the outside shapes. The four small shapes move from the second shape to the outside one.

292: 3,650 square inches (9,271 square centimeters). Each 20 x 20 square (1,016 square centimeters) represents 400 square inches. 4 squares, 6 half-squares, 2 half-square triangles, 3 quarter squares, and 3 eighth square triangles are used.

293:

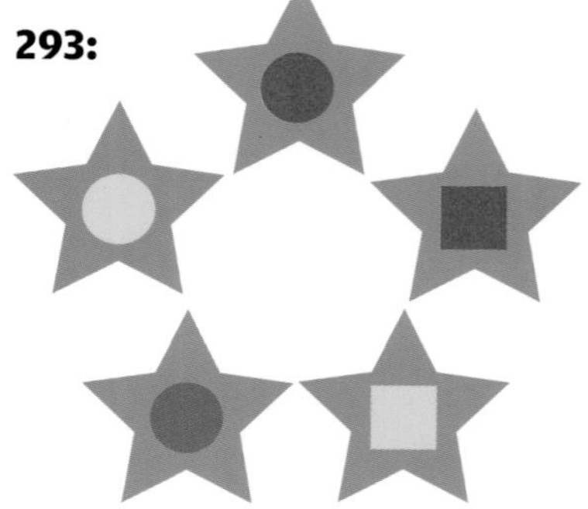

294: b) 15 c) 12 d) 10 a) 8.

295: C and I are the pair.

296: A and C.

297:
A) 8. Subtract the numbers opposite each other.
B) 18. Add the opposite numbers.

298: B. Each row and column in the grid contains four dark and three light squares, and numbers that total 10.

299:

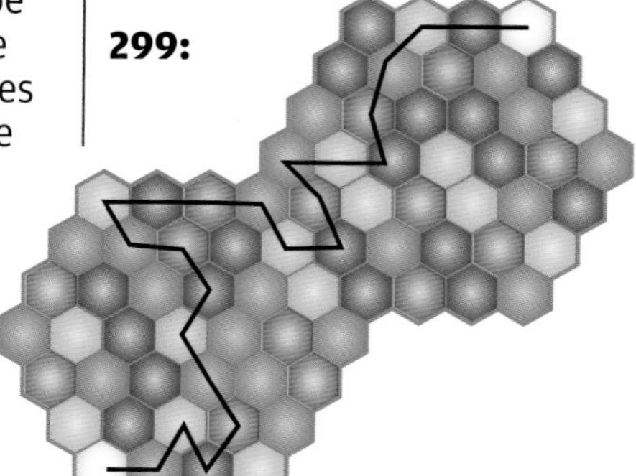

300:

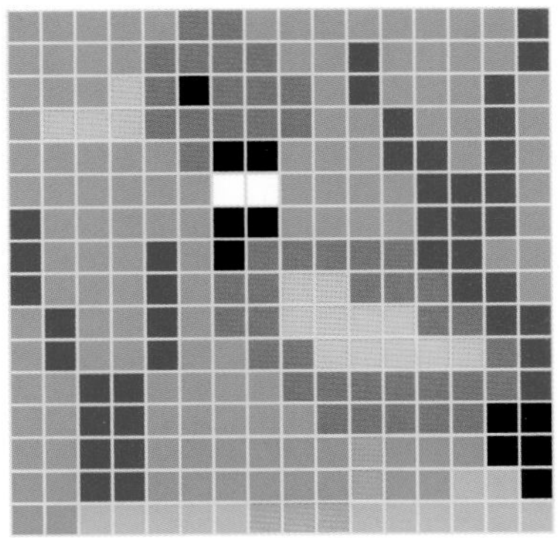

301: G is the odd one out.

302:
Pink = Left
Red = Right
Black = Down
Yellow = Up
Purple = Up Right
Brown = Down Right
Blue = Up Left
Green = Down Left.
The final die in your trip is the red 4, sixth die down in the second column.

303:

2	1	6	3	4	5
3	2	5	4	1	6
4	3	2	6	5	1
1	4	3	5	6	2
6	5	4	1	2	3
5	6	1	2	3	4

304:
1. 5.
2. Green.
3. 0.
4. 1.
5. Green.

305:

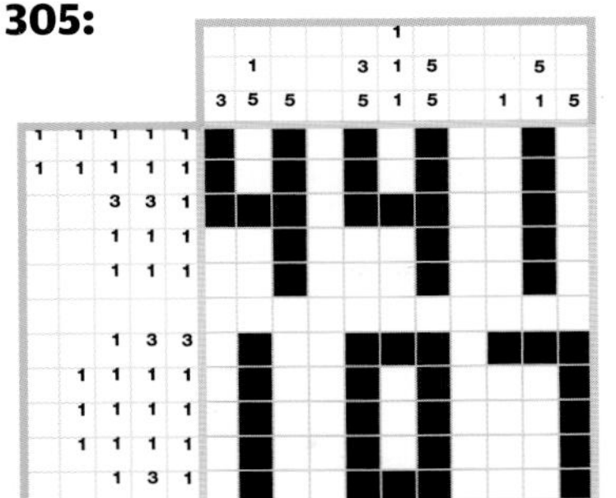

306:

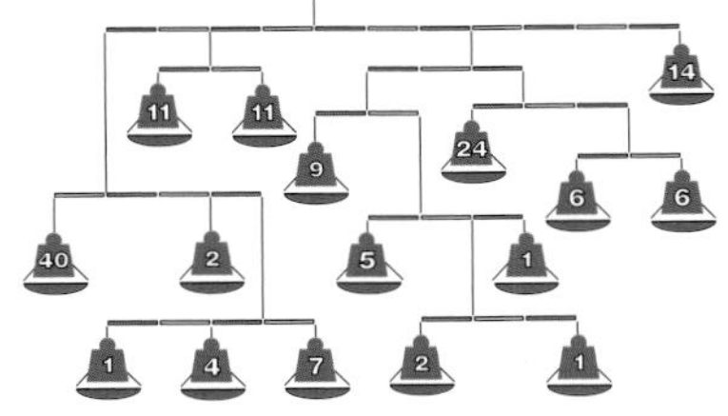

307: Cleopatra.

308: A red 2. Two numbers the same are followed by a red number. Two numbers of different colors are followed by a 2.

309:

310:

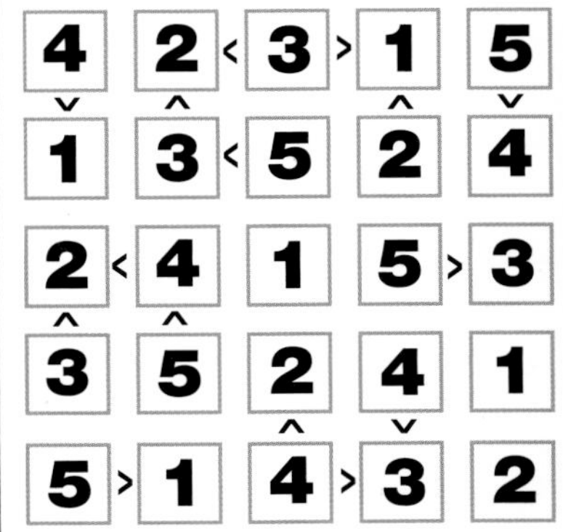

311: The boat finishes the race at the buoy in square 4C.

312: A and F are the pair.

313:

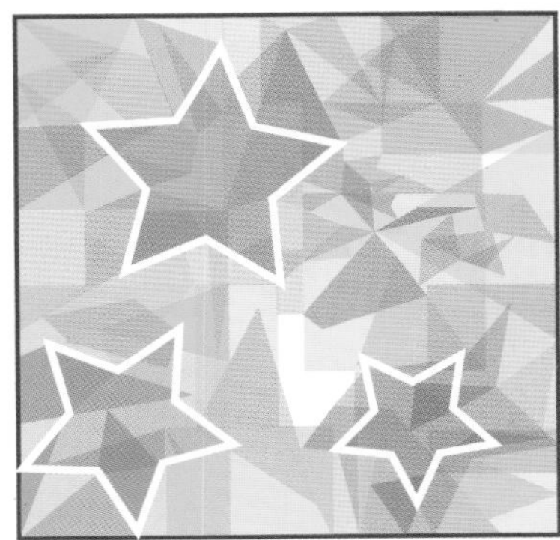

314: Originally, the men paid $30, but they each got $1 back, so they have only paid $27. $25 of this went into the driver's cash box while $2 went into his pocket.

315: A and C.

316:

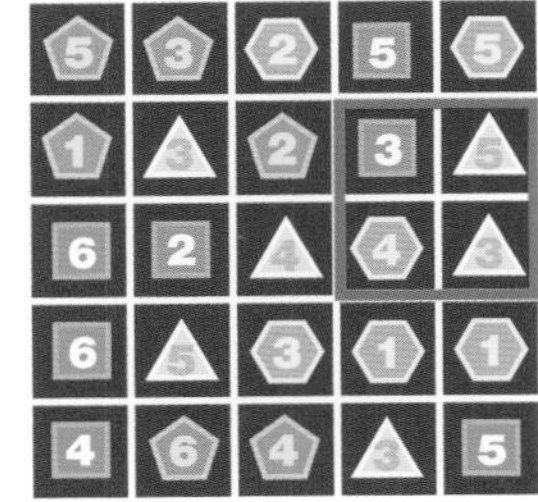

317: Mozart.

318: A and E are the pair.

319:

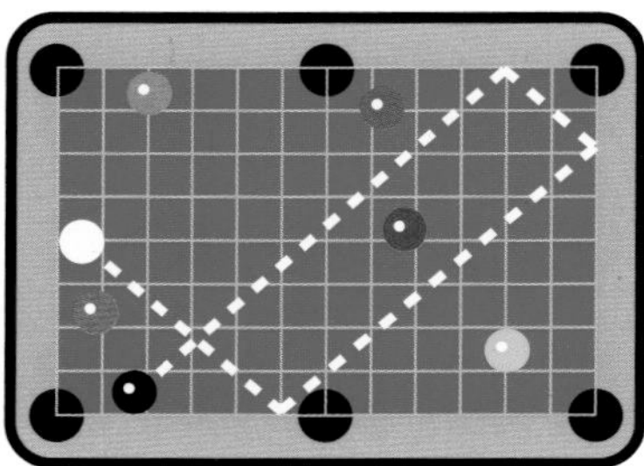

320: A.

321:

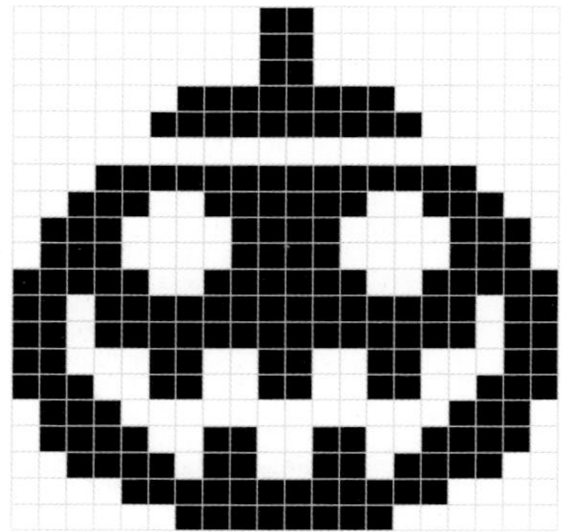

322: A, C, and E.

323: Ziplock is alien G.

324: Thumper had 50 and Cottontail had 30.

325: D.

326: E.

327: C. Each row and column in the grid contains two green squares and a letter B, and numbers that total 8.

328:

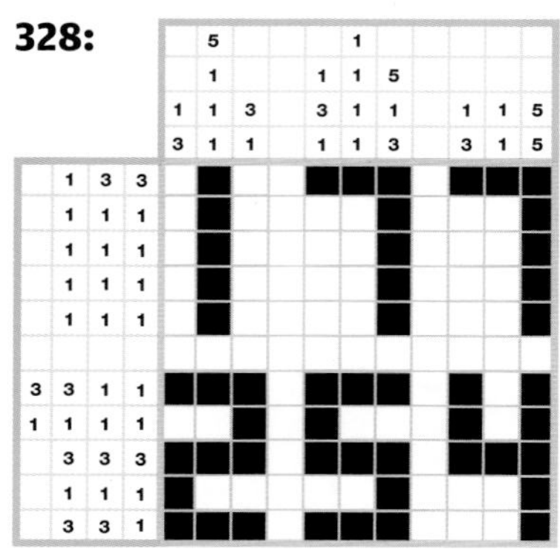

329: A. With each new image, the stars take the color of the previous double stripes. The double stripes take the color of the previous background, the background takes the color of the previous central stripe, and the central stripe takes the color of the previous stars.

330: If its bordering squares (not diagonals) are predominantly purple, a square becomes purple. If they are predominantly orange, it becomes orange. If the bordering cell colors are equal in number, the square becomes black, and if the bordering squares have now become predominantly black, a square also becomes black.

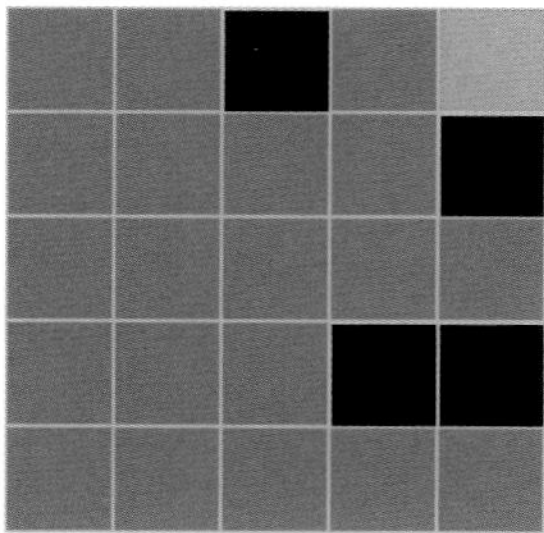

331:

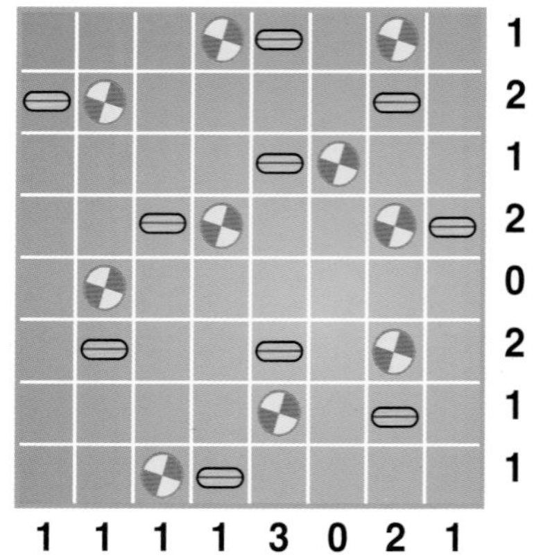

332: 948.

333: A line on the left or right of this square will give up only one box to your opponent.

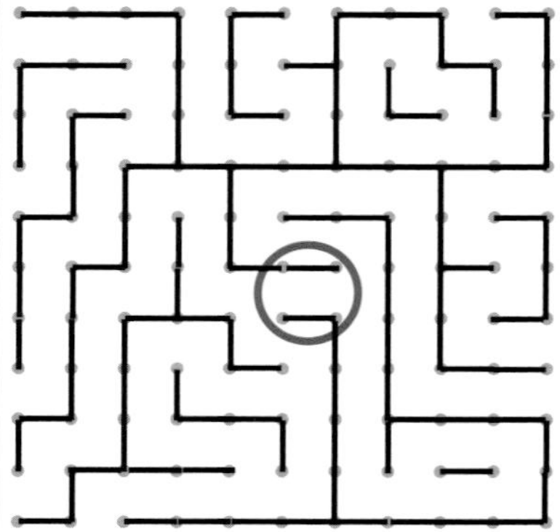

334:
1. 14.
2. 15.
3. Red and yellow.
4. 4.
5. 3.

335:

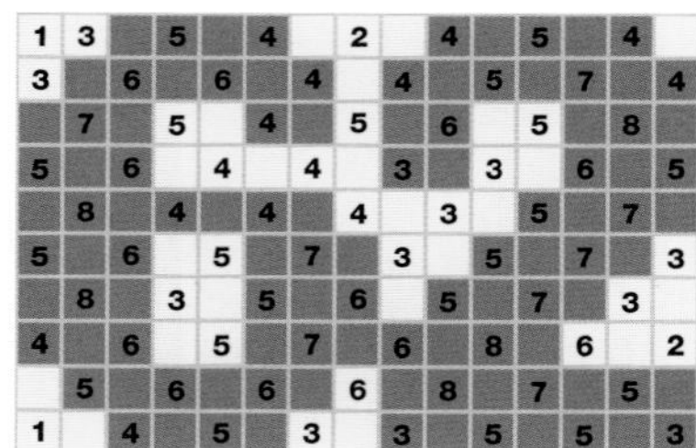

336: Four spoons and five boxes of teabags.

337:
Pink 1.
Purple 2.
Red 3.
Green 4.

338:

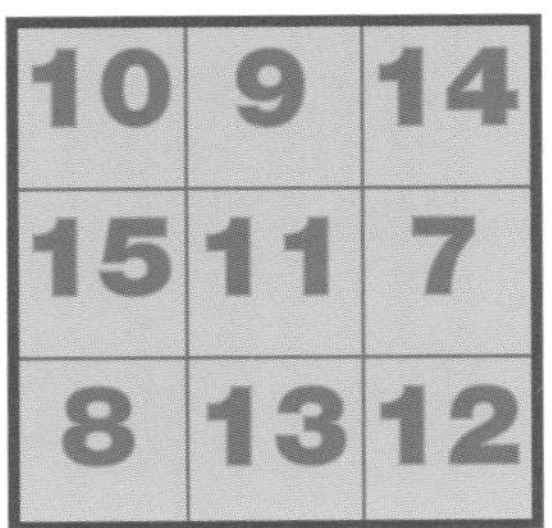

339:

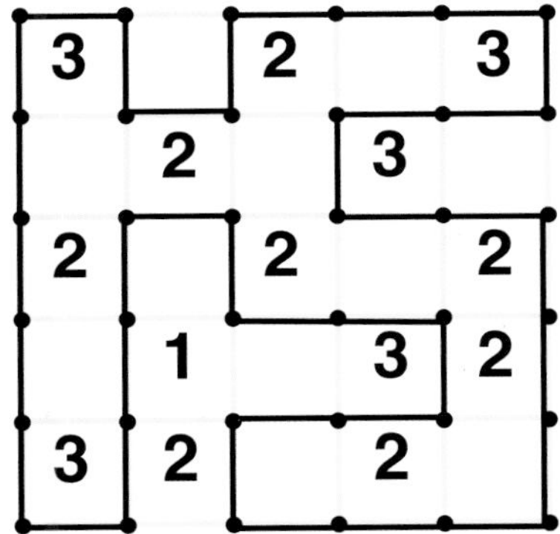

340: D and B.

341: D. Each row and column in the grid contains 2 pink squares, 2 black dots, and two white Xs.

342:

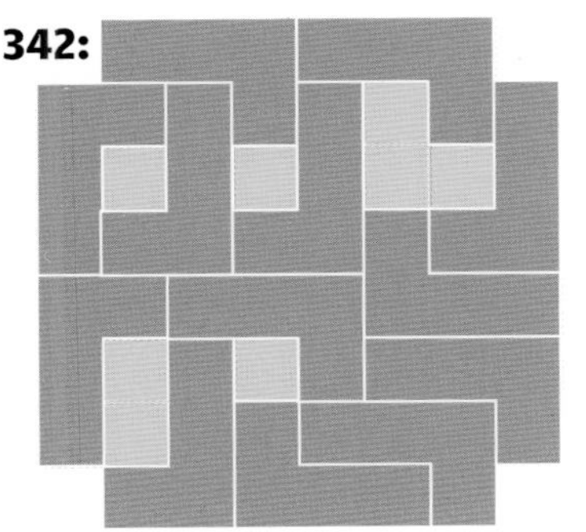

343: Cream.

344: B.

345:

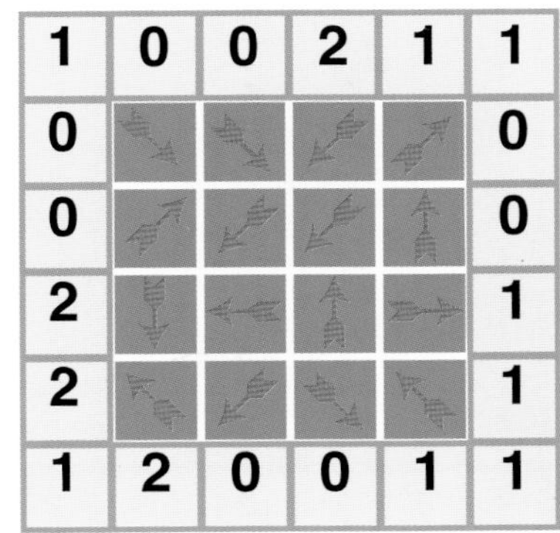

346:
The final die in your trip is the red 4, top die in the sixth column.

347: 91. Take the alphabetical position of the first letter of the city, and multiply by the number of letters in the word. 13 (M) x 7 = 91.

348:

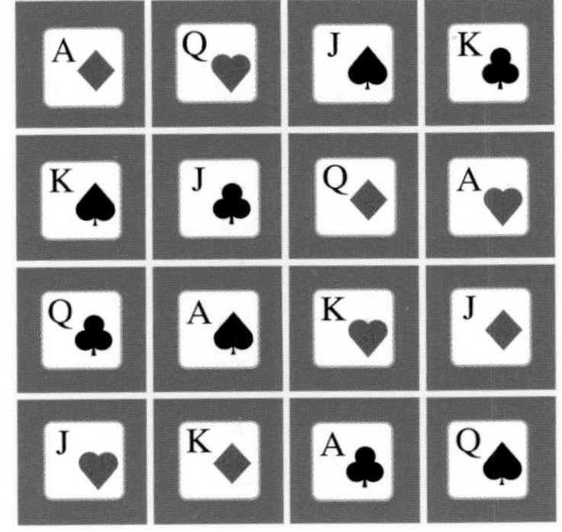

349: Second tile on the bottom row.

350: 4/9ths did, and 5/9ths didn't. 1/9th of 459 is 51. 4 x 51 is 204 (153 + 51) and 5 x 51 is 255 (136 + 119).

351:

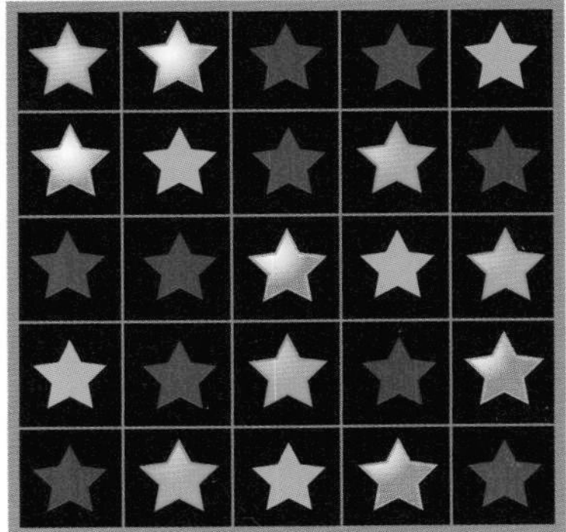

352: 6,950 square inches (17,653 square centimeters). Each 20 x 20 square represents 400 square inches (1,016 square centimeters). 9 squares, 11 half squares, 5 quarter squares, and 13 eighth-square triangles are used.

353: E8, L11, F7, K2.

354: 75.

355:

K	M	I	G	A	L
M	A	G	L	I	K
A	G	K	I	L	M
I	L	M	A	K	G
G	I	L	K	M	A
L	K	A	M	G	I

4	3	2	6	1	5
5	6	1	2	3	4
3	5	6	4	2	1
6	1	4	3	5	2
2	4	5	1	6	3
1	2	3	5	4	6

G + 5 = L I + 6 = O M + 1 = N
A + 3 = D K + 4 = O L + 2 = N
Solution: LONDON

356: Blue. If Jules and Jim were both wearing red caps, Janet would know hers was blue, and similarly if Janet and Jim were both in red caps, Jules would know hers was blue. So when Janet says she can't work out which color her cap is, that means that Jules and Jim are either both wearing blue caps, or that they have one of each. Assuming Jules has worked this out, if she sees Jim in a red cap, she will know hers must be blue. If she can't work out her own cap color, Jim's cap must also be blue.

357:

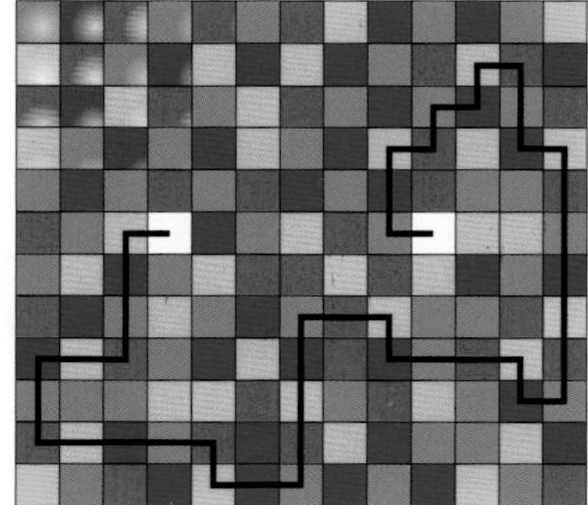

358: 288. The numbers represent the number of sides in the shape they occupy. When shapes overlap, the numbers are multiplied.
A: 3 x 4 x 4 x 5 = 240.
B: 4 x 4 x 3 = 48.

359:

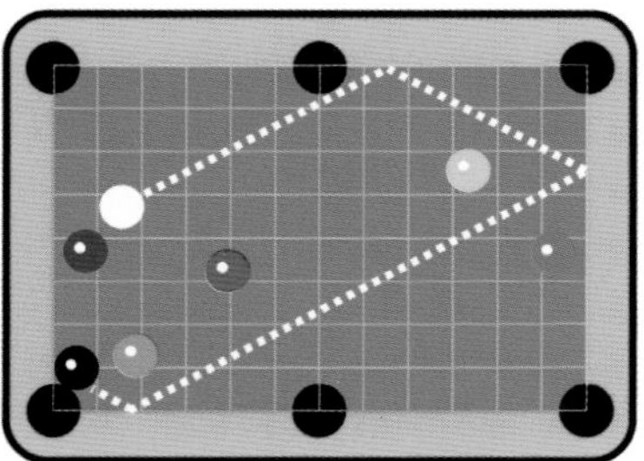

360: C.

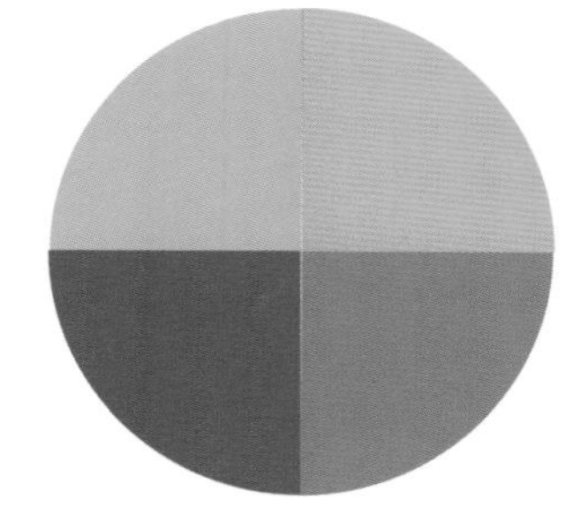

361: B and F are the pair.

362:

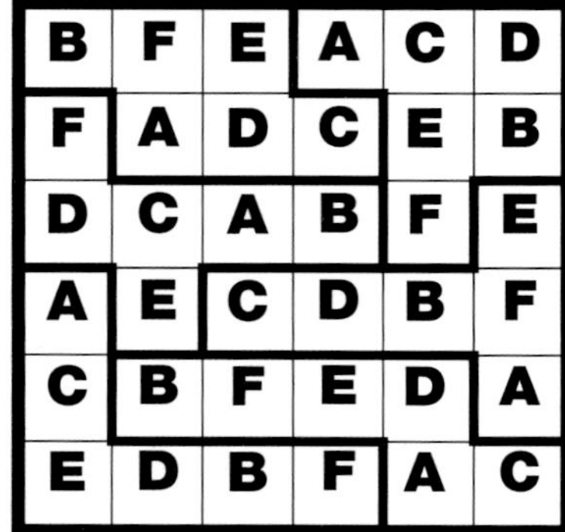

B	F	E	A	C	D
F	A	D	C	E	B
D	C	A	B	F	E
A	E	C	D	B	F
C	B	F	E	D	A
E	D	B	F	A	C

363: A and B.

364: 36. There are 21 dots on every die and we can see 27. 63 - 27 = 36.

365: If its bordering triangles are predominantly brown, a triangle becomes green. If they are predominantly green, it becomes brown. If the bordering cells are equal in number, the triangle becomes pink, and if the bordering triangles have now become predominantly pink, it also becomes pink.

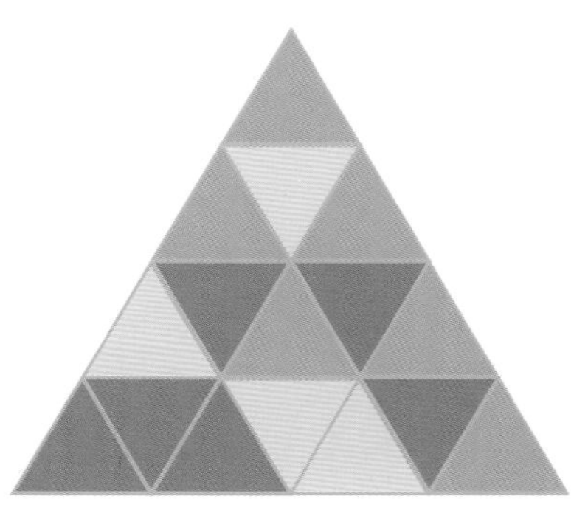